Scie

EY STA

3

EVELS

5-7

RACTICE PAPER

3B

Key Stage 3

Science Test

Practice Paper 3B

Read this page, but don't open the booklet until your teacher says you can start. Write your name and school in the spaces below.

First Name ______________________________

Last Name ______________________________

School ______________________________

Remember

- The test is one hour long.
- Make sure you have these things with you before you start: pen, pencil, rubber, ruler, angle measurer or protractor, calculator.
- The easier questions are at the start of the test.
- Try to answer all of the questions.
- Don't use any rough paper — write all your answers and working in this test paper.
- Check your work carefully before the end of the test.
- If you're not sure what to do, ask your teacher.

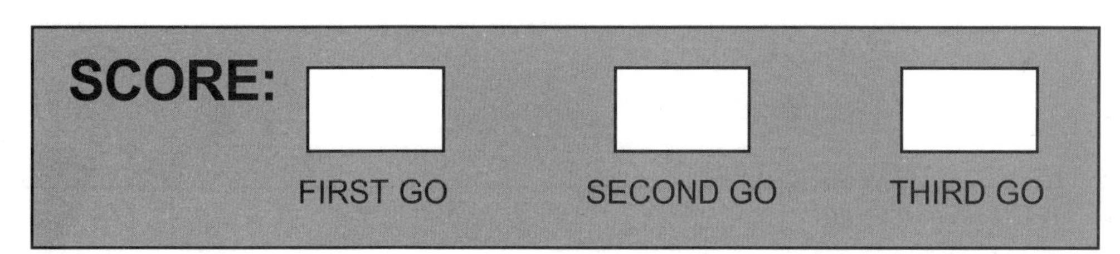

Exam Set SHGP31

1. Some friends are having a tug of war. The diagram shows the two teams and the force with which each person is pulling.

Which team will win, if each person pulls with a constant force?
Show your working.

....

....

....

3 marks

Maximum 3 marks

2. Look at the two pyramids of numbers shown below.

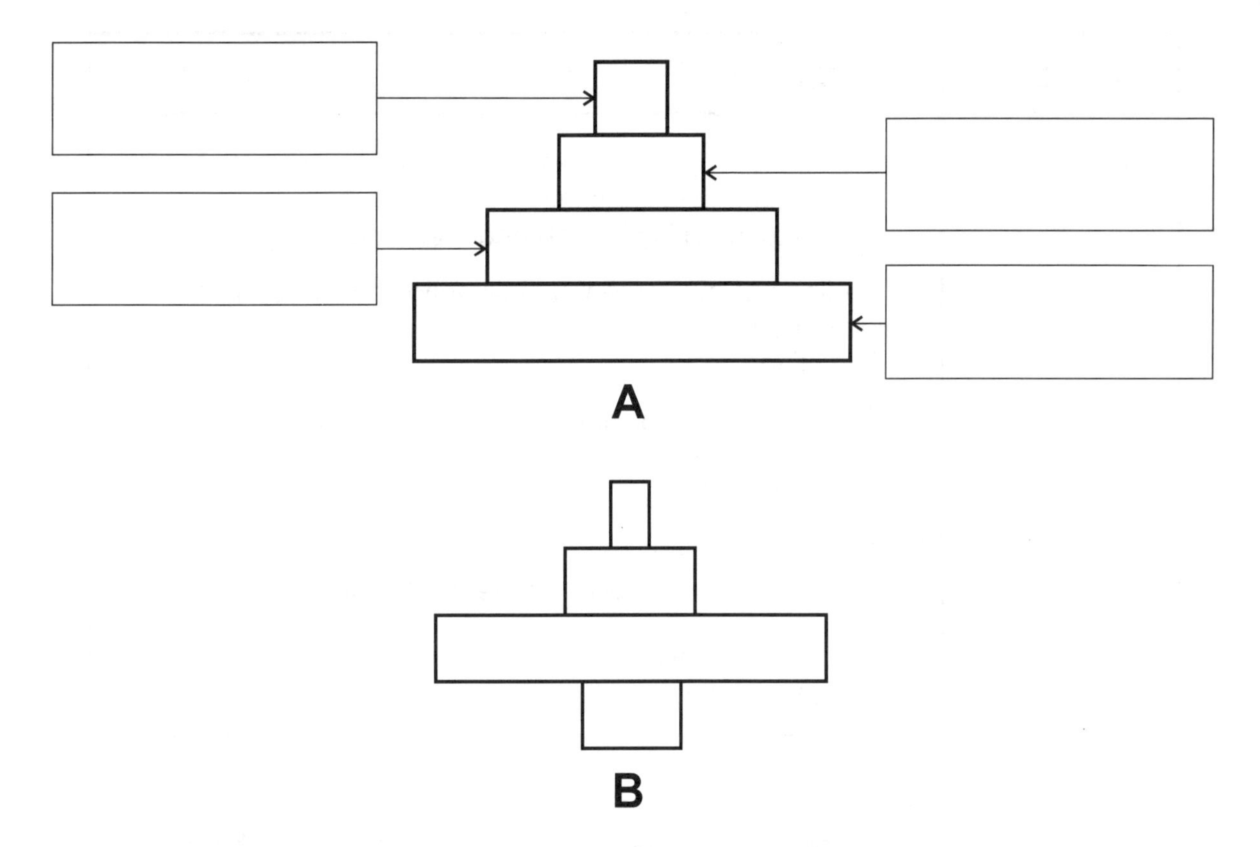

(a) Label pyramid A, choosing from the labels in the box below.

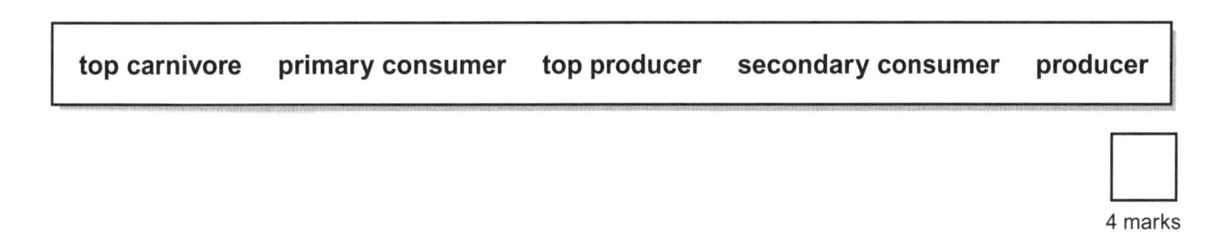

4 marks

(b) Which pyramid, **A** or **B**, could represent the following food chain?

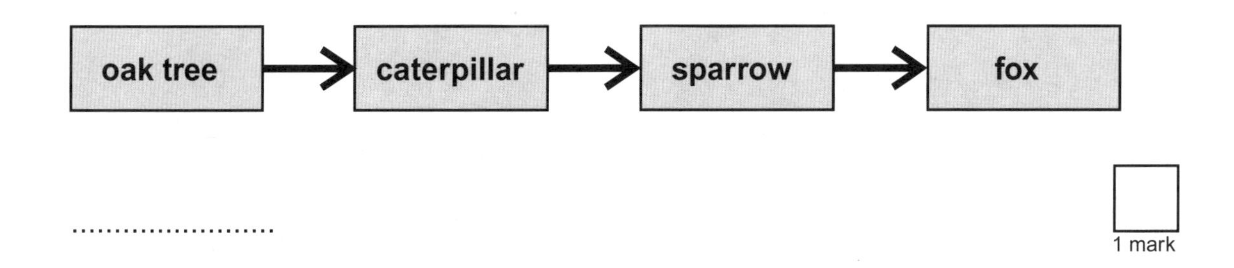

....

1 mark

Maximum 5 marks

3. Look at the table below showing some of the effects of some drugs.

DRUG	EFFECT
Cannabis	Causes feelings of relaxation and wellbeing. May cause hallucinations. Linked to infertility in men and mental health problems.
Cocaine	Feelings of excitement usually followed by depression. Overdose can kill. Addictive.
Heroin	Causes feelings of happiness and wellbeing. Overdose can kill. Highly addictive.
LSD	Causes hallucinations. Regular use linked with mental health problems.
Sedatives	Helps people relax. Dangerous (can be fatal) if mixed with alcohol.

(a) Using information in the table, name two drugs or types of drug that can cause hallucinations.

1. .... 2. ....

2 marks

(b) Name one drug or type of drug listed above that has a medical use.

....

1 mark

(c) Explain what the term 'addictive' means.

....

1 mark

Maximum 4 marks

4. Use the information in the table below to answer the questions that follow.

SUBSTANCE	CHEMICAL FORMULA
water	H_2O
carbon dioxide	CO_2
alcohol (ethanol)	C_2H_5OH
glucose	$C_6H_{12}O_6$
oxygen	O_2

(a) Which substance is an element?

....

1 mark

(b) Which element is present in all the substances?

....

1 mark

(c) How many atoms are there in one molecule of glucose?

....

1 mark

Maximum 3 marks

5. Wayne is investigating friction in liquids. He times how long it takes a marble to fall through a tube filled with wallpaper paste.

Here are his results:

Distance fallen by marble (cm)	Time taken (s)
10	2.1
20	4.3
30	6.0
40	8.4
50	9.9

(a) Use the blank graph paper below to draw a graph of Wayne's results. Draw a line of best fit.

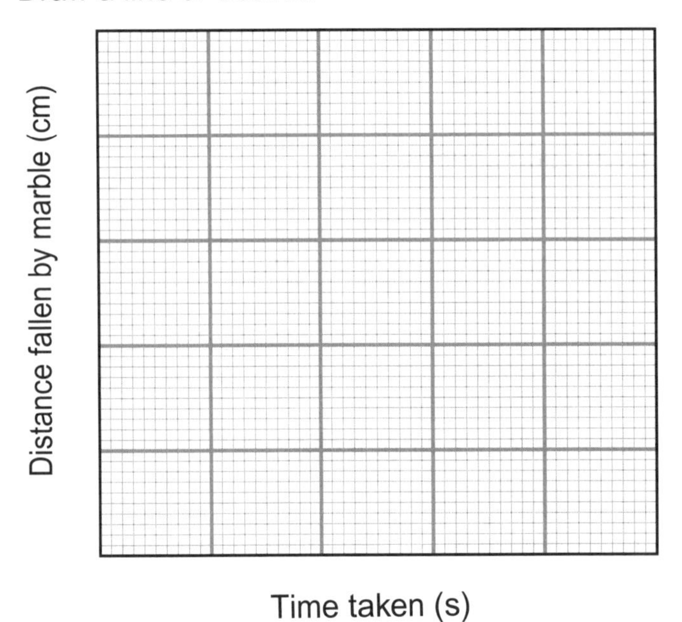

3 marks

(b) What do his results tell Wayne about the speed of the falling marble?

....

....

1 mark

Maximum 4 marks

6. A general equation for a neutralisation reaction is:

Acid + base → a salt + water

(a) Draw lines to connect each of the salts below to the acid and the base that would react to form them.

Acid	Salt	Base
hydrochloric acid	calcium chloride	copper oxide
sulfuric acid	iron nitrate	calcium oxide
nitric acid	copper sulfate	iron oxide

3 marks

(b) Complete the word equation for the following neutralisation reaction:

sodium hydroxide + ... → sodium chloride + water

1 mark

(c) Write down the name of the acid that has the chemical formula: $\mathbf{HNO_3}$.

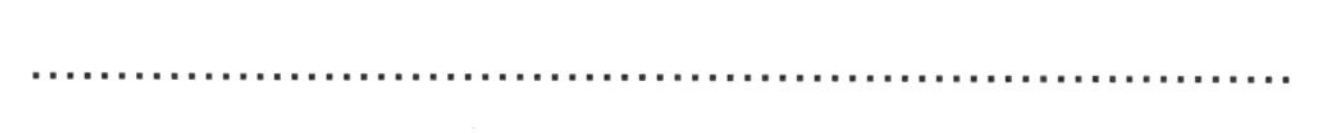

1 mark

Maximum 5 marks

7. Follow the key below to match each animal shown to its correct group.

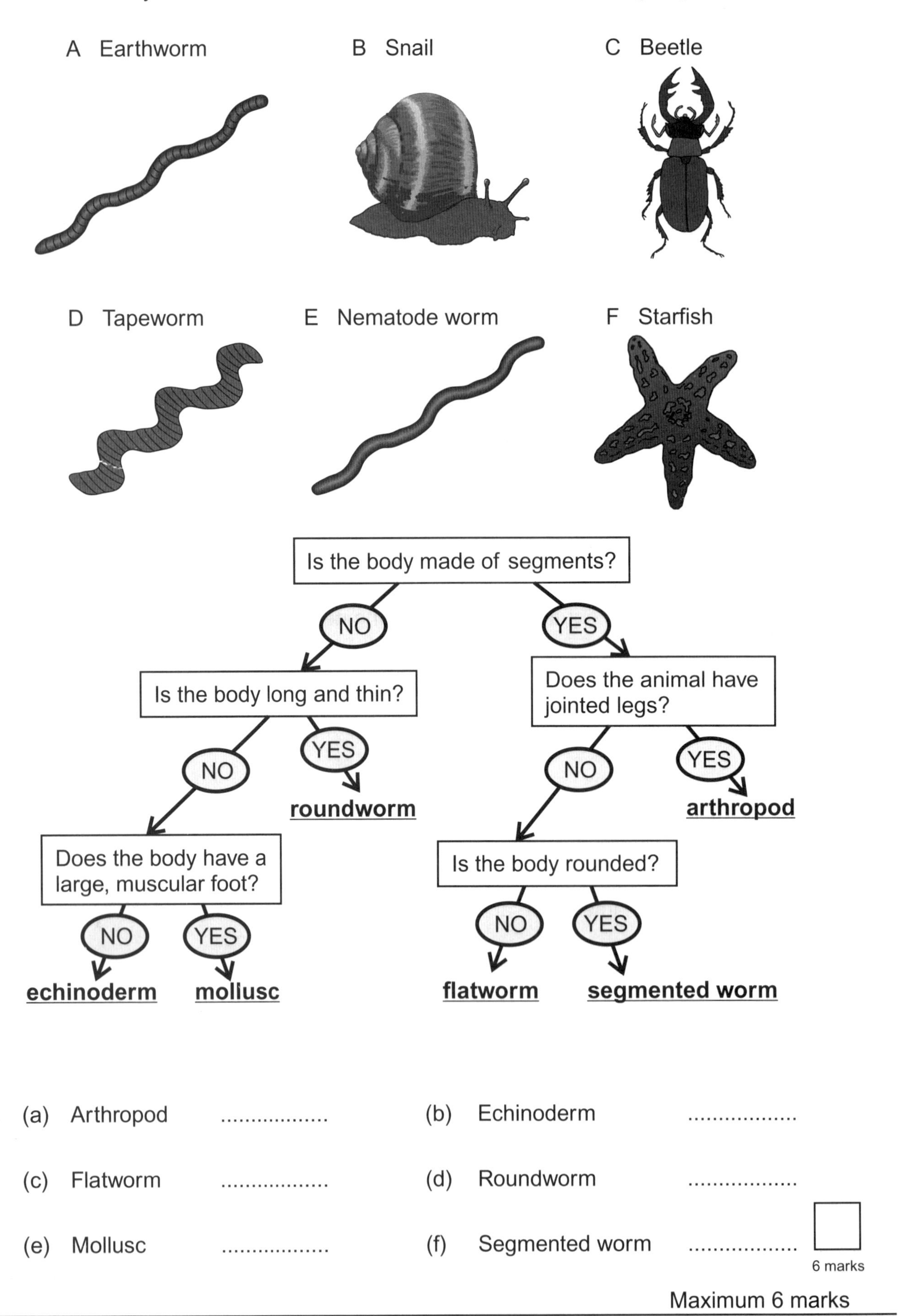

(a) Arthropod .... (b) Echinoderm ....

(c) Flatworm .... (d) Roundworm ....

(e) Mollusc .... (f) Segmented worm ....

6 marks

Maximum 6 marks

8. Methane is a gas. A molecule of methane consists of one carbon atom chemically joined to four hydrogen atoms.

(a) Write a word equation for the reaction that happens when methane burns in air.

....

2 marks

(b) If pure methane is burnt in a closed container, how will the air inside the container be different afterwards? Tick any answers that apply.
The air inside the container will contain:

- ☐ More hydrogen
- ☐ More carbon dioxide
- ☐ Less hydrogen
- ☐ Less carbon dioxide
- ☐ More oxygen
- ☐ More sulfur dioxide
- ☐ Less oxygen
- ☐ Less sulfur dioxide

2 marks

(c) When methane was burnt in a closed container, carbon (soot) and carbon monoxide were formed, as well as the usual products.
Which of the following is the best explanation for this?

A The methane burned too quickly.

B The air inside the container was too damp.

C There was not enough oxygen for the methane to burn completely.

D The methane contained impurities.

Answer: ....

1 mark

Maximum 5 marks

9. Mr Ahmed demonstrates a model steam engine connected to a generator to make electricity.

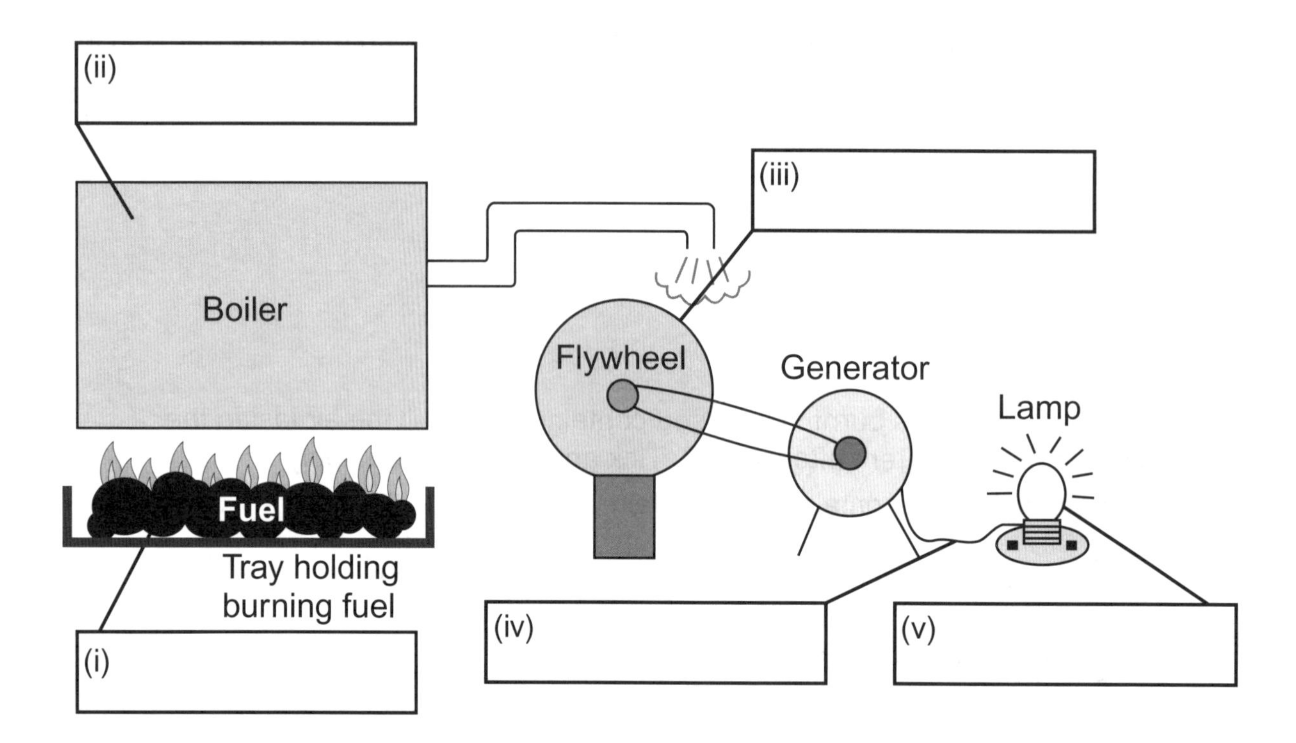

(a) Using the words below, complete the labels on the diagram to show the types of useful energy at each stage. Use each label once only.

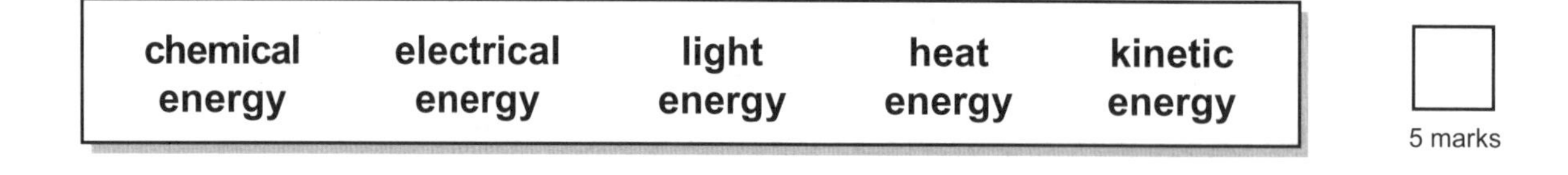

chemical energy
electrical energy
light energy
heat energy
kinetic energy

5 marks

(b) Match up the different types of heat transfer below with the correct examples from the steam engine.

conduction	warm air from above the boiler circulates the room
convection	heat flows from the white-hot filament in the bulb to its surroundings
radiation	the metal tray holding the burning fuel gets hot

2 marks

Maximum 7 marks

10. Tony is carrying out an experiment to compare the rate of photosynthesis of two types of algae. The following diagram shows the reaction that happens.

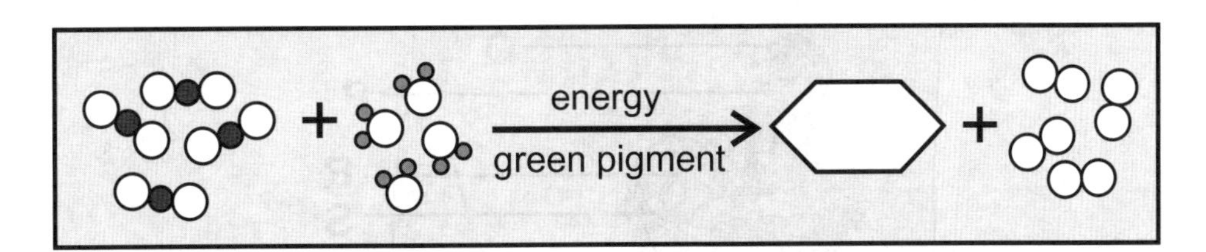

(a) Write out the word equation for this reaction.

....

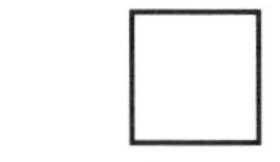

1 mark

The diagram shows the equipment Tony is using for the experiment.

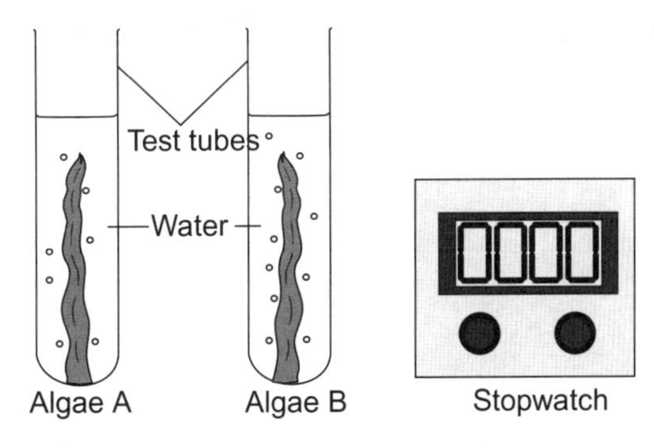

(b) How can Tony use this equipment to measure the rate of photosynthesis?

....

1 mark

(c) What can Tony do to make his results reliable?

....

1 mark

(d) Name the green pigment needed for photosynthesis to happen.

....

1 mark

(e) What type of energy is used to drive this reaction?

....

1 mark

Maximum 5 marks

11. The diagram shows the human female reproductive system.

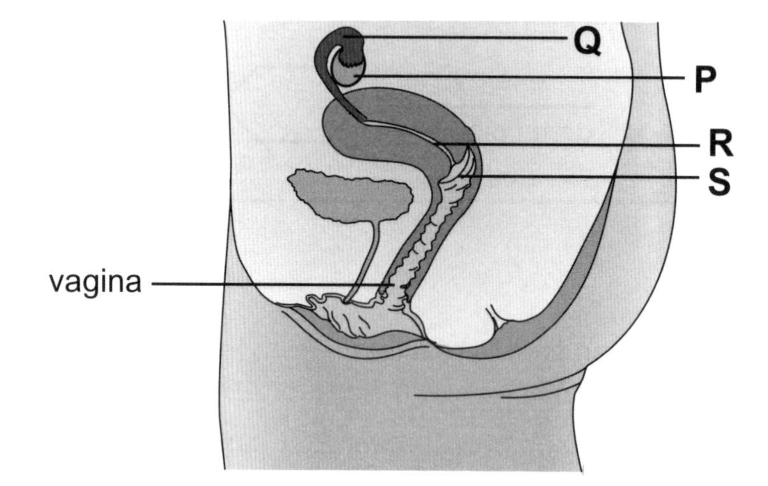

(a) Give the correct labels for the structures P, Q, R and S.

P .... Q ....

R .... S ....

4 marks

(b) From which part are the ova or eggs released at ovulation?

....

1 mark

(c) On approximately which day in the menstrual cycle does ovulation occur (if day one is when menstruation begins)?

....

1 mark

(d) Explain how the uterus changes each month to prepare for a fertilised egg.

....

1 mark

Maximum 7 marks

12. In an experiment, a ray of sunlight was directed onto a triangular prism made out of glass, as shown below.

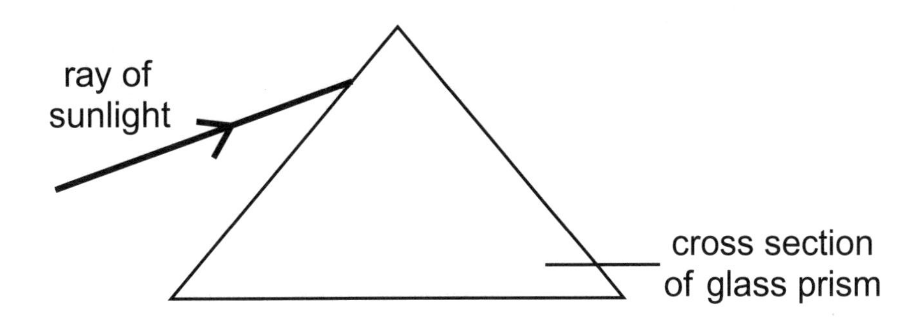

(a) Complete the diagram to show what happens to the ray of light.

☐
3 marks

(b) Which of the following words correctly describe what happens to the ray of light? Tick **two** boxes.

☐ absorption

☐ dispersion

☐ refraction

☐ radiation

☐
2 marks

Maximum 5 marks

13. A teacher shows her class two different experiments. She pushes a metal coin through a slot into a money box.

Next, she takes the coin out and heats it strongly. She tries to put the heated coin into the money box, but it won't fit through the slot.

In her second experiment, the teacher stands at the end of the classroom and opens a bottle of rose-water. It takes about a minute for everyone in the class to smell the rose-water. After lunch she does the same thing, but this time she warms the bottle slightly before opening it. This time it only takes half as long for everyone to smell the perfume.

(a) Explain, in terms of the particles in the coin, why the heated coin won't fit through the slot.

....

....

....

2 marks

(b) Explain, in terms of particles, why the class smelled the rose-water more quickly when it had been warmed.

....

....

....

2 marks

(c) What do both of your explanations have in common?

....

....

2 marks

Maximum 6 marks

14. Look at this circuit diagram.

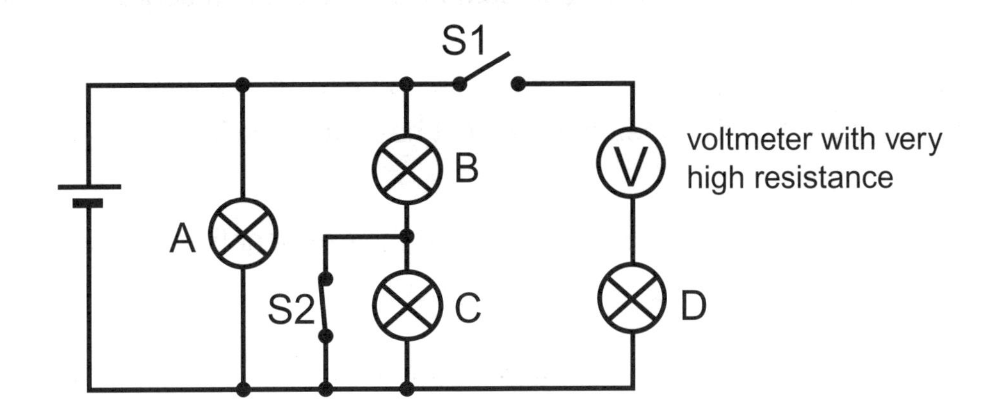

There are four bulbs, **A**, **B**, **C** and **D**, in the circuit.

(a) In the spaces below, state which bulbs are lit and which are not lit when switch S1 is open and S2 is closed as shown above.

Lit bulbs ....

Unlit bulbs ....

2 marks

(b) What three changes should be made to the circuit shown above to make sure all the bulbs are lit?

1. ....

2. ....

3. ....

3 marks

Maximum 5 marks

15. Potassium chloride is a white, crystalline solid at room temperature. Tim and Sarah are carrying out an experiment to see what happens when they mix potassium chloride crystals (KCl) with water. They add some KCl crystals to a beaker of water and stir it.

Tim says the KCl disappears because it is no longer in the water.
Sarah says the KCl disappears because it has dissolved in the water.

(a) Suggest how Tim and Sarah could test their explanations to find out who is right.

....

.... 2 marks

Sarah suggests testing their explanations by putting a piece of magnesium into the beaker. She says that the potassium will leave a deposit on the magnesium as they react. They try this, but there is no reaction.

Tim says the lack of a reaction proves there was no KCl in the solution.
Sarah is confused because her textbook says that KCl dissolves in water.

(b) Use the data below to explain why Tim is wrong.

.... 1 mark

Reactivity Series

Potassium
Sodium
Calcium
Magnesium
Aluminium

(c) Would it be better for Sarah and Tim to rely on their first-hand experience or a secondary source? Give a reason for your answer.

....

.... 2 marks

Maximum 5 marks

END OF TEST

Coordination Group Publications

Key Stage 3 Science

Answer Book

SATS Practice Papers

Levels 5-7

Contents

Using the Practice Papers P2
Working Out Your Grade P3
Answers P4

Exam Set SHGP31

These practice papers won't make you better at Science...

... but they will show you what you **can** do, and what you **can't** do.

The papers are just like the ones you'll get on the day — so they'll tell you what you need to **work at** if you want to do **better**.

Do a test, **mark it** and look at what you **got wrong**.
That's the stuff you need to learn.

Go away, **learn** those tricky bits, then **do the same test again**. If you're **still** getting questions wrong, you'll have to do even **more practice** and **keep testing** yourself until you get all the questions right.

It doesn't sound like a lot of **fun**, but how else do you expect to **learn** it?

There are two big ways to improve your score

1) **Keep practising the things you get wrong**
If you keep getting the energy questions wrong, practise energy. If you keep making a hash of the plants questions, practise plants. And so on...

2) **Don't throw away easy marks**
Even if a question looks dead simple you have to check your answer and make sure it's sensible.

Doing the Tests

There are **three sets** of practice papers in this pack.
Each set has:

Paper A
1 hour test **75 marks**

Paper B
1 hour test **75 marks**

Follow all the instructions

1) The most important thing is to **understand** the questions.
   Read everything really **carefully** to be sure you're doing what they want.

2) If you're going to do the practice papers more than once,
   then write your answers on a separate bit of paper.

Working out your Grade

- Do a complete exam (Paper A and Paper B).
- Mark both exam papers, and add up the marks (which gives you a mark out of 150).
- Look it up in this table to see what grade you got.

Mark	150 – 105	104 – 73	72 – 42	41 – 36	under 36
Level	7	**6**	**5**	**4**	**N**

Important

Any level you get on these practice papers is **no guarantee** of getting that in the real SAT — **but** it is a pretty good guide.

Published by Coordination Group Publications Ltd

Contributors:
Rebecca Harvey, Frederick Langridge, Jim Wilson.

Editors:
Amy Boutal, Ellen Bowness, Tom Cain, Katherine Craig, Sarah Hilton, Rose Parkin, Kate Redmond, Ami Snelling, Julie Wakeling.

Many thanks to Steve Parkinson for proofreading.

Groovy website: www.cgpbooks.co.uk
Jolly bits of clipart from CorelDRAW
Printed by Elanders Hindson, Newcastle upon Tyne.

1A KS3 Levels 5-7 Science Paper 1A

Q	Marks	Correct answer	Useful tips
1.	1	Immune — Helps protect the body against infections.	
	1	Reproductive — Produces sperm or egg cells.	
	1	Digestive — Breaks down complex food molecules and absorbs them.	
	1	Circulatory — Transports substances such as food and oxygen around the body.	
	1	Respiratory — Replaces oxygen and removes carbon dioxide from the blood.	
2. a	2	Peter's muscles convert chemical energy into movement energy **[One mark]** and Peter's muscles convert chemical energy into heat energy **[One mark]**.	
b	1	Because light travels faster than sound.	
c	2	Speed = distance ÷ time. 200 ÷ 25 = 8 m/s. **[One mark for answer, one mark for correct unit]**	
3.	1	The amount / volume / mass / weight of the tea / water used.	
	1	The temperature of the tea.	
	1	Initial temperature **OR** size / shape of cup **OR** material cup was made from / amount of insulation **OR** time Tim left the cups of tea for **OR** where the cups were left.	
4. a i	1	Solid — C.	*Tip: Subliming, as you might have gathered, is where a substance turns straight from a solid into a gas (or vice versa) without going through the liquid stage. Not many substances do it and you don't really need to know much about it for the exam, so don't worry about it too much.*
ii	1	Melting — D.	
iii	1	Condensing — F.	
iv	1	Liquid — A.	
v	1	Freezing — G.	
vi	1	Gas — B.	
vii	1	Boiling — E.	
b	1	Condensing (F) **OR** Freezing (G)	
5. a	3	Zinc — zinc nitrate — nitric acid **[One mark]**. Iron — iron sulfate — sulfuric acid **[One mark]**. Lead — lead chloride — hydrochloric acid **[One mark]**.	*Tip: All acids contain hydrogen. Metals like zinc, iron and lead, on the other hand, are pure elements. The only atoms they contain are the metal atoms.*
b i	1	E.g. Universal indicator solution **[One mark]**.	
ii	1	E.g. The solution would turn red or orange **[One mark]**.	
c	1	The acid.	
6. a	3	A — cell wall **[One mark]**. B — chloroplast **[One mark]**. C — vacuole **[One mark]**.	
b	1	To support the cell.	*Tip: Never make the mistake of thinking that all plant cells have chloroplasts. There's not much point unless the cell photosynthesises, now is there?*
c	2	Roots are found underground where there is no light **[One mark]**. They don't need chloroplasts as they don't photosynthesise **[One mark]**.	
7. a	4	A quiet high note — B **[One mark]**. A quiet low note — D **[One mark]**. A loud high note — A **[One mark]**. A loud low note — C **[One mark]**.	
b	1	Its frequency is too high **OR** is outside the human hearing range **OR** is above 20 kHz.	
8.	5	Order: H_2SO_4, HNO_3, reduced, increased, $CaCO_3$.	
9. a i	1	It is an addictive drug that raises the heart beat **OR** it narrows the arteries **OR** it causes high blood pressure **OR** it leads to heart disease. **[One mark]**.	
ii	1	It coats the lining of the lungs, making them less able to take in oxygen **OR** it contains carcinogens which cause lung cancer **[One mark]**.	

Q	Marks	*Correct answer*	*Useful tips*
iii	1	It (is a poisonous gas which) reduces the ability of red blood cells to carry oxygen **[One mark]**.	
b	3	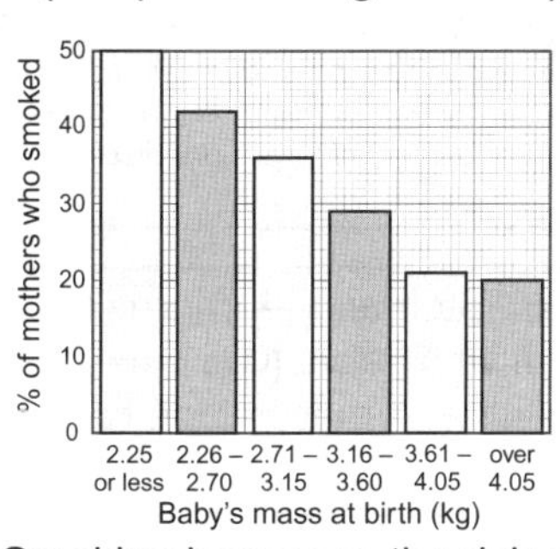	*Tip: If they ask you to do a graph and you have to come up with the scales for the axes yourself, the rule is that you use as much of the available space as you can. Try not to end up with a tiny graph cramped in one corner of the graph paper. Having said that, it's even more important you pick a sensible scale — don't have each small square being worth 3.25 units or anything silly like that.* **[One mark for labelling the axes correctly, one mark for both scales shown correctly on the axes, one mark for showing each bar with the correct height]**
c	1	Smoking increases the risk of the baby having a smaller birth mass, which can lead to health problems.	
10. a	2	A **[One mark]**, because it is the closest to the star **[One mark]**.	
b	2	E **[One mark]**, because it has the greatest mass **[One mark]**.	
11. a	1	To spread out its weight and stop it sinking into the sand.	
b	1	To store fat for food without insulating its body all over (which would make it hotter).	
c	1	To protect its eyes from sand.	*Tip: Even if you haven't learned this, a bit of calm thought and common sense should get you through. Which is nice.*
d	1	To allow it to eat tough / spiky desert plants.	
12. a	1	There was a bright flame **OR** ash formed **OR** the magnesium metal turned into white powder.	
b	1	Magnesium oxide.	
c	1	Magnesium + oxygen $\rightarrow$ magnesium oxide.	
13. a	1	A mixture of compounds.	
b i	1	It is a gas.	
ii	1	Cold water flowing through the condenser cools the naphtha, so it turns back into a liquid.	
14. a	3	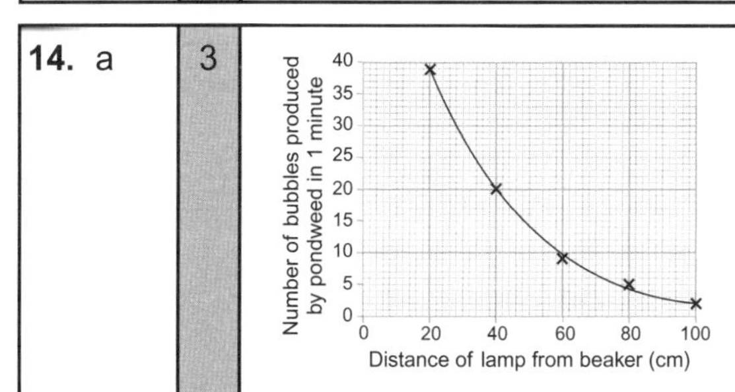	**[One mark for correctly plotting all the points, one mark for labelling the axes correctly, one mark for a smooth curve through the points similar to that shown]**
b	2	The rate of photosynthesis / amount of gas/oxygen produced is lower **[One mark]** the further the lamp is from the plant / the lower the light intensity is **[One mark]**.	
15. a i	1	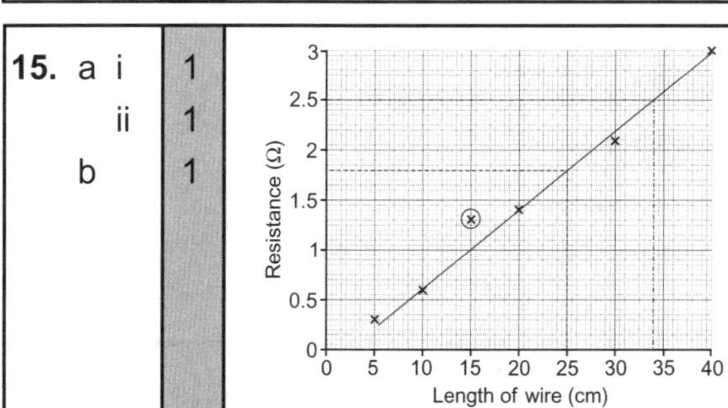	**[One mark for correctly plotting all the points, one mark for a line of best fit similar to that shown]**
ii	1		
b	1		**[One mark for circling the anomalous result as shown]**
c i	1	Accept 1.7 - 1.9 **[One mark]**	
ii	1	Accept 33 - 35 **[One mark]**	
d	1	As the length of the wire increases, the resistance increases **[One mark]**.	

1B KS3 Levels 5-7 Science Paper 1B

Q	Marks	Correct answer	Useful tips
1. a i	1	Water.	
ii	1	Syrup.	*Tip: When something dissolves, it hasn't disappeared — its particles have just got so spread out among the particles of solvent that you can't see them any more. So anything that helps them spread out, like stirring or giving them more energy, will help them dissolve.*
iii	1	Sugar.	
b	1	Heat the mixture **OR** stir the mixture.	
2.	5	Small intestine — absorbs nutrients into the bloodstream **[One mark]**. Stomach — churns up food and mixes it with acid and enzymes **[One mark]**. Teeth — grind up food and mix it with saliva **[One mark]**. Large intestine — absorbs water from the food waste **[One mark]**. Gullet — moves food to the next part of the digestive system by peristalsis **[One mark]**.	
3.	3	See table below. **[Three marks for all correct, one mark for two correct, two marks for three correct]**	*Tip: If you're still getting mixed up with atoms and compounds and elements and molecules, now's the time to get it all worked out. Molecules are made from more than one atom joined together, and they can be elements (if both atoms are the same) or compounds (if the atoms are of different elements).*

Description	Letter
An element made up of molecules	B
Molecules in a compound	C
A mixture of different elements	D
An element made up of atoms	A

Q	Marks	Correct answer	Useful tips
4. a	1	60 × 10 = 600 N	
b	1	Sophie must weigh more than Colin.	
c	2	Any two of: They could add more weight to Colin's end of the seesaw. They could move the plank so the pivot is nearer Sophie / Sophie's end is shorter. **[One mark each]**	
d	2	Set up a balance, putting a heavier weight on one end than the other. Add weights to the lighter end until the heavier end is lifted **[One mark]**. Move the pivot in stages until the heavier end is lifted **[One mark]**.	
5. a	2	Gas A — oxygen **[One mark]**. Gas B — carbon dioxide **[One mark]**.	
b	1	Respiration.	
c	1	glucose + oxygen → carbon dioxide + water (+ energy).	
6. a	2	calcium carbonate + sulfuric acid → calcium sulfate + water + carbon dioxide **[Lose one mark for each mistake]**.	
b	1	A base.	
7.	1	Skin — Forms a physical barrier to most microbes.	
	1	Mucus — Sticky substance that traps microbes in places like the nose and lungs.	
	1	Blood clot — Seals wounds quickly to prevent entry of microbes.	
	1	Stomach acid — Chemical that kills most microbes.	
	1	Immune system — Made up of white blood cells that engulf microbes or release antibodies.	
8. a	1	B.	
b	1	A.	*Tip: There's no excuse for mixing up the rock types. Sedimentary rocks are made from sediments — little crumbs of old rock and dead matter that gradually build up into new rock. Metamorphic rocks have metamorphosised (the fancy word for changed) from one type to another. Then all that's left to remember are igneous rocks — they're the, erm, interesting ones, made from volcanoes and lava and stuff.*
c	1	D.	
d	1	E.	
e	1	C.	
9. a	2	copper sulfate + magnesium → magnesium sulfate + copper **[Lose one mark for each mistake]**.	
b	1	Because the magnesium takes the place of the copper in the copper sulfate solution, forcing the copper out.	
c	1	Magnesium.	*Tip: Don't get confused — the more reactive element would never be left sitting on its own as a pure metal.*

Q	Marks	Correct answer / Useful tips
10. a	2	When it's summer in England the northern half of the Earth is tilted towards the Sun **[One mark]**, so as the Earth turns, the Sun's rays reach it for more of the day **[One mark]**.
b	2	Because of the tilt of the Earth **[One mark]**, the Sun appears much lower in the sky in winter than in summer time **[One mark]**.
11. a	1	The concentration of the acid **[One mark]**.
b	2	Any two of: the volume of acid / mass of marble chips / the size/surface area of the marble chips **[Two marks]**.
c	1	Repeat her experiment and take an average of the results **[One mark]**.
d i	3	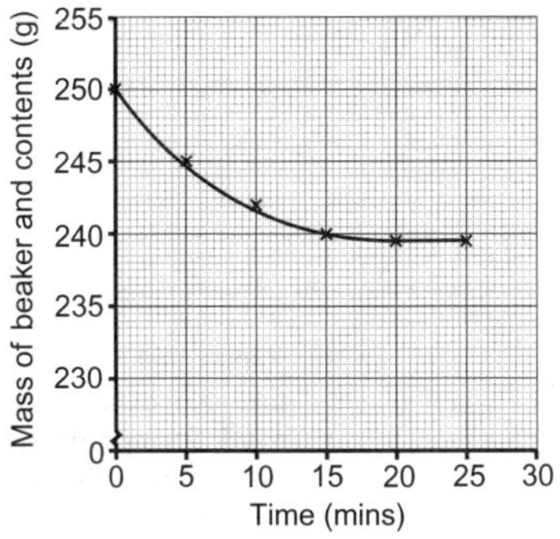 Graph: Mass of beaker and contents (g) (0, 230–255) against Time (mins) (0–30). **[One mark for numbering and labelling the axes correctly, one mark for plotting the points correctly, one mark for joining the points with a smooth curve]**
3ii	1	E.g. the mass of the beaker and contents decreases for 20 minutes and then stays the same **[One mark]**.
iii	1	18½ minutes. *The mass was still changing after 15 minutes, but had stopped by 20, meaning the reaction had finished.*
iv	2	250.0 – 239.5 = 10.5 g. **[One mark for correct answer, one mark for correct unit]**
12. a	1	Primary colours.
b i	2	If only red and blue light shine on the dress, it absorbs the blue light **[One mark]** and reflects only the red light and so appears red **[One mark]**.
ii	2	Yellow light is made up of red and green light **[One mark]**. When both red and green light are shining on it, the dress reflects both colours and appears yellow **[One mark]**.
iii	1	Yellow.
13. a	1	Ball and socket joint.
b	2	One muscle contracts to bend the joint **[One mark]** and the other contracts to straighten the joint **[One mark]**.
c	1	A
14. a	1	The arrow should be drawn pointing directly upwards from the sliding bolt, towards the electromagnet.
b	1	Gravity.
c	1	iron **OR** steel **OR** nickel **OR** cobalt.
d	1	Use a higher voltage/current/more powerful battery **OR** have more turns in the coil of wire of the electromagnet **OR** use a better (more easily magnetised) material for the core of the electromagnet.
15. a	3	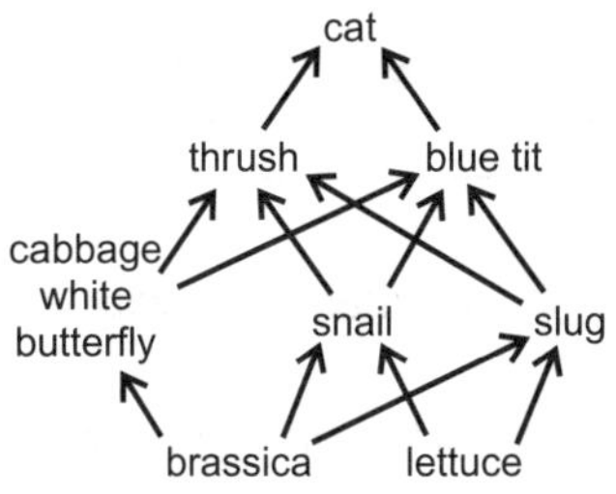 Food web: cat, thrush, blue tit, cabbage white butterfly, snail, slug, brassica, lettuce. **[Take away one mark for each mistake or omission]**
b	1	There are many variables that cannot be controlled when working in the field **[One mark]**.
c	1	By counting the number of slugs and snails using a quadrat. **[One mark]**
d	2	The number of blue tits will decrease **[One mark]**, as there will be less food/fewer slugs and snails for them **[One mark]**.

2A KS3 Levels 5-7 Science Paper 2A

Q	Marks	Correct answer	Useful tips
1.	2	Carbon dioxide — Global warming Sulfur dioxide — Acid rain Solid particles — Asthma **[Three correct for two marks, one correct for one mark]**.	
2.	3	A — carbon dioxide **[One mark]**. B — hydrogen **[One mark]**. C — oxygen **[One mark]**.	
3. a	1	The note would be louder.	
b	2	High frequency **[One mark]** and high pitch **[One mark]**.	
4.	3	Muscle — tissue **[One mark]**. Heart **AND** Brain — organ **[One mark]**. Sperm **AND** Neurone — cell **[One mark]**.	
5. a	1	conduction	
b	3	Your graph should look similar to →	**[One mark for a sensible scale and correctly-labelled axes, one mark for correctly plotting all the points, one mark for good line of best fit.]**
c	2	She could use metal blocks made of different metals (but of the same mass) **[One mark]**. She would need to calculate the change in temperature over time **[One mark]**.	
d	1	Accept 55 °C - 57 °C.	
e	1	It is easier to see the trend.	

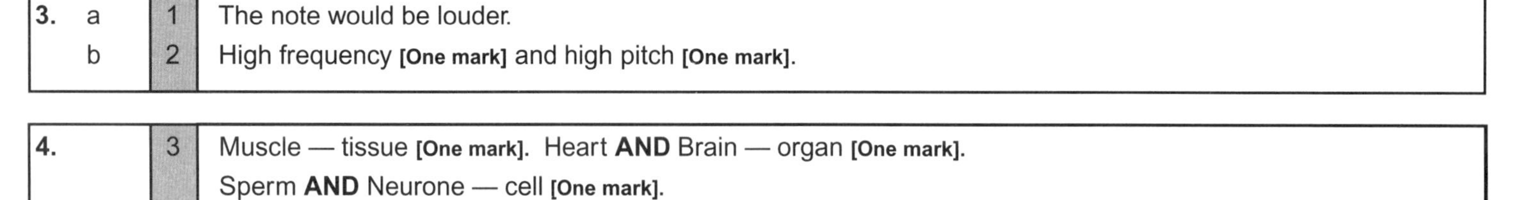

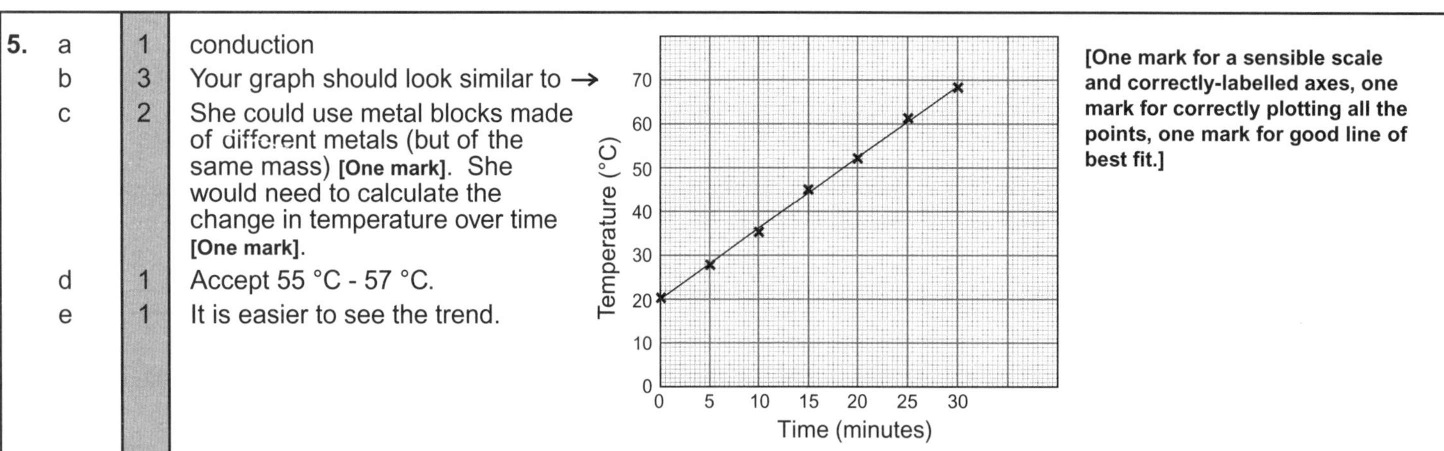

Q	Marks	Correct answer	Useful tips
6. a	1	The ice melted.	*Tip: So, kinetic energy. Sounds a bit technical, but it's simple really. All particles move about a bit — even in solids they vibrate, and in gases they rush about like crazy. When something warms up, the kinetic energy of its particles increases. When something cools down, the kinetic energy of its particles decreases. That's why solids tend to be quite stiff and dense, and gases are floaty and, well, mainly empty space.*
b	1	Their kinetic energy increased.	
c	1	Their kinetic energy decreased.	
d	1	10 °C	
e	1	20 °C	
7. a	1	1 cm	
b	1	E.g. she could measure the height of all the girls in her class and calculate an average **OR** Kath could be measured by someone other than herself.	
c	2	No **[One mark]**. Only a small group of boys and one girl have been included in this study **[One mark]**..	
d i	2	Any two of: facial hair begins to grow, voice deepens, pubic hair begins to grow, testes begin to produce sperm, genitals become more developed, muscles may become more developed **[One mark each]**.	
ii	2	Any two of: hips widen, breasts develop, ovulation / periods start, pubic hair grows **[One mark each]**.	
8. a	1	kinetic	
b	1	The wind energy is free **OR** it causes less environmental problems/pollution than electricity produced by burning fossil fuels **OR** it uses a renewable energy resource.	
c	1	Any one of: it's less reliable because the wind doesn't always blow, it spoils the view, it is noisy, there is a low energy output, it is expensive to build.	
d	1	The Sun.	

Q	Marks	Correct answer	Useful tips
9. a	1	A and Y	
b	1	It is made of a mixture of substance A and substance B.	
c	1	An ink line would be separated out by the solvent and make the chromatogram unclear.	
d	1	If it was below the surface the substances would wash out into the solvent instead of moving up the paper.	
10. a	2	Any two of: brown hair, blue eyes, her sex **[One mark each]**.	*Tip: Don't be fooled — the question asked for features that were due to Rhiannon's genes only, and her height would be due to a combination of genes and her environment.*
b	1	They have different hair colours and different eye colours.	
c	1	She inherits some genes from her mother and some from her father.	
11. a	3	E.g. **[Circuit complete for one mark, lamps connected in parallel for one mark, switches to isolate the lamps independently for one mark.]**	
b	2	The battery might run out more quickly / need replacing more often **[One mark]** because more energy would be needed to power both the lamps **[One mark]**.	
12.	4	Protista — Include algae and amoeba **[One mark]**. Fungi — Moulds, yeasts, mushrooms and toadstools **[One mark]**. Plants — Ferns, mosses, conifers and flowers **[One mark]**. Animals — Insects, fish, birds **[One mark]**.	
13. a	1	magnesium + water $\rightarrow$ magnesium oxide + hydrogen	
b i	2	potassium + water $\rightarrow$ potassium hydroxide **[One mark]** + hydrogen **[One mark]**.	
ii	1	alkali	
ii	1	pH 12	
14. a	1	They live in the hottest climate, so they need long ears to help them keep cool.	
b	1	To enable them to hear predators.	
c	2	They would have small ears **[One mark]** because they live in a cold climate and need to conserve heat **[One mark]**.	
d	1	They use their large ears to keep cool in their warm climate.	
15. a	1	A	*Tip: Remember, air resistance isn't a fixed thing. It changes depending on how fast you're going and how big you are.*
b	1	C	
c	1	B	
d	1	C	
e	2	speed = distance ÷ time = 100 ÷ 15 = 6.7 m/s **[Correct answer for one mark, correct unit for one mark.]**	
16. a	2	Tablet B **[One mark]**. Because it neutralised more acid than tablet A **[One mark]**.	
b	2	Any two of: e.g. strength/concentration of acid / volume of drops / temperature **[One mark each]**.	
c	1	Type of tablet	
d	1	He could repeat the experiment and calculate an average.	

2B KS3 Levels 5-7 Science Paper 2B

Q	Marks	*Correct answer* / *Useful tips*
1. a	3	Copper — 1 **[One mark]**. Sulfur — 1 **[One mark]**. Oxygen — 4 **[One mark]**.
b	1	Copper sulfate. *Tip: If you've recognised the copper, the sulfur and the oxygen, the name of the salt should be pretty obvious.*
2. a	2	E.g. **[One mark for a straight line from any point on the child to the mirror, a straight line from the top mirror to the bottom mirror and a straight line from the mirror to the driver's eye, one mark for direction of light going from child to driver.]** *Tip: Of course, there are other rays of light bouncing off every bit of the child he can see. Luckily you only have to show one of them — otherwise things would get very complicated.*
b	2	**[One mark for showing that the light is reflected onto the opposite surface. One mark for showing that it is then reflected back in the direction from which it originally came.]**
3. a	2	Nucleus — controls the cell. Cytoplasm — where all the chemical reactions take place. Cell membrane — controls what passes into and out of the cell. **[One correct for one mark, all correct for two marks.]**
b i	1	Respiration.
ii	3	Oxygen — used **[One mark]**. Glucose — used **[One mark]**. Carbon dioxide — made **[One mark]**.
c	1	In the blood.
4. a	3	E.g. **[Two marks if all points are plotted correctly, one mark if four or more points are plotted correctly. One mark for straight line of best fit]**
b	1	D
c	1	Accept any answer between 6 and 8.
5. a	2	It is repelled by magnet A **[One mark]**, so moves downwards away from it **[One mark]**.
b	2	If it's the wrong way up it will attract the small magnet **[One mark]**, which will move in the wrong direction and give a result that's off the scale **[One mark]**.
c	1	So that the arm is balanced before any magnets are tested **OR** to increase the sensitivity / accuracy / precision of the pointer / so that the pointer moves more.
d	1	The stronger magnet will give a bigger reading / make the pointer move further up the scale.
6. a	2	The water has become more acidic **[One mark]**, because the universal indicator has turned from green (neutral) to orange (weak acid) **[One mark]**.
b	2	Ordinary air didn't affect the pH of the water after 2 minutes **[One mark]**, because the universal indicator stayed green (neutral) **[One mark]**.
c	2	Becky's experiment showed that breathing into water made it more acidic **[One mark]**, and Huang's showed that this was due to a substance in her breath and not just due to air bubbling through it **[One mark]**.
7. a	1	Enzymes.
b	1	Amylase.

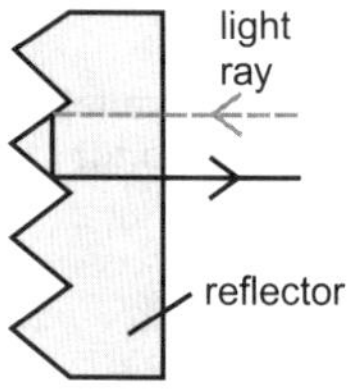

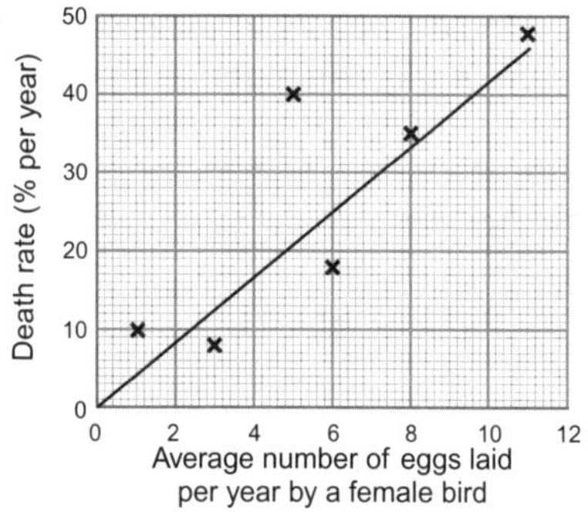

Q	Marks	Correct answer	Useful tips
c	2	X — protein **[One mark]**. Y — amino acid **[One mark]**.	
d	1	Meat **OR** fish **OR** eggs **OR** cheese **OR** beans **OR** lentils.	
8. a	2	Rock B **[One mark]**, because its crystals are bigger due to it cooling more slowly/underground **[One mark]**.	
b	2	Marble — metamorphic. Limestone — sedimentary. Granite — igneous. **[One mark one correct, two marks for all]**.	
9. a	2	Its speed stays constant because there's no friction to slow it down **[One mark]**. It needs to be moving to stay in orbit **[One mark]**.	
b	1	Surveying **OR** spying **OR** mapping **OR** telephones **OR** navigation **OR** research (accept other sensible answers).	*Tip: Satellites are used for loads of things. The only one you can't say is TV, because they already told you that in the question.*
c	1	The Moon.	
10. a	1	friction **OR** air resistance	
b	2	Bar chart: Distance Travelled (cm) (0–60) against Colour of Car (red, blue, green, black). **[One mark for two bars plotted correctly, two marks for all bars plotted correctly (including labels on x-axis).]**	*Tip: They've done the first one for you here, so use that to your advantage and make sure your bars are the same width and in the same position within the space.*
c	2	E.g. different mass, different amounts of friction between floor and wheels, different amount of air resistance due to different shapes, rolled down slope from different heights **[One mark for each]**.	
11. a	1	It is wasted as heat.	
b	2	The cost of electrical energy **[One mark]** and the price of each bulb **[One mark]**.	
c	2	She won't have to bother changing it so often **[One mark]** and less CO_2 is produced by the low power bulbs **[One mark]**.	
d	1	20% of 60 = (60 ÷ 100) × 20 = 12 watt	
12. a	1	Because the same atoms are present.	
b i	1	Oxygen	
ii	1	2 g	
c	1	Zinc oxide	
13. a	2	They produce mucus to trap particles and microorganisms **[One mark]**. They are lined with cilia to push the particles and microorganisms back out of the lungs **[One mark]**.	
b	1	Nicotine.	
c	1	The cilia are destroyed so can't remove microorganisms from the lungs.	
d	1	It prevents the red blood cells carrying oxygen around the body properly.	
14. a	1	A solution in which no more solid can dissolve.	
b i	2	**[One mark for correct axes, one mark for points correctly plotted.]** →	Graph: solubility (g / 100 g water) (0–60) against temperature (°C) (0–40)
ii	1	The point at 24 °C should be circled.	
iii	1	This could have been caused by, e.g. not stirring enough, overheating the solution, a weighing error **[One mark]**.	
iv	1	The curve should pass through all the points apart from the circled one. →	
c	1	The solubility of potassium nitrate increases as the temperature increases.	
d i	1	Accept answer between 30 and 33 g / 100 g	
ii	1	Accept answer between 43 and 45 g / 100 g	

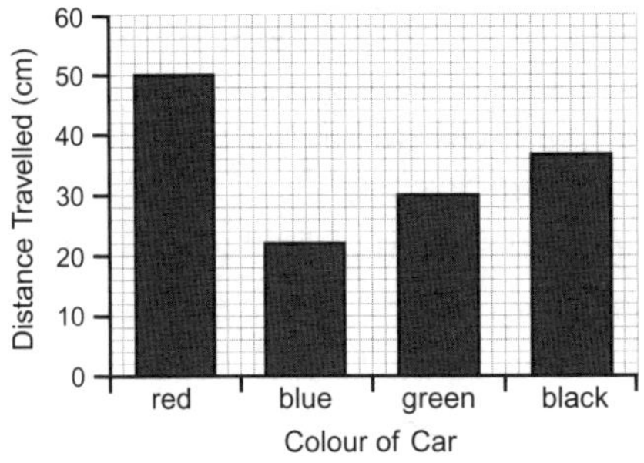

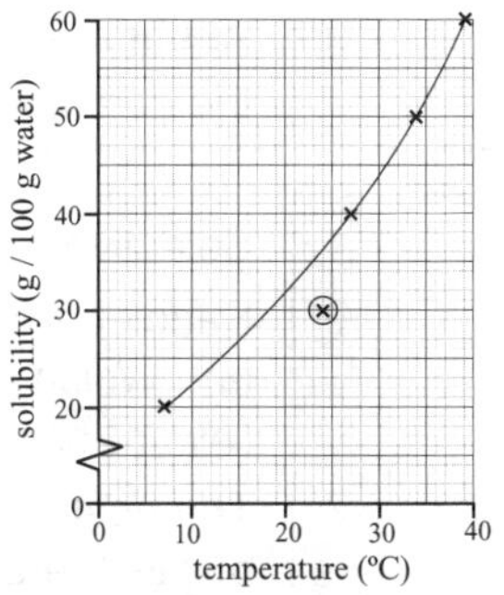

3A KS3 Levels 5-7 Science Paper 3A

Q	Marks	Correct answer	Useful tips
1. a i	1	Lamp **OR** bulb.	
ii	1	Ammeter.	
iii	1	Battery.	*Tip: Don't forget that there's a wire going through the middle of the fuse — people are always missing that off, and you won't get the mark if you do.*
iv	1	Voltmeter.	
b	1	The fuse should be drawn as shown:	
2.	4	Stomach acid — red — 1 **[One mark]**. Soap powder — blue — 10 **[One mark]**. Lemon juice — orange — 3 **[One mark]**. Salt water — green — 7 **[One mark]**.	
3. a i	1	... there is no air on the Moon.	
ii	1	... the Moon has a much smaller mass than the Earth.	
b	2	300 000 × 1.25 = 375 000 km. **[One mark for correct answer, one mark for correct units]**	
4. a	1	He used the same type of plant (geranium) **OR** same size of plant **OR** he left them for the same length of time (two weeks) **OR** he watered them all with the same frequency (daily).	
b	3	Plant A — Couldn't photosynthesise in the dark so grew spindly in search of light **[One mark]**. Plant B — Had plenty of light for photosynthesis so grew well **[One mark]**. Plant C — Had enough light for photosynthesis, but still grew towards the light to absorb more **[One mark]**.	
c	1	My results show that plants are sensitive to the amount of light available.	
5. a i	1	It is a renewable energy resource **OR** it doesn't produce any pollution **OR** it doesn't give out carbon dioxide / add to the greenhouse effect.	
ii	1	The land is flooded, which destroys habitats **OR** Animals and plants living in the flooded valley might be killed, including rare species.	
b	2	Any two of: coal, oil, natural gas (accept 'fossil fuels' if a specific example is not used for the second mark), wind, wave, tidal, nuclear, biomass, solar, geothermal **[One mark each]**.	
6. a	2	From top to bottom, the column should read: 20, 24, 29, 21, 28 **[Lose one mark for each mistake]**	
b	2	Any two of: always use the same mass of cornflakes, always use the same volume of water, keep the boiling tube the same distance from the burning cornflakes, keep the thermometer at the same height in the boiling tube **[One mark each]**.	
c	1	They could repeat the experiment several times and take an average.	
d	1	They could insulate the apparatus **OR** use a wider-bottomed container for the water (to absorb more of the heat from the cornflakes).	
7. a	1	Distillation.	
b	1	They have different boiling points **OR** alcohol boils at a lower temperature than water does.	
c	1	The alcohol is cooling and turning back into a liquid / condensing.	
d	2	Brandy **[One mark]**, because the alcohol in the wine evaporates off first and runs into the container of brandy **[One mark]**.	
8. a	1	Selective breeding.	
b	2	Saddleback, so it will be hardy enough to live outside **[One mark]**, and Welsh, so it will have lean meat and large litters **[One mark]**. (Award one mark only if correct varieties are given but no reasons.)	*Tip: What a shame if you knew the answer but lost marks for not giving reasons. Especially as the question clearly says 'Explain your answer.' Always read the question carefully.*
c	2	The best of the offspring would be chosen and bred together **[One mark]**, and after many generations of this there could be a new variety with new features **[One mark]**.	

Q	Marks	Correct answer	Useful tips
9. a	3	P — breastbone **OR** sternum **[One mark]**. Q — ribs **[One mark]**. R — backbone **OR** spine **OR** vertebral column **[One mark]**.	
b i	1	Protection.	
ii	1	Support **OR** movement.	
10. a i	2	Plastic **OR** wood **[One mark]**, because it is not a good conductor of heat so will stop his hand being burnt **[One mark]**.	*Tip: That's right, there was more than one correct answer. That might happen now and again, so don't let it confuse you — don't sit there for hours trying to come up with a reason why wood wouldn't be any good as a handle.*
ii	2	Copper **OR** steel **[One mark]**, because it has a high melting point **OR** because it is not flammable **[One mark]**.	
b	1	The smoke is hotter than the air in the room, meaning it is less dense, so it rises — straight up the chimney.	
c	1	The heat energy is given out in the form of a wave by radiation.	
11. a	1	Any one of: wear goggles, use a heat-proof mat, handle the hot crucible with tongs **[One mark]**.	
b	2	Element: 1 **OR** 2 **[One mark]**. Compound: 4 **[One mark]**.	
c i	1	Iron sulfide.	
ii	1	FeS.	
d	1	8.8 g.	
12. a	1	Virus.	
b i	2	She has been injected with a harmless form of the microorganism **[One mark]** to make her immune to it **[One mark]**.	
ii	2	No, her immune system still fights the microorganism **[One mark]** — the vaccine just prepares it in advance to deal with future infections **[One mark]**.	
13.	4	(see grid below) **[One mark for every four squares filled in correctly]**	*Tip: It's amazing how many people get these wrong, because all you really need to know is that a more reactive metal takes the place of a less reactive one in a solution. And the reactivity series is right there, showing you who's more reactive than who.*

	calcium	magnesium	iron	copper
calcium nitrate	✗	✗	✗	✗
magnesium nitrate	✓	✗	✗	✗
iron nitrate	✓	✓	✗	✗
copper nitrate	✓	✓	✓	✗

Q	Marks	Correct answer	Useful tips
14. a	2	Any two of: Amount of food available, number of sparrowhawks or other predators, amount of competition (for food, shelter etc.) from other animals, amount of disease in the population, number of nesting sites available, weather **[One mark each]**.	
b	2	The populations of both birds go up and down with time **[One mark]**. The number of sparrowhawks rises and falls shortly after the same change in the number of sparrows **[One mark]**.	
c	2	When there are lots of sparrows, there's a lot of food for the sparrowhawks and so more survive **[One mark]**. However, if a lot of sparrowhawks survive, there are a lot of predators for the sparrows and their numbers fall, leaving less food for the sparrowhawks so their numbers also drop shortly after **[One mark]**.	
15.	2	The elephant's weight is spread out over a much bigger area **[One mark]**, so it exerts less pressure on the floor than Mrs Lightfoot's heels which cover a much smaller area **[One mark]**.	
16. a	1	$800 \times 10 = 8000$ N.	
b	2	Pressure = force ÷ area. Pressure = $8000 \div 0.25 = 32\ 000$ N/m^2 **[One mark for correct answer, one mark for correct units]**	

3B KS3 Levels 5-7 Science Paper 3B

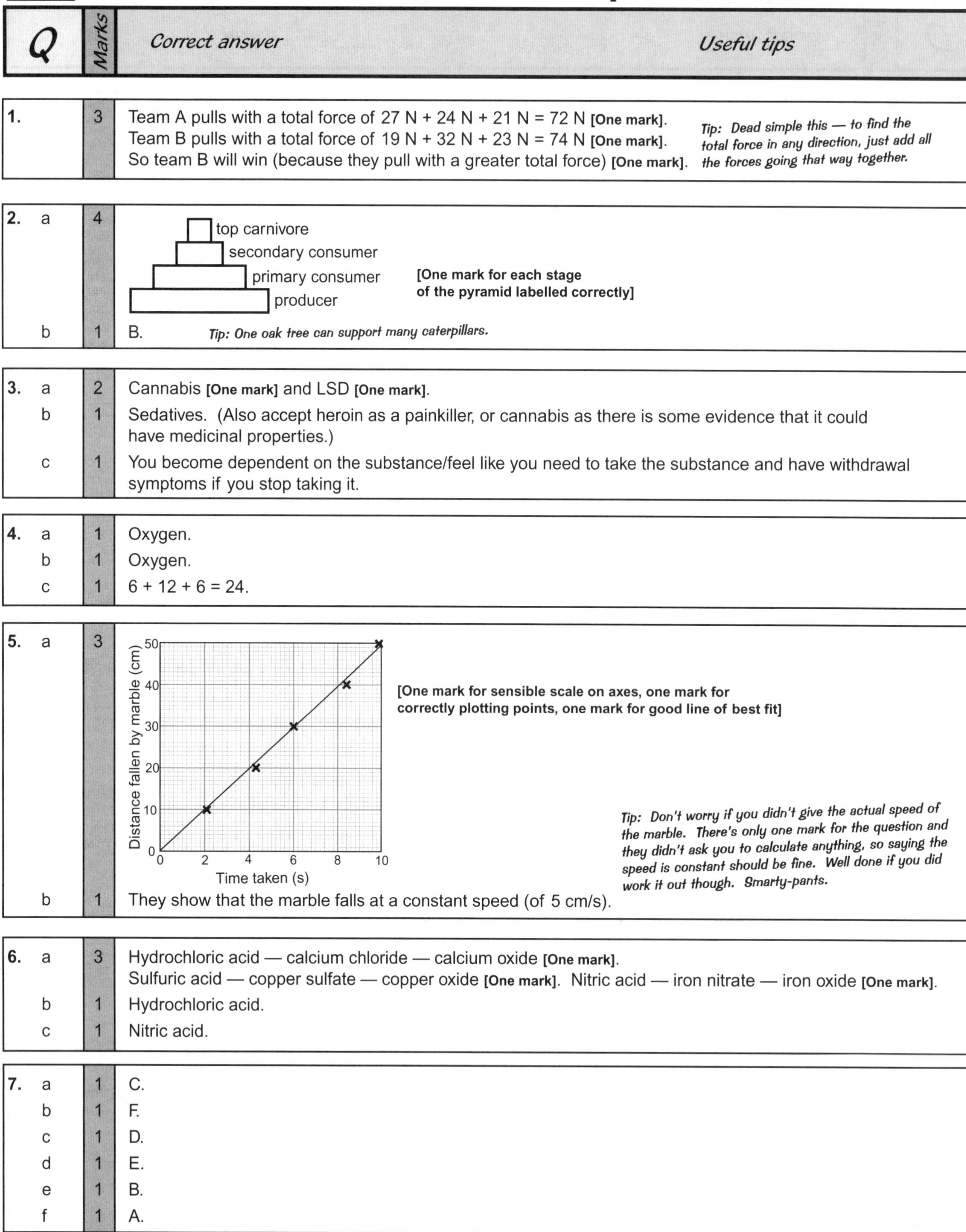

Q	Marks	Correct answer	Useful tips
1.	3	Team A pulls with a total force of 27 N + 24 N + 21 N = 72 N **[One mark]**. Team B pulls with a total force of 19 N + 32 N + 23 N = 74 N **[One mark]**. So team B will win (because they pull with a greater total force) **[One mark]**.	*Tip: Dead simple this — to find the total force in any direction, just add all the forces going that way together.*
2. a	4	Pyramid (top to bottom): top carnivore; secondary consumer; primary consumer; producer **[One mark for each stage of the pyramid labelled correctly]**	
b	1	B.	*Tip: One oak tree can support many caterpillars.*
3. a	2	Cannabis **[One mark]** and LSD **[One mark]**.	
b	1	Sedatives. (Also accept heroin as a painkiller, or cannabis as there is some evidence that it could have medicinal properties.)	
c	1	You become dependent on the substance/feel like you need to take the substance and have withdrawal symptoms if you stop taking it.	
4. a	1	Oxygen.	
b	1	Oxygen.	
c	1	6 + 12 + 6 = 24.	
5. a	3	Graph: Distance fallen by marble (cm), 0–50, against Time taken (s), 0–10 **[One mark for sensible scale on axes, one mark for correctly plotting points, one mark for good line of best fit]**	
b	1	They show that the marble falls at a constant speed (of 5 cm/s).	*Tip: Don't worry if you didn't give the actual speed of the marble. There's only one mark for the question and they didn't ask you to calculate anything, so saying the speed is constant should be fine. Well done if you did work it out though. Smarty-pants.*
6. a	3	Hydrochloric acid — calcium chloride — calcium oxide **[One mark]**. Sulfuric acid — copper sulfate — copper oxide **[One mark]**. Nitric acid — iron nitrate — iron oxide **[One mark]**.	
b	1	Hydrochloric acid.	
c	1	Nitric acid.	
7. a	1	C.	
b	1	F.	
c	1	D.	
d	1	E.	
e	1	B.	
f	1	A.	
8. a	2	Methane + oxygen → carbon dioxide + water **[Take away one mark for each mistake or omission]**.	
b	2	More carbon dioxide **[One mark]** and less oxygen **[One mark]**.	*Tip: Any compound of just hydrogen and carbon produces water and carbon dioxide when it burns.*
c	1	C.	

Q	Marks	Correct answer	Useful tips
9. a i	1	Chemical energy.	
ii	1	Heat energy.	
iii	1	Kinetic energy.	
iv	1	Electrical energy.	
v	1	Light energy.	
b	2	Conduction — the metal tray holding the burning fuel gets hot. Convection — warm air from above the boiler circulates the room. Radiation — heat flows from the white-hot filament in the bulb to the surroundings.	**[Two marks for all correct, one mark for one correct]**

Q	Marks	Correct answer	Useful tips
10. a	1	Carbon dioxide + water $\rightarrow$ glucose + oxygen.	
b	1	By counting the number of bubbles produced in a given time.	
c	1	Repeat the experiment and take an average of his readings.	
d	1	Chlorophyll.	
e	1	Light energy **OR** sunlight	

Q	Marks	Correct answer	Useful tips
11. a	4	P — ovary **[One mark]**. Q — oviduct **OR** Fallopian tube **[One mark]**. R — uterus **OR** womb **[One mark]**. S — cervix **[One mark]**.	
b	1	An ovary.	
c	1	Day 14.	
d	1	Its lining thickens.	

Q	Marks	Correct answer	Useful tips
12. a	3	Similar to: 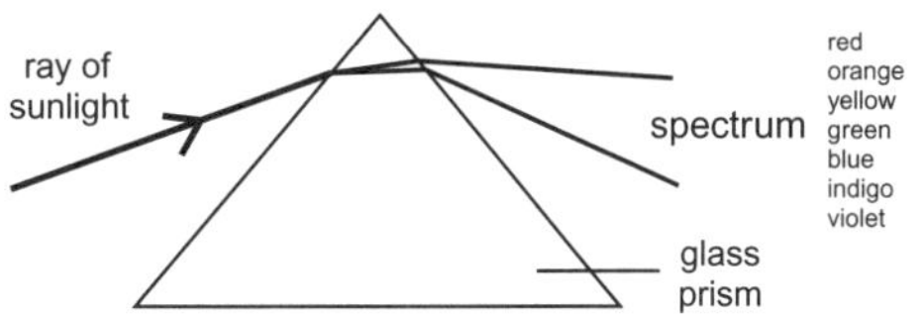 ray of sunlight spectrum: red, orange, yellow, green, blue, indigo, violet glass prism	**[One mark for showing the direction of the ray changing correctly, one mark for showing that the ray spreads out, one mark for giving a spectrum of colours]**
b	2	Dispersion **[One mark]** and refraction **[One mark]**.	

Q	Marks	Correct answer	Useful tips
13. a	2	Heating the coin gives the particles more energy, so they vibrate more strongly **[One mark]**. This means that each particle takes up a slightly bigger volume, so the coin expands **[One mark]**.	
b	2	The particles of rose-water had more energy after heating **[One mark]**, so they turned into gas particles (which could spread around the room) more readily **[One mark]**.	
c	2	They both involve the particles of the substances **[One mark]** changing their behaviour after being given more energy **[One mark]**.	

Q	Marks	Correct answer	Useful tips
14. a	2	Lit: A, B **[One mark]**. Not lit: C, D **[One mark]**.	
b	3	Close switch S1 **[One mark]**. Open switch S2 **[One mark]**. Remove the voltmeter **OR** connect the voltmeter in parallel not in series **[One mark]**.	

Q	Marks	Correct answer	Useful tips
15. a	2	By evaporating all the water **[One mark]** to see if a solid is left behind (because KCl will only be left if it was dissolved in the water) **[One mark]**.	
b	1	There was no reaction because potassium is more reactive than magnesium.	
c	2	A secondary source **[One mark]** because their conclusions are based on an error **[One mark]**.	

Set A

Vampires

Contents

Yikes! Vampire Bats Can Run, Too....................page 3

Writing Horror — Forbidden Treats....................page 5

Extract from *Dracula*....................page 7

The idea of bloodsucking vampires has frightened and fascinated people for centuries. There are many superstitions and legends about them. Writers describe imaginary vampires in fiction. Scientists are still discovering more about the powers of the only real vampires — vampire bats — which have some very surprising abilities.

© TOM MCHUGH / SCIENCE PHOTO LIBRARY

Common vampire bats live in Mexico and most countries in Central and South America. They roost in dark caves and tree hollows and feed on the blood of birds and mammals such as cows and horses. This article by Robert Ray Britt for the LiveScience *website reports on a new discovery about how they can move around.*

Yikes! Vampire Bats Can Run, Too

As if nature really needed to endow vampire bats with anything more unusual than the ability to fly and a propensity to drink blood, the creatures have been found to sprint along the ground, too. 1

All the better to sneak up on a victim, scientists say. 2

A new study found fleet-footed vampire bats can break into a loping run on all fours, at least when coaxed on a treadmill. 3

Bad news for cows

Bats are the only mammals that fly. Scientists think they generally stopped running long ago, as evolution gave flight capabilities to their forelimbs. Most species of bats, if asked to run, can do little more than flop around like fish out of water. 4

Vampire bats must have regained the ability to run, says Cornell University researcher Daniel Riskin, who led the new experiments. The skill might have been useful for chasing down small, swift animals that wouldn't sit still for a feeding event, Riskin told *LiveScience*. 5

Thing is, the common vampire bat rarely chases small animals any more. Instead, it feeds mostly on dozing cattle that have been introduced into the bats' range — mostly from northern Mexico down to Argentina and Chile — over the past few hundred years, Riskin said. In labs, a vampire bat will feed on anything — even a snake — but in the wild they prefer cows, whose blood they drink mostly at night while the livestock sleep. 6

"Cows just seem to be the easiest," he said. 7

The ability to run is not so critical when gorging on a sleeping cow, and therefore it has gone unnoticed by scientists, Riskin figures. 8

Hopping is good, when you're a bat slurping cow blood, because cows are heavy and can kick or roll over and squash a bat, Riskin explained in a telephone interview. 9

On to the treadmill

Scientists knew previously that the legs of vampires were stronger than those of other bats, enabling them to crawl and hop. In the March 17 issue of the journal *Nature*, Riskin and his colleagues write: "The common vampire bat (*Desmodus rotundus*) walks forwards, sideways and backwards, and initiates flight with a single vertical jump from standing." Researchers still don't know exactly why they can walk. 10

And nobody had ever documented bats doing the 4-yard dash. 11

To study this movement, captive bats were put on a treadmill — safely inside a Plexiglas cage — and photographed. At slow treadmill speeds, the bats walked in a manner similar to mice. When the treadmill was cranked up, the clever little mammals dutifully kept pace, using mostly their powerful forelimbs to reach speeds exceeding 2.7 miles per hour (1.2 metres per second). 12

"Bats with a little more room to manoeuvre can probably move twice that fast," Riskin said. 13

For the record, a reasonably fit human can run much more quickly. 14

The swift gait of the vampire bat is unlike that of any other animal, the study found. The scientists call it running "because it includes a notable aerial phase." You might want to jog across the room with a nice spring in your step to understand what that means. 15

Vampire bats, it seems, are over-evolved, now that their prey are just lumbering cattle. 16

"It's as if they were designed to chase race cars," Riskin said, "and they find themselves running after school buses." 17

Blood Suckers?

A vampire bat's wingspan is typically 8 inches, though its body is about the size of an adult human thumb. It feeds on the blood of horses, pigs and even birds. The common vampire bat, *Desmodus rotundus*, prefers cows, however. 18

The vampire hunts at night, when other animals are sleeping. It doesn't suck blood. It uses heat sensors to find a victim's veins. Sharp teeth cut the animal — about like a shaving nick — and the bat simply laps up what oozes out. 19

A chemical in the bat's saliva keeps the blood from clotting, so it keeps flowing (a blood-thinning drug developed from vampire bat saliva helps prevent strokes and heart attacks). Another chemical numbs the victim's skin so it won't wake up. 20

"They sit there licking the wound for up to a half hour," says Daniel Riskin of Cornell University. A bat will drink about a tablespoon of blood in a sitting. 21

Vampires have attacked humans, but such reports are rare. 22

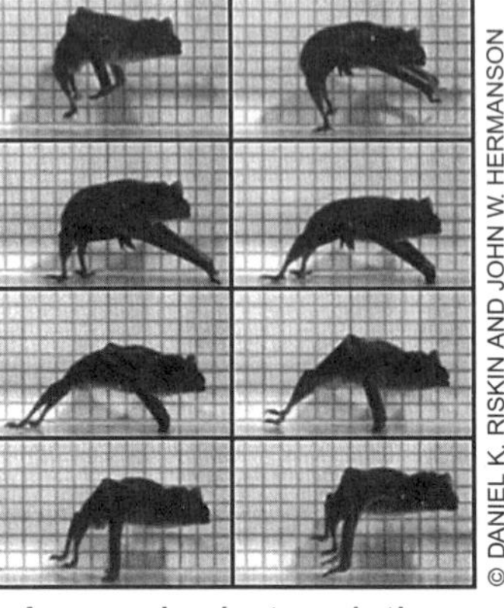

A vampire bat sprinting.

Darren Shan is an author who writes for teenagers. His series of vampire stories — which feature a teenage hero whose name is Darren Shan — began with the novel "Cirque Du Freak". In this article for a children's book website, Kidsreads, he explains some of the ideas behind the story.

Writing Horror — Forbidden Treats

by Darren Shan

I remember somehow catching the hammy* Vincent Price film, "Theater Of Blood," when I was 6 years old. It's the one where he plays a lambasted** Shakespearean actor who sets out to silence his critics with artistic murderous licence. In one scene he feeds a critic the mashed-up remains of his beloved poodles, on which the poor man duly chokes. I was blown away! This was story-telling as I'd never experienced it, and even at that tender age, while other kids were glued to nice, safe, anodyne*** stuff, I knew I wanted more!!! 1

That thirst for "more" has never left me. As a child and teenager I sought out all the horror that I could, be it in movies, books or comics. I craved creepiness. If nightmares were the result — all the better! Over the years, I moved on and found other loves (horror is fun, but it can be limiting), though nothing ever had the same effect on me as those old Hammer movies, or Stephen King's early novels, or the short stories of Edgar Allan Poe. 2

When I came to write Cirque Du Freak, I had only one mandate**** in mind: I was going to write the sort of book that I'd have loved to read as an 11/12 year old. It didn't matter that, as a twentysomething, I wasn't as stoked-up by horror as I'd once been. I wasn't writing for twenty year olds: I was writing for kids, and for the kid I'd once been — and I was determined to treat them to the sort of gruesome helter-skelter ride I believed they deserved. 3

** hammy = dramatically over-acted*

*** lambasted = strongly criticised*

****anodyne = dull*

*****mandate = rule*

Cirque Du Freak isn't a reckless, irresponsible book. Although it's about vampires and circus freaks, I wasn't interested in sickening readers or pushing back the boundaries of what is acceptable. It explores such themes as friendship, the importance of family, and the need to make personal sacrifices for the good of others. But, like "Theater Of Blood," it certainly isn't for the squeamish! While there are no poodles in the book, there are vampires and poisonous tarantulas; a savage Wolf Man and a Snake Boy; one character winds up in a coma, whilst another gets buried alive. It's a book designed to play on a reader's emotions. There are out-and-out scary scenes ("boo! moments" as I like to call them), but also darker, less bombastic* scenes, which will linger in your mind for days (and nights!) to come. 4

That, for me, is the secret of good horror: the subtle menace between the sudden bursts of action and violence. Cirque Du Freak is designed not just to thrill you, but to set your nerves on edge. It's sometimes shocking, but also thought-provoking. Because that's where I believe the greatest horrors lie: not in having something leap at you out of the darkness, but in staring into the shadows of the night and brooding about what lurks within...waiting...staring back... 5

** bombastic = extremely dramatic to impress*

Jonathan Harker has travelled to Transylvania to have a business meeting with Count Dracula. While staying in the Count's castle in the Carpathian mountains, he realises that he is a prisoner. Here he records a strange event in his journal. This is an extract from the 19th-century novel, Dracula, by Bram Stoker.

Dracula

When he left me I went to my room. After a little while, not hearing any sound, I came out and went up the stone stair to where I could look out towards the South. There was some sense of freedom in the vast expanse, inaccessible though it was to me, as compared with the narrow darkness of the courtyard. Looking out on this, I felt that I was indeed in prison, and I seemed to want a breath of fresh air, though it were of the night. I am beginning to feel this nocturnal existence tell on me. It is destroying my nerve. I start at my own shadow, and am full of all sorts of horrible imaginings. God knows that there is ground for my terrible fear in this accursed place!
I looked out over the beautiful expanse, bathed in soft yellow moonlight till it was almost as light as day. In the soft light the distant hills became melted, and the shadows in the valleys and gorges of velvety blackness. The mere beauty seemed to cheer me. There was peace and comfort in every breath I drew. As I leaned from the window my eye was caught by something moving a storey below me, and somewhat to my left, where I imagined, from the order of the rooms, that the windows of the Count's own room would look out. The window at which I stood was tall and deep, stone-mullioned*, and though weatherworn, was still complete. But it was evidently many a day since the case had been there. I drew back behind the stonework, and looked carefully out.

1

** stone-mullioned = with a stone frame*

What I saw was the Count's head coming out from the window. I did not see the face, but I knew the man by the neck and the movement of his back and arms. In any case I could not mistake the hands which I had had some many opportunities of studying. I was at first interested and somewhat amused, for it is wonderful how small a matter will interest and amuse a man when he is a prisoner. But my very feelings changed to repulsion and terror when I saw the whole man slowly emerge from the window and begin to crawl down the castle wall over the dreadful abyss*, face down with his cloak spreading out around him like great wings. At first I could not believe my eyes. I thought it was some trick of the moonlight, some weird effect of shadow, but I kept looking, and it could be no delusion. I saw the fingers and toes grasp the corners of the stones, worn clear of the mortar by the stress of years, and by thus using every projection and inequality move downwards with considerable speed, just as a lizard moves along a wall. 2

What manner of man is this, or what manner of creature is it in the semblance** of man? I feel the dread of this horrible place overpowering me. I am in fear, in awful fear, and there is no escape for me. I am encompassed*** about with terrors that I dare not think of. 3

** abyss = deep drop*

***semblance = likeness*

****encompassed = surrounded*

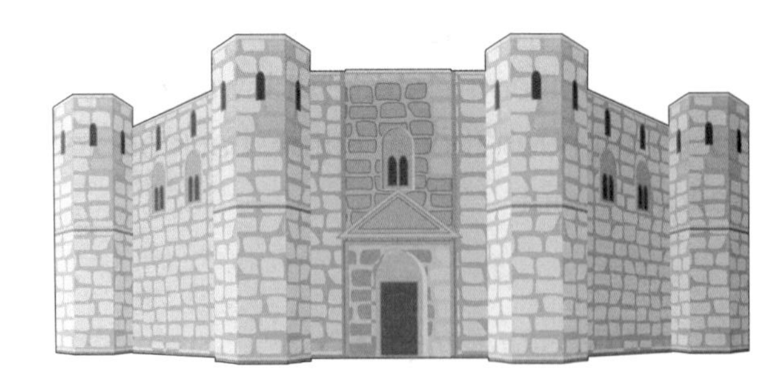

Set B

Changing Schools

Contents

Extract from *Harry Potter and the Philosopher's Stone*................................page 3

Starting 'big' school..page 5

Wingrave School...page 7

For many people, starting a new school is the first time they've had to adapt to a sudden change. It can be scary and intimidating but it can also be an exciting opportunity to make new friends and experience new things.

This is an extract from the book 'Harry Potter and the Philosopher's Stone' by J. K. Rowling. Harry Potter is just getting used to being at Hogwarts, his new school. Like most people in a new place he is finding it difficult to work out where he is going, especially as things keep moving.

Harry Potter and the Philosopher's Stone

There were a hundred and forty-two staircases at Hogwarts: wide, sweeping ones; narrow, rickety ones; some that led somewhere different on a Friday; some with a vanishing step halfway up that you had to remember to jump. Then there were doors that wouldn't open unless you asked politely, or tickled them in exactly the right place, and doors that weren't really doors at all, but solid walls just pretending. It was also very hard to remember where anything was, because it all seemed to move around a lot. The people in the portraits kept going to visit each other and Harry was sure the coats of armour could walk. 1

The ghosts didn't help, either. It was always a nasty shock when one of them glided suddenly through a door you were trying to open. Nearly Headless Nick was always happy to point new Gryffindors in the right direction, but Peeves the poltergeist was worth two locked doors and a trick staircase if you met him when you were late for class. He would drop waste-paper baskets on your head, pull rugs from under your feet, pelt you with bits of chalk or sneak up behind you, invisible, grab your nose and screech, 'GOT YOUR CONK!' 2

Even worse than Peeves, if that was possible, was the caretaker, Argus Filch. Harry and Ron managed to get on the wrong side of him on their very first morning. Filch found them trying to force their way through a door which unluckily turned out to be the entrance to the out-of-bounds corridor on the third floor. He wouldn't believe they were lost, was sure they were 3 trying to break into it on purpose and was threatening to lock them in the dungeons when they were rescued by Professor Quirrell, who was passing.

Filch owned a cat called Mrs Norris, a scrawny, dust-coloured creature with bulging, lamp-like eyes just like Filch's. She patrolled the corridors alone. Break a rule in front of her, put just one toe out of line, and she'd whisk off for Filch, who'd appear, wheezing, two seconds later. Filch knew the secret passageways of the school better than anyone (except perhaps the Weasley twins) and could pop up as suddenly as any of the ghosts. The students all hated him and it was the dearest ambition of many to give Mrs Norris a good kick.

And then, once you had managed to find them, there were the lessons themselves. There was a lot more to magic, as Harry quickly found out, than waving your wand and saying a few funny words.

They had to study the night skies through their telescopes every Wednesday at midnight and learn the names of different stars and the movements of the planets. Three times a week they went out to the greenhouses behind the castle to study Herbology, with a dumpy little witch called Professor Sprout, where they learnt how to take care of all the strange plants and fungi and found out what they were used for.

The experience of moving from primary to secondary school is shared by almost everyone. In this article, some Year 7 students and their headmaster talk about the first day at secondary school. This article is from the BBC website.

Starting 'big' school

September. New school year. New shoes and uniform, new books and pencil case. Leaving cosy primary school behind and entering those big gates with those bigger pupils and a frightening day ahead. Was that you?? 1

Do you remember your first day at 'big' school? The rumours about having your head flushed in the toilet, the daunting view of the big building, the other pupils so much bigger than you, the prospect of real homework and strict teachers? Oh yes, it can be such a scary time and it happens to us all. 2

New pupils starting at the Royal Wolverhampton Senior School have sent us their impressions of their first day. See what they have to say. 3

Alexandra

I woke up about 7.00 in the morning feeling nervous but at the same time excited. I quickly ate my breakfast and rushed to the door and then my mum and dad stopped me and took lots of pictures of me. 4

I could tell they were proud of me. My dad walked me to the bus station but we had to wait about 15 minutes before it came. Soon it arrived and I was waving to my dad and I set off. 5

When I got there we went straight to Chapel and I met a girl called Erin who was really nice. After Chapel we did some games, then after break we had a tour of the school. 6

By then it was time for lunch and we ate. Then we had to find bits of string that were in our house colour. It took a long time but it was great fun. Mr Thomas said at the end to me that I did impress him. After that we went to have tea it was very nice. I really like this school and I can't wait for another day to come. 7

Chenise

As I walked through the grand double door, I saw many people hanging around the wooden table. There was a crowd of people there, waiting to be welcomed to the start of the Senior School. Finally a member of staff welcomed my mom and I. We were sent to Victoria Hall. After a few minutes, and after all our hugs and kisses, parents/guardians left. 8

Later on we visited Reynolds. It was like the Year 7/year 8 base. I was amazed when I first saw it. There is a work room, kitchen, common room and the sofa room. I am looking forward to using these facilities. 9

After Chapel we were told which Form we were in. I am now in 7.1 which is Mr Rayner. We then went to our Form room, Room 9. In there we wrote in our diaries the timetable for the year. Then we wrote what subjects the teachers taught. 10

A few minutes later we doubled up (7.1 and 7.2) and Mr Rayner and Mr Thomas gave us a quick tour of the school. 11

After that, it was lunch time. I had a jacket potato with butter and mixed fruits for the drink. 12

Later on we played games. We had to communicate with each other, but not by talking. We had to arrange ourselves in height order and age. 13

Sunjay

I arrived at school at about eight o'clock this morning. After that I went into the school office and met Ms Tate, she then told me which Competition House I was in and told me to go to Victoria Hall and wait for everybody else to arrive. Year 7 then went up to the Year 7 Common Room. 14

After Ms Tate had told us a few things we all went to Chapel. When the service was over we went back to the Common Room. Mr Rayner then took us (7.1) to either room 6 or room 9. We then wrote down our timetables. Then we had break. 15

After break we went on a tour of the school with Mr Rayner and Mr Thomas, to find our classrooms for Thursday's lessons. We then went to lunch (it was great)! When I came out of lunch I got lost and ended up next to the cricket pitch. I managed to find my way back but I was late for class. My first day was fab!! 16

Tim Waters, Headmaster

"The first day at a new school is always daunting, but I'm glad to say that for most pupils it ends up being remembered for all the right reasons. 17

Eighty four new pupils joined Senior School at the Royal this term, an equal mix of day pupils and boarders. 18

Wherever a child arrives from, the emotions are the same, a mix of excitement, anxiety and, if it is a big school, disorientation. 19

Schools these days work very hard to induct pupils, with "taster" days the previous year to help familiarize them and new pupils are teamed up with "buddies" to help. Provided that the ethos of the school is welcoming, it takes very little time for newcomers to fit in and feel at home". 20

During the Second World War it was considered dangerous to remain in London because of German bombing raids. Lots of children were sent to live with families in the countryside — sometimes with complete strangers. This was called "evacuation". This article describes the experiences of two evacuated children, Cherry-Anne and Lisbeth, as their London school and the local school are combined.

Wingrave School

In September 1939, 84 schoolchildren with their teachers were evacuated from Tufnell Park in North London to Wingrave*. Among them were Cherry-Anne, who was nine years old and Lisbeth, who was just six. Cherry-Anne and Lisbeth's mother accompanied the group as an official assistant to the staff. 1

By today's standards, conditions were tough for the young evacuees. The schoolroom was crowded, dark and cold, food and sweets were rationed, and they were initially billeted** with a Wingrave couple. Despite these conditions, Cherry-Anne and Lisbeth have happy memories of their schooldays during the war in Wingrave. 2

The arrival of the evacuees in Wingrave more than doubled the size of the village school and inevitably created organisational problems. The evacuees were allocated the main room of the school, but this had to be subdivided into three classrooms by hanging war issue blankets from the ceiling. The blankets did little to stop the noise from one class disturbing the next one, but they did stop the heat from the single stove in the hall reaching the far end. Cherry-Anne was lucky — she was near the stove, but Lisbeth had to wear her outdoor coat all day to keep warm in winter. 3

The academic background and abilities of the London evacuees were very different from those of the local Wingrave children, and it was initially decided to teach the two schools separately. This approach did not find favour with the Wingrave headmaster, Mr Stubbs, who made representations to the Education Committee, and achieved integration*** of the two schools in January 1940. 4

** Wingrave = a village in Buckinghamshire*
*** billeted = given temporary lodgings*
**** integration = joining together*

Extracts from the school logbook illustrate the difficulties of organising school life in the autumn term of 1939. 5

Extracts from the logbook:

September 19th 1939. *School reopened at 9am. The Burghley contingent of teachers declined to combine the two schools and work as one. In order to avoid friction, they were given the main room to themselves. As they are entirely a junior girls school difficulty with regard to text books is being encountered. Neither are there sufficient desks to accommodate the children.* 6

November 21st 1939. *Eight boys went after the hunters at mid day and did not arrive at school until 2.30pm (one and a quarter hours late). They were marked absent and were each given one stroke with the cane on the hand.* 7

December 29th 1939. *A letter has been received from the Secretary of State for Education following Mr Blocksidge's visit suggesting reorganisation of the school by amalgamating* all of the children into three sections — seniors, juniors and infants. I propose to carry out this reorganisation as soon as the teachers' Christmas leave has been worked out.* 8

** amalgamating = joining together*

Children waiting to be evacuated at a London railway station during the Second World War.

Set C

Sporting Lives

Contents

Extract from *The Loneliness of the Long-distance Runner* .... page 3

Be Active! .... page 5

On your marks .... page 7

Keeping active is important for health but can also be fun. It doesn't matter what sport people are involved in — if it's something they love then they can get a lot more out of it than just keeping fit.

This is an extract from the short story 'The Loneliness of the Long-distance Runner' by Alan Sillitoe. The main character, Smith, has been sent to an institution for young offenders. There he has become a favourite with the staff because of his talent as a long-distance runner.

The Loneliness of the Long-distance Runner

Told to go, I trotted down the pavilion steps, out on to the field because the big cross-country was about to begin and the two entries from Gunthorpe had fixed themselves early at the starting line and were ready to move off like white kangaroos. The sports ground looked a treat: with big tea-tents all round and flags flying and seats for families — empty because no mam or dad had known what opening day meant — and boys still running heats for the hundred yards, and lords and ladies walking from stall to stall, and the Borstal* Boys Brass Band in blue uniforms; and up on the stands the brown jackets of Hucknall as well as our own grey blazers, and then the Gunthorpe lot with shirt sleeves rolled. The blue sky was full of sunshine and it couldn't have been a better day… 1

"Come on, Smith," Roach the sports master called to me, "we don't want you to be late for the big race, eh? Although I dare say you'd catch them up if you were." The others cat-called and grunted at this, but I took no notice and placed myself between Gunthorpe and one of the Aylesham trusties, dropped on my knees and plucked a few grass blades to suck on the way round… My knees felt the cool soil pressing into them, and out of my eye's corner I saw Roach lift his hand. The Gunthorpe boy twitched before the signal was given; somebody cheered too soon; Medway bent forward; then the gun went, and I was away. 2

We went once around the field and then along a half-mile drive of elms, being cheered all the way, and I seemed to feel I was in the lead as we went out by the gate and into the lane, though I wasn't interested enough to find out. The five-mile course was marked by splashes of whitewash gleaming on gateposts and trunks and stiles and stones, and a boy with a waterbottle and bandage box stood every half-mile waiting for those that dropped out or fainted. Over the first stile, without trying, I was still nearly in the lead but 3

** Borstal = a detention centre for young offenders*

one; and if any of you want tips about running, never be in a hurry, and never let any of the other runners know you are in a hurry even if you are. You can always overtake on long-distance running without letting the others smell the hurry in you; and when you've used your craft like this to reach the two or three up front then you can do a big dash later that puts everybody else's hurry in the shade because you've not had to make haste up till then. I ran to a steady jog-trot rhythm, and soon it was so smooth that I forgot I was running, and I was hardly able to know that my legs were lifting and falling and my arms going in and out, and my lungs didn't seem to be working at all, and my heart stopped that wicked thumping I always get at the beginning of a run. Because you see I never race at all; I just run, and somehow I know that if I forget I'm racing and only jog-trot along until I don't know I'm running I always win the race. For when my eyes recognize that I'm getting near the end of the course — by seeing a stile or cottage corner — I put on a spurt, and such a fast big spurt it is because I feel that up till then I haven't been running and that I've used up no energy at all…

I trotted on along the edge of a field bordered by the sunken lane, smelling green grass and honeysuckle, and I felt as though I came from a long line of whippets trained to run on two legs, only I couldn't see a toy rabbit in front and there wasn't a collier's cosh* behind to make me keep up the pace. I passed the Gunthorpe runner whose shimmy** was already black with sweat and I could just see the corner of the fenced-up copse*** in front where the only man I had to pass to win the race was going all out to gain the half-way mark. Then he turned into a tongue of trees and bushes where I couldn't see him anymore, and I couldn't see anybody, and I knew what the loneliness of the long-distance runner running across country felt like, realizing that as far as I was concerned this feeling was the only honesty and realness there was in the world and I knowing it would be no different ever, no matter what I felt at odd times, and no matter what anybody else tried to tell me. The runner behind me must have been a long way off because it was so quiet, and there was even less noise and movement than there had been at five o'clock of a frosty winter morning. It was hard to understand, and all I knew was that you had to run, run, run, without knowing why you were running, but on you went…

4

** collier's cosh = a blunt weapon used to encourage whippets to race*
*** shimmy = loose running shirt*
**** copse = a dense growth of trees*

We're often told we should be doing more exercise, but it can be difficult to know where to start. This article from the British Heart Foundation promotes physical activity, and includes an interview with a teenager who's already found a sport she loves.

Be Active!

It only takes **60 minutes** a day to keep active. 1

Yes, that's all it takes! You just need to do something physical like ***dancing, cycling, swimming or even walking your dog!*** So long as it makes you slightly out of breath. 2

YOU could do it as 4 slots of 15 mins each day if time is tight. 3

Team sports like football, basketball and netball are also great. It just depends what you're into. Or, you can stay in the comfort of your own home, and use an exercise tape or video. 4

Ready, Steady, GO! 5

1. Put on your favourite music and dance! 6

2. Take your dog (or someone else's) for a walk. 7

3. Don't catch the bus, leave home a bit earlier and have a brisk walk. It's **FREE!** Think of ALL the money you will save on fares! 8

4. Borrow an exercise video or tape — workout to your own routine. (some libraries have them or try the health and fitness section of your nearest record shop, bookshop) 9

5. Always run up stairs! 10

Check this out BEFORE you start 11

- Set yourself an activity routine. 12
- **Always start and end each session with a few minutes of gentle activity to warm up and cool down.** 13
- The best form of activity is something you enjoy and can fit into your daily routine. This way, once you have started you won't be tempted to find an excuse for not keeping it up! 14
- Sixty minutes a day will make all the difference. 15

Felicity

1. What activity do you do? 16

Figure skating.

2. What first made you interested in it?

I started skating at a public rink when I was three, and I just continued doing it. But my passion for it really started about five years ago, from watching it on TV. 17

3. How easy is it to do?

It's hard! Learning how to skate is a scary experience, especially when you fall for the first time. But once you get past being afraid of the ice, and get more comfortable with skating in general, it gets a lot easier. 18

4. Does it need special equipment or clothing?

All that you need is a pair of skates with sharpened blades. But it's best to skate in loose clothing, nothing too tight or constricting. And make sure whatever you're wearing is warm enough! 19

5. Where do you do the activity? 20

At a skating rink. Preferably with ice, not wax.

6. How much does it cost?

The cost of buying or renting skates, then however much it costs for a public skating session. But private lessons are much more expensive. 21

7. What makes you want to keep on doing it?

The thrill I get when I jump, or when I land a new jump. Also, figure skating is an extremely creative sport, and I love thinking up new spin positions and trying things that I've seen famous skaters do. 22

8. What are you aiming for?

I hope to land my double toe and double loop jumps by the end of the year! 23

9. Where can other people find out about this activity? 24

Through the yellow pages, or from a search engine on the internet.

Future competitors in the Olympics are usually identified while they're still at school. This abridged version of an article from the Times Educational Supplement investigates how they balance their sporting dreams with their education.

On your marks

Stephen Manning
Published: 16 March 2007

It's five years, four months and 11 days until the start of the London Olympics in 2012. Time to grow a few medal-winners? Not really. All the athletes who could compete in five years' time have been identified in each of the 26 sports. Some will already have competed in the UK School Games held last September in Glasgow. Some may not stay the course, but they all share a fervent desire to be Olympians. And some of them are still at school. 1

Finding a balance between school and Olympic-level athletics can be daunting, says James English, PE teacher at The Coopers' Company and Coborn School, a specialist sports college in Upminster, Essex. As mentor co-ordinator, he has been involved with some very promising pupils and knows the responsibility that carries. 2

"We call it the Team You — parents, teachers, coaches are all on the team to make you, the young athlete, the best you can be," he says. 3

Coopers' has a number of promising athletes earmarked for a great, possibly Olympian, future, such as Rebecca Carson, 17, Britain's national under-18s fencing champion. She won the Commonwealth team event for Scotland at last year's Commonwealth Games and is one of 10 teenage fencers on the Talented Athlete Scholarship Scheme. 4

5 She has to work hard to balance her commitments to her school and her sport. "In an average month I'll have two competitions, mainly at weekends," she says. "But the school will be flexible if there is something major."

6 Last April, just before her GCSEs, she needed a week to prepare for the World Junior Championships in South Korea. "I left revision for when I got back," she says. "I concentrated on training from January to April. Then, as soon as it was over I was back to revising — I was doing it on the plane home." And she didn't do badly: 11 passes, with two A*s and two As.

7 Rebecca is not the only talented athlete at her school: it boasts a number of other potential Olympians, such as 13-year-old Nicole Raymond, part of the school team that won the National Schools Cross-Country Championship. She hopes to compete in the triathlon. Her studies have not suffered: she is top of her year academically.

8 Two of the great hopes in sailing are Frances Peters, 15, and her brother James, 14. They were among 100 of the country's best athletes aged 14 to 17 who attended the first National Talent Orientation Camp. The pupils were coached by Olympic champions and sports stars such as Dame Kelly Holmes.

9 "It gave us an insight into the decisions we'd have to make about our priorities," says Frances. "So we want to be Olympians? How much do we really want it? This is what 'wanting it' means. Although you shouldn't give up education, you have to be aware of the demands and you need to be able to prioritise."

10 The four-day camp was intense. "We got up at 6.30am and went to the gym for an hour of circuit training or aerobics — hard on the first day, but it's a good habit to get into. It's good to see other young athletes in different sports sharing a similar vision."

11 Britain's stated aim, as expressed by the British Olympic Association, is to come fourth in the medal table (behind the United States, Russia and China).

12 Nothing in recent — or indeed ancient — memory has captured the spirit of so many youngsters and their teachers as the build-up to the London Games.

English

KEY STAGE
3

LEVELS
4-7

PRACTICE PAPER
Reading
Set C

Key Stage 3

English Test

Reading Paper
Sporting Lives
Set C

Instructions

- Before you start to write, you have **15 minutes** to read the Reading Booklet.
- From that point you will have **1 hour** to write your answers.
- Try to answer **all** of the questions.
- There are **13** questions, worth **32 marks**.
- Check through all of your work carefully before the end of the test.
- If you're not sure what to do, ask your teacher.

First Name ______________________

Last Name ______________________

School ______________________

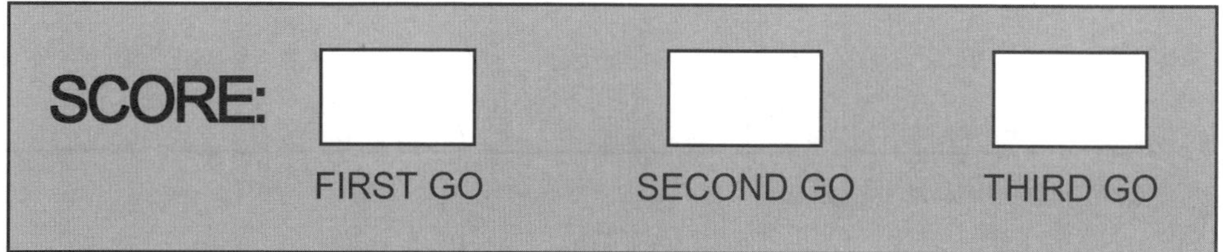

Exam Set ER3P33, ETTP32 or EMAP34

Questions 1-4 are about *The Loneliness of the Long-distance Runner* (pages 3-4 in the Reading Booklet)

1. From the first paragraph, pick out one phrase that shows the setting is not a normal school.

....

....

(1 mark)

1 mark

2. How does the writer build up tension in the final sentence of paragraph 2? Explain one way and support your answer with a quotation.

....

....

....

(2 marks)

2 marks

3. In paragraph 4, the author describes Smith running through the countryside.

   a) Write down two phrases from paragraph 4 that describe the setting.

....

....

(1 mark)

1 mark

   b) Why do you think the author describes the setting in detail? Give one reason.

....

....

(1 mark)

1 mark

4. In the whole text, how does the writer use language to help us understand how the narrator is feeling?

You should comment on:

- how the writer sets the scene;
- the narrator's tone of voice;
- the way running is described.

....

....

....

....

....

....

....

....

....

....

....

....

....

....

....

....

(5 marks)

5 marks

Questions 5-8 are about *Be Active!*
(pages 5-6 in the Reading Booklet)

5. Pick out two examples of presentational features the writer uses and explain why they are effective.

Presentational features:

1. ....

2. ....

Why they are effective:

1. ....

2. ....

(2 marks)

2 marks

6. Why does the writer include the interview with Felicity? Suggest one reason.

....

....

(1 mark)

1 mark

7. Write down one piece of advice the article gives about exercise.

....

....

(1 mark)

1 mark

8. How does the whole article encourage people to do more exercise?

You should comment on:

- the language of the article;
- the tone of the article;
- the organisation of the article.

....

....

....

....

....

....

....

....

....

....

....

....

....

....

....

....

(5 marks)

5 marks

Questions 9-12 are about *On your marks*
(pages 7-8 in the Reading Booklet)

9. Explain one way in which the first paragraph captures the attention of the reader. Support your answer with a quotation.

....

....

....

....

(2 marks)

2 marks

10. From paragraph 6 describe one way Rebecca had to balance school and sport.

....

....

(1 mark)

1 mark

11. Paragraphs 9 and 10 suggest that the Olympic Dream is difficult to achieve.

a) Pick out two words or phrases that show this.

....

....

(1 mark)

1 mark

b) Explain how these words or phrases are effective.

....

....

....

(2 marks)

2 marks

12. The article includes quotations from some of the people it describes.
Give one reason why the writer may have done this.

....

....

(1 mark)

1 mark

Question 13 is about *Be Active!* and *On your marks*

13. *Be Active!* and *On your marks* are both about participation in sports but have been written for different purposes.

Complete the table below suggesting the purpose of each text and its effect on the reader. Support each answer with a quotation.

	Be Active!	*On your marks*
Purpose of text		
Effect on reader		
Quotation		

(6 marks)

6 marks

English

KEY STAGE
3

LEVELS
4-7

PRACTICE PAPER
Reading
Set B

Key Stage 3

English Test

Reading Paper
Changing Schools

Set B

Instructions

- Before you start to write, you have **15 minutes** to read the Reading Booklet.
- From that point you will have **1 hour** to write your answers.
- Try to answer **all** of the questions.
- There are **13** questions, worth **32 marks**.
- Check through all of your work carefully before the end of the test.
- If you're not sure what to do, ask your teacher.

First Name ____________________

Last Name ____________________

School ____________________

Exam Set ER3P33, ETTP32 or EMAP34

Questions 1-4 are about *Harry Potter and the Philosopher's Stone* (pages 3-4 in the Reading Booklet)

1. From the first paragraph, write down why it was difficult for Harry to remember where things were in his new school.

....

....

(1 mark) 1 mark

2. a) In paragraph 2, the writer lists the ways that Peeves is unpleasant. Write down one phrase that shows he is unpleasant.

....

(1 mark) 1 mark

b) Explain why the list of ways Peeve's is unpleasant is an effective way of describing his personality to the reader.

....

....

(1 mark) 1 mark

3. The writer uses humour in her descriptions of the school. Give one example of humour and explain why it is effective.

Example from text

....

Why it is effective

....

(2 marks) 2 marks

Questions 5-8 are about *Starting 'big' school* (pages 5-6 in the Reading Booklet)

scribe one technique the writer uses to attract the reader's attention in ragraph 1. Explain why it is effective.

....

....

....

(2 marks)

2 marks

m Chenice's account, give one impression you get of the school. pport your answer with a quotation.

....

....

....

(2 marks)

2 marks

mplete the table below to show how the way the article is organised makes ore useful to the reader.

How the article is organised	How this helps the reader
General introduction to changing schools	Helps the reader to understand what the students are going to talk about
Sections describing different pupils' experiences	
Headline and subheadings	

(2 marks)

2 marks

4. In the whole text, how does the writer create a magical atmosphere Hogwarts School?

You should comment on:

- the language the writer uses;
- the unusual features of the school building and lessons;
- the descriptions of characters.

4. In the whole text, how does the writer create a magical atmosphere for Hogwarts School?

You should comment on:

- the language the writer uses;
- the unusual features of the school building and lessons;
- the descriptions of characters.

....

....

....

....

....

....

....

....

....

....

....

....

....

....

....

....

(5 marks)

5 marks

Questions 5-8 are about *Starting 'big' school*
(pages 5-6 in the Reading Booklet)

5. Describe one technique the writer uses to attract the reader's attention in paragraph 1. Explain why it is effective.

....

....

....

(2 marks)

2 marks

6. From Chenice's account, give one impression you get of the school. Support your answer with a quotation.

....

....

....

(2 marks)

2 marks

7. Complete the table below to show how the way the article is organised makes it more useful to the reader.

How the article is organised	How this helps the reader
General introduction to changing schools	Helps the reader to understand what the students are going to talk about
Sections describing different pupils' experiences	
Headline and subheadings	

(2 marks)

2 marks

8. What impression does the article give about what it's like to start secondary school?

You should comment on:

- the feelings described by the children;
- the language used in the introduction;
- the headmaster's comment.

5 marks

(5 marks)

Questions 9-12 are about *Wingrave School*
(pages 7-8 in the Reading Booklet)

9. From paragraphs 1 and 2 what overall impression do you get of the evacuees' experience? Give one quotation to support your answer.

....

....

....

(2 marks)

2 marks

10. How do the logbook extracts suggest that the school is old-fashioned compared to today's schools? Give one example.

....

(1 mark)

1 mark

11. Why do you think the extracts from the logbook are included in the article? Suggest one reason.

....

....

(1 mark)

1 mark

12. Pick out three phrases from paragraph 3 that show that the school was uncomfortable for the children. Explain the effect of these phrases on the reader.

Phrase 1

....

....

Effect on Reader

....

....

Phrase 2

....

....

Effect on Reader

....

....

Phrase 3

....

....

Effect on Reader

....

....

(3 marks)

3 marks

Question 13 is about *Harry Potter and the Philosopher's Stone* and *Wingrave School*

13. Both *Wingrave School* and *Harry Potter and the Philosopher's Stone* describe characters adapting to unusual conditions at school. However, they are very different types of text.

Complete the table below by:

- Circling what you think the purpose of each text is.
- Explaining your choices.

	Wingrave School	*Harry Potter and the Philosopher's Stone*
Purpose of the text (circle your answer)	entertaining informing persuading	entertaining informing persuading
Give a reason for your choice		

(4 marks)

4 marks

English

KEY STAGE
3

LEVELS
4-7

PRACTICE PAPER
Reading
Set A

Key Stage 3

English Test

Reading Paper Vampires

Set A

Instructions

- Before you start to write, you have **15 minutes** to read the Reading Booklet.
- From that point you will have **1 hour** to write your answers.
- Try to answer **all** of the questions.
- There are **14** questions, worth **32 marks**.
- Check through all of your work carefully before the end of the test.
- If you're not sure what to do, ask your teacher.

First Name ____________________

Last Name ____________________

School ____________________

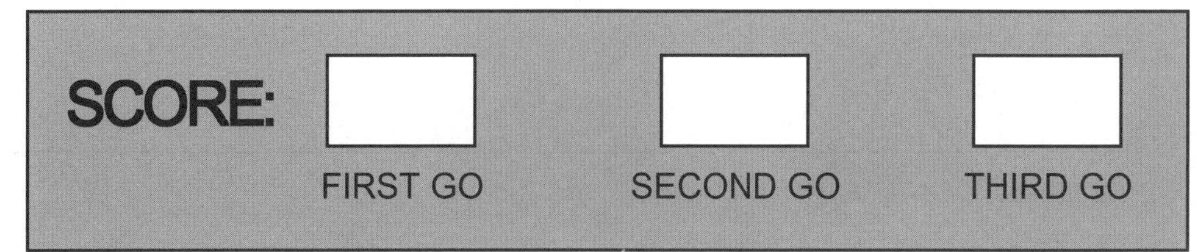

Exam Set ER3P33, ETTP32 or EMAP34

Questions 1-5 are about *Yikes! Vampire Bats Can Run, Too*
(pages 3-4 in the Reading Booklet)

1. From the first paragraph of the article, write down three things a vampire bat can do.

• .... • .... • ....

(1 mark)

1 mark

2. How does the title of the article grab the reader's attention? Explain one way.

....

....

(1 mark)

1 mark

3. Look at paragraphs 5 and 6. Explain one way in which the writer links these paragraphs together smoothly. Support your answer with a quotation.

....

....

....

(2 marks)

2 marks

4. a) From the first three paragraphs, write down a phrase which tells the reader that vampire bats can be quite fast.

....

(1 mark)

1 mark

b) Write down a word from the section "On to the treadmill" which suggests that cattle move slowly.

....

(1 mark)

1 mark

5. In the whole article, how does the writer try to make the information entertaining and easy to understand for the reader?

You should comment on:

- the way the article is organised;
- the writer's use of informal language;
- the comparisons the writer uses.

....

....

....

....

....

....

....

....

....

....

....

....

....

....

....

....

(5 marks)

5 marks

Questions 6-9 are about *Writing Horror — Forbidden Treats* (pages 5-6 in the Reading Booklet)

6. Look at paragraph 1. Give one way in which the writer makes the opening of the article interesting for a teenage audience.

....

(1 mark)

1 mark

7. Give one reason from paragraph 4 why Darren Shan thinks that "Cirque Du Freak" is *not* a reckless or irresponsible book.

....

....

(1 mark)

1 mark

8. In paragraph 5, what two elements does Darren Shan argue are needed for a good horror story?

....

....

....

(2 marks)

2 marks

9. Explain how the whole article shows the author Darren Shan's enthusiasm for horror stories.

You should comment on:

- the language he uses to describe his own reactions to horror stories;
- the effects of the range of punctuation he uses;
- the way he writes about how a reader of horror stories should be affected.

....

....

....

....

....

....

....

....

....

....

....

....

....

....

....

....

(5 marks)

5 marks

Questions 10-13 are about the extract from *Dracula* by Bram Stoker (pages 7-8 in the Reading Booklet)

10. Give one detail in paragraph 1 that tells us that it is night-time.

....

(1 mark)

1 mark

11. In the first 10 lines of paragraph 1, the narrator tells the reader how he feels about being in Count Dracula's castle. Pick out two phrases or sentences and explain what each one suggests about the narrator's feelings.
Write your answers in the table below.

Words from the text	What they suggest

(2 marks)

2 marks

12. The narrator's feelings change between the middle of paragraph 1 and the middle of paragraph 2.

a) Describe the narrator's feelings in the middle of paragraph 1.
Support your answer with a quotation.

....

....

b) Describe the narrator's feelings by the middle of paragraph 2.
Support your answer with a quotation.

....

....

(4 marks)

4 marks

13. In the last paragraph, the narrator repeats certain words. Pick out one example of repetition. Explain what it suggests to the reader about the narrator's state of mind.

Example

....

....

What it suggests about the narrator's state of mind

....

....

(1 mark)

1 mark

Question 14 is about *Yikes! Vampire Bats Can Run, Too* and *Dracula*

14. *Yikes! Vampire Bats Can Run Too* and *Dracula* each have a different tone and atmosphere. Complete the table below by explaining how each phrase makes the reader feel about the creature it is describing.

	Words from text	Effect on the reader
Yikes! Vampire Bats Can Run, Too	"Hopping is good, when you're a bat slurping cow blood, because cows are heavy and can kick or roll over and squash a bat"	
	"the clever little mammals dutifully kept pace"	
Dracula	"down the castle wall over the dreadful abyss, face down with his cloak spreading out around him like great wings."	
	"what manner of creature is it in the semblance of man?"	

(4 marks)

4 marks

English

KEY STAGE
3

LEVELS
4-7

PRACTICE PAPER
Writing
Set C

Key Stage 3

English Test

Writing Paper

Set C

Instructions

This paper is **1 hour and 15 minutes** long.

You should spend about:
45 minutes on Section A
30 minutes on Section B

Section A, the longer writing task, is worth **30 marks**.

Section B, the shorter writing task, is worth **20 marks**.

You should spend 15 minutes planning your answer to Section A, using the planning grid provided.

Check through all of your work carefully before the end of the test.

If you're not sure what to do, ask your teacher.

First Name ______________________

Last Name ______________________

School ______________________

Exam Set ER3P33, ETTP32 or EMAP34

Section A — Longer writing task

Bad Behaviour

Spend about 45 minutes on this section.

You are a pupil on the school council.

You receive this note from the head teacher:

> I have been sent a letter by an elderly lady who lives near the school. She has complained about the behaviour of pupils leaving school each afternoon. She says they talk too loudly, kick footballs around and eat too many sweets.
>
> I have already replied to her letter to explain that the pupils here are well behaved, but I think it would help if she received a letter from you as well. Please would you try to persuade her to come into school and see for herself that you and your friends are a well mannered and well behaved bunch?
>
> You could also tell her about some of the things you and your friends do to contribute to the local community.

Write a letter to the elderly lady, persuading her that pupils at your school are well behaved and inviting her to visit so that she can see this for herself.

(30 marks)

Use this page to plan your work.

This page will not be marked.

- Why do you think pupils at your school are well behaved?

- What examples could you give of good behaviour?

- How do pupils at your school make a positive contribution to the local community?

- Why should the elderly lady visit your school?

Section B — Shorter writing task

Relaxation Area

Spend about 30 minutes on this section.

Your after-school youth club has received money to create a relaxation area and is running a competition to decide what it will be like. The poster advertising the competition says:

> Have you got a winning idea?
>
> You're about to get a new relaxation area, but we need ideas for what it should be like.
>
> Tell us what you think we should put in this area and why. The best idea will become reality.

Write an entry for the competition, describing the new relaxation area you would like to see and why.

(20 marks including 4 for spelling)

English

KEY STAGE
3

LEVELS
4-7

PRACTICE PAPER
Writing
Set B

Key Stage 3

English Test

Writing Paper

Set B

Instructions

This paper is **1 hour and 15 minutes** long.

You should spend about:
45 minutes on Section A
30 minutes on Section B

Section A, the longer writing task, is worth **30 marks**.

Section B, the shorter writing task, is worth **20 marks**.

You should spend 15 minutes planning your answer to Section A, using the planning grid provided.

Check through all of your work carefully before the end of the test.

If you're not sure what to do, ask your teacher.

First Name ____________________

Last Name ____________________

School ____________________

Exam Set ER3P33, ETTP32 or EMAP34

Section A — Longer writing task

Teen Readers

Spend about 45 minutes on this section.

You have a Saturday job at the local library.

Your boss gives you this information:

> I would like to encourage more teenagers to use the library. Maybe we need to make the teenage book section more attractive. Or we could offer more services to teenagers — libraries are about more than books. Other libraries in the area are offering:
>
> - free internet access for school pupils
> - homework clubs
>
> Please write a report advising me about why teenagers don't like using the library at the moment and what we could do to encourage them to use the library more.

Write a report to advise your boss about why teenagers aren't using the library now, and how you think more teenagers could be encouraged to use the library in the future.

(30 marks)

Use this page to plan your work.

This page will not be marked.

- Why don't teenagers like the library at the moment?

- What could the library do to attract more teenagers?

- Why would these things attract teenagers?

Section B — Shorter writing task

Talent Contest

Spend about 30 minutes on this section.

You have volunteered to help organise the school's talent contest.
The teacher in charge gives you this note:

> Pupils entering the contest need to know what they're letting themselves in for!
>
> They need to know how long they have to perform for and the sorts of things they could do.
>
> They also need to know what time it's on, where it's being held and what they need to bring with them.

Write a leaflet informing pupils about the details of the talent contest.

(20 marks including 4 for spelling)

English

KEY STAGE
3

LEVELS
4-7

PRACTICE PAPER
Writing
Set A

Key Stage 3

English Test

Writing Paper

Set A

Instructions

This paper is **1 hour and 15 minutes** long.

You should spend about:
45 minutes on Section A
30 minutes on Section B

Section A, the longer writing task, is worth **30 marks**.

Section B, the shorter writing task, is worth **20 marks**.

You should spend 15 minutes planning your answer to Section A, using the planning grid provided.

Check through all of your work carefully before the end of the test.

If you're not sure what to do, ask your teacher.

First Name ______________________________

Last Name ______________________________

School ______________________________

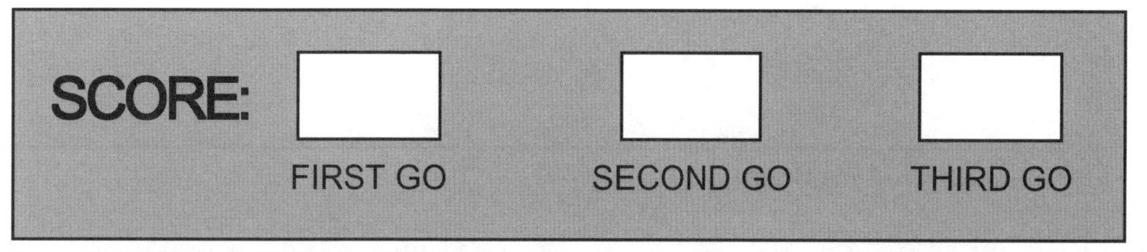

Exam Set ER3P33, ETTP32 or EMAP34

Section A — Longer writing task

Improving the Common Room

Spend about 45 minutes on this section.

You are a member of your school's Student Council. Earlier in the year, the Council received some money from the Parents' Association to spend on improving the Year 9 common room. You get this note from the head of the Student Council:

> It's nearly the summer holidays, so I want to thank you for your help with the Student Council's work this year. I think we've achieved a lot!
>
> There's one last job to do before we enjoy that well earned rest. Do you remember that, earlier in the year, the Parents' Association gave us £100 to spend on the common room? Well, they're having a meeting soon and I need someone to write a formal report for them on how we spent the money. The report needs to explain what we've done, how it's improved things and what else still needs doing.
>
> Could you do this for me please?
> Thanks!

Write a report for the Parents' Association, explaining how the Student Council have spent the £100 on improving the Year 9 common room and what improvements are needed in the future.

(30 marks)

Use this page to plan your work.

This page will not be marked.

- Details of what you spent the money on and why

- How this has improved the facilities for Year 9 students

- What improvements are still needed in the common room and why

Section B — Shorter writing task

Summer Fair Fundraising

Spend about 30 minutes on this section.

You are helping to organise your school's summer fair. You receive this note from one of the other organisers:

> Hi! How's it going?
>
> I'm hoping we can raise over £1,000 this year — which would beat last year's target by £200. Since all profits go to charity, it's worth a try.
>
> I'm having trouble getting enough volunteers for the stocks — you know, where you can pay to throw wet sponges at people. I've persuaded three Year 11 students to volunteer, but no teachers have yet.
>
> Could you write a couple of paragraphs for the staff newsletter to try to persuade some of them to volunteer? You can keep it quite light-hearted. It would only be for ½ hour each, the sponges would be soaked in WARM water — and it is for charity!

Write a short article for the staff newsletter to persuade teachers to volunteer for a turn in the stocks at this year's summer fair.

(20 marks including 4 for spelling)

CGP

Key Stage 3

English

SATS Practice Papers Answer Book

Levels 4-7

Contents

Using the Practice Papers........................P2
Reading Answers.......................................P6
Writing Answers.......................................P12
Shakespeare Answers............................P20

Exam Set ER3P33, ETTP32 or EMAP34

These practice papers won't make you better at English

... but they will show you what you **can** do, and what you **can't** do yet.

The papers are just like the ones you'll get on the day — so they'll tell you what you need to **work at** if you want to do **better**.

Do a test, **get it marked** and look at what you **got wrong**.
That's the stuff you need to work on.

Go away, **learn** those tricky bits, then **do the *same* test again**.
If you're **still** getting questions wrong, you'll have to do even **more practice** and test yourself **again**.

It doesn't sound like a lot of **fun**, but it **really will help**.

There are three big ways to improve your score

1) **Keep practising the things you get wrong.**
   If you keep mucking up the Shakespeare questions, you'll need to look at the scenes all over again. If your spelling's lousy then go away and practise that.

2) **Don't throw away easy marks.**
   Read each question really carefully and make sure you do exactly what it says. And don't do anything silly like forgetting to write in clear paragraphs.

3) **Don't rush the Reading questions.**
   If you don't read the passages properly you can't possibly get good marks. You've got to pay attention to every single word.

Published by Coordination Group Publications Ltd

Contributors:
Thomas Harte
Elisabeth Sanderson
Katherine Reed
Nicola Woodfin

Many thanks to Glenn Rogers *and* Paula Barnett *for proofreading.*

Groovy website: www.cgpbooks.co.uk
Jolly bits of clipart from CorelDRAW®
Printed by Elanders Hindson Ltd, Newcastle upon Tyne.

Doing the Tests

There are **three sets** of practice papers in this pack.
Each set has:

Reading Paper
15 minutes reading time, 1 hour writing time
32 marks *(goes towards overall Reading Score)*

Writing Paper
Section A, longer writing task — 15 minutes planning time,
30 minutes writing time
30 marks *(goes towards overall Writing Score)*
Section B, shorter writing task — 30 minutes writing time
20 marks *(goes towards overall Writing Score)*

Shakespeare Paper
45 minutes writing on extracts from Shakespeare scenes
18 marks *(goes towards overall Reading Score)*

The **Reading Paper** has **three** bits of writing to read.
You have to answer about five questions on each bit of writing.

In the **Writing Paper** you have to write **two** pieces of writing.

The last paper's the **Shakespeare Paper**. You have to read two bits from your **scenes** and answer a question on them. This booklet contains a **general mark scheme** which can be used to mark all the Shakespeare questions.

You need these things

A **pen**.

Lined paper. ← *Do the Reading questions on a separate bit of paper if you want to do the test more than once.*

Answering the questions

- The most important thing is to **understand** the questions.
  Read everything really **carefully** to be sure you're doing what they ask.
- Remember to **plan** carefully for the Writing Paper longer task. You don't really have time for big mistakes, and it's **clear**, **well-organised** writing that gets the best marks.
- Be especially careful about your **punctuation** and **spelling** on the writing questions. There are marks put aside for spelling in the shorter writing question.
- Put lots of **quotations** in your Shakespeare answer, and remember to explain why you've chosen them — it's the best way to prove that you know the scenes well, and that you're giving a relevant answer.

Follow all the instructions

- In the Reading Paper look at the **number of marks** you can get for each question. Spend more time on questions worth more marks.
- The questions give you a list of things to think about — include them **all** in your answer. You'll get **more marks** if you do.

How to Mark the Tests

It's pretty straightforward. You can mark all the tests using this booklet. Ask an adult to mark them for you if you like — it's good to get someone else's opinion of your work.

There are **lots** of good ways to answer every single one of the questions in these practice papers. That means we can't tell you **word for word** what kind of work gets a level 4, 5, 6 or 7.

Instead we've given a description of the **kind** of answer that'll get you a certain number of marks. It might look a bit complicated, but once you get stuck in, it should all become clear.

Reading Paper

- Mark the **Reading** questions just for reading comprehension. Don't knock off marks for badly written answers, or give more marks for well written ones.
- Tot up the marks to get a score out of **32**.

Writing Paper

- This is marked for **sentence structure and punctuation**, **text structure and organisation** and **composition and effect**.
- Add up the separate marks for each task to get a mark out of **50**.

Shakespeare Paper

- The Shakespeare question is only marked for **understanding** — there are no marks for the written style.
- The Shakespeare question is marked out of **18**.

Using the Mark Schemes for the Writing Paper

- Read the work and then look at the **mark scheme tables** for each question. Decide which of the "What's the Answer Like?" descriptions matches it **most closely**.
- Each description gives a **range** of possible marks. If the answer does **every single thing** in one particular description, and does them well, give it a mark from the top end of the range. If the answer **doesn't** do everything in the description, but does do **some of it**, give it a mark from the bottom of the range.
- And obviously, the longest answers aren't necessarily the best ones.

Working Out the Level

Reading Score

Add the score (out of 32) for the **Reading Paper** to the score (out of 18) for the **Shakespeare Paper** to get a total **Reading Score** out of **50**, and look it up here:

TOTAL score out of 50	10→15	16→25	26→33	34→50
LEVEL	4	5	6	7

Writing Score

Add the score (out of 30) for **Section A** of the **Writing Paper** to the score (out of 20) for **Section B** of the **Writing Paper** to get a total **Writing Score** out of 50, and look it up here:

TOTAL score out of 50	7→13	14→24	25→33	34→50
LEVEL	4	5	6	7

Overall Level

To get an overall level, add together the **Reading** and **Writing Scores** to get a mark out of **100**, then look it up here:

TOTAL score out of 100	17→29	30→50	51→67	68→100
LEVEL	4	5	6	7

Important!

Getting Level 4, 5, 6 or 7 on one of these practice papers is **no guarantee** of getting that in the real SATs — **but** it's a pretty good guide.

Set A — Reading Paper

Page 4 of this booklet has some really helpful points about marking — make sure you read it first.

1. 1 mark for an answer which gives all three abilities:
   - fly
   - drink blood
   - run / sprint
2. 1 mark for any valid explanation, e.g.
   - He uses an exclamation mark to make it sound like something dramatic has happened.
   - He uses a slang word "Yikes" to amuse us and encourage us to think we'll understand the article.
3. 2 marks for a clear explanation, including a quotation, e.g.
   - He starts paragraph 6 with the phrase "Thing is," which expresses a reservation about what has gone before.
   - He repeats the words "small animals," which shows that the two paragraphs have a subject in common.

4a. 1 mark for a valid phrase, e.g.
   - "fleet-footed"
   - "sprint along the ground"
   - "break into a loping run"

4b. 1 mark for the word "lumbering"

5. A good answer is likely to cover points like the high number of quotes, use of comparisons (e.g. "flop around like fish out of water" or "It's as if they were designed to chase race cars…"), mixing of scientific quotes with simple explanations (e.g. "You might want to jog across the room… to understand what that means") and the way subheadings identify section topics.

   1 or 2 marks for an explanation that recognises that the tone is light-hearted and picks out some examples but does not cover all three prompts.

   3 marks for an explanation that comments on the effects of specific details and quotations but does not cover all three prompts in detail.

   4 or 5 marks for a detailed answer in which all three prompts are dealt with and comments are supported with appropriate quotations and explanations.
6. 1 mark for a valid answer, e.g.
   - He writes as though he is talking directly to the reader in chatty, informal language.
   - He uses multiple exclamation marks to show excitement about the topic.
   - He describes a grotesque and humorous scene from a film.
7. 1 mark for a valid answer, e.g.
   - The book explores important themes (such as family, friendship, making sacrifices).
8. 1 mark for the point that it should contain shocking, thrilling, action-packed, violent events.

   1 mark for the point that it should contain more subtle moments that make the reader think and brood.
9. A good explanation might cover the enduring nature of his enthusiasm e.g. "That thirst for 'more' has never left me"; the range and type of emotions triggered by horror stories, e.g. it "explores" themes, "lingers" in the mind and contrasts "the subtle menace between the sudden bursts of action and violence"; the effect of single and multiple exclamation marks, and the unsettling effect of ellipses ("...") in paragraph 5.

   1 or 2 marks for general comments which recognise Shan's enjoyment of reading and writing horror. There will be some reference to the text but some of the prompts may not be covered.

   3 marks for an answer that comments on the effects of specific details and quotations. Some of the prompts may not be covered in detail.

   4 or 5 marks for a detailed answer in which all three prompts are dealt with and comments are supported with appropriate quotations and explanations.
10. 1 mark for a valid answer, e.g.
    - He saw everything by "moonlight."
    - "a breath of fresh air, though it were of the night" — he is describing night air.
    - "this nocturnal existence" — he is making it clear that he only moves around at night.
11. 1 mark for each row completed, to a maximum of 2 marks. **Must include a valid quotation** and an explanation e.g.
    - "I felt that I was indeed in prison" — He feels trapped.
    - "It is destroying my nerve" — He is starting to get jumpy and scared.
    - "there is ground for my terrible fear in this accursed place" — He is convinced that the castle is dangerous.

12a. 1 mark for a valid description of a feeling and 1 mark for a supporting quotation, e.g. he's beginning to relax as he looks at the beautiful landscape — "there was peace and comfort in every breath I drew."

12b. 1 mark for a valid description of a feeling and 1 mark for a supporting quotation, e.g. he is disgusted and frightened by the strange sight of the Count — "my very feelings changed to repulsion and terror".

Set A — Reading Paper

Page 4 of this booklet has some really helpful points about marking — make sure you read it first.

13. 1 mark for a valid answer — must include an example with an explanation, e.g.
    - "I am in fear, in awful fear" — repeating the word fear emphasises how extreme his emotion is.
    - "What manner of man is this, or what manner of creature" — repeating the word "manner" shows how uncertain he is about the creature he can see.
14. 1 mark for each valid explanation in the "Effect on the reader" column, up to a maximum of 4 marks, e.g.

    For *"Hopping is good…roll over and squash a bat"*
    - "slurping" makes the bat sound comical.
    - The idea of it being squashed makes it seem more vulnerable.

    For *"the clever little mammals…"*
    - The phrase "little mammals" makes them sound endearing.
    - Calling them "clever little mammals" suggests that we could admire the bats, not fear them.

    For *"down the castle wall…like great wings"*
    - The description of the Count above the "dreadful abyss" makes him sound confident and frightening.
    - The words "like great wings" emphasise his power and strangeness.

    For *"what manner of creature is it…"*
    - Imprecise words like "manner" and "semblance" create a feeling of mystery about who or what the Count is.
    - The use of a question helps emphasise the narrator's confusion to the reader.

Set B — Reading Paper

Page 4 of this booklet has some really helpful points about marking — make sure you read it first.

1. 1 mark for any valid answer e.g.
   - It was because things kept moving around, e.g. the people in the portraits.

2a. 1 mark for any one of the following phrases:
   - "He would drop waste-paper baskets on your head"
   - "pull rugs from under your feet"
   - "pelt you with bits of chalk"
   - "sneak up behind you, invisible, grab your nose"

2b. 1 mark for a reasonable explanation e.g.
   - The list shows he's unpleasant in many ways.
   - The list emphasises how unpleasant he is.

3. 1 mark for a valid example e.g.
   - Doors that won't open unless you ask them politely or tickle them in the right place.
   - The poltergeist Peeves drops waste-paper baskets on people's heads.

   1 mark for a valid explanation e.g.
   - The humour is quirky and surprising.
   - The description has a slapstick humour, like a cartoon.

4. Ideas for answering this question include the writer's use of descriptive language, her matter-of-fact telling of magical events and the way her characters have adapted to them in practical ways.

   1 or 2 marks for a simple answer that attempts to answer the question but doesn't cover all three of the prompts.

   3 marks for an answer that covers all three prompts but isn't developed.

   4 or 5 marks for an answer that covers all three prompts, is clear and detailed and has points supported with quotations.

5. 1 mark for any valid technique, e.g.
   - first paragraph is printed in bold
   - short sentences
   - repetition
   - emotive language

   1 mark for a valid explanation, e.g.
   - Short sentences stop the reader from becoming bored.
   - Repetition makes the reader curious about what is coming next.
   - Emotive language makes the reader care about what is happening.

6. 1 mark for a valid impression, 1 further mark for a supporting quotation, e.g.
   - It's imposing — "the grand double door".
   - It's got lots of facilities — "there is a work room, kitchen, common room and the sofa room."

7. 1 mark for each row of the table completed with a valid description of how that aspect of the article helps the reader.

   Example answers for "Sections describing different pupils' experiences":
   - They show the reader different points of view.
   - They help the reader remember what it felt like to start a new school.

   Example answers for "Headline and subheadings":
   - They make it clear what the article and different sections are about.
   - They divide the article up so that it isn't so daunting.

8. Answers for this question could comment on the excitement expressed by all three students, the use of direct questions in the introduction to make the reader think about their own experience and the use of the headmaster's comment to make general rather than specific statements.

   1 or 2 marks for a simple answer that attempts to address some but not all of the prompts.

   3 marks for an answer that attempts to address all three prompts but isn't detailed or doesn't use quotations to support ideas.

   4 or 5 marks for an answer that clearly addresses all three prompts and answers the question using quotations or examples from the text.

9. 1 mark for a valid comment e.g.
   - It seemed tough but happy.
   - It sounds unpleasant and difficult.

   1 further mark for a relevant supporting quotation e.g.
   - "Despite these conditions, Cherry-Anne and Lisbeth have happy memories..."
   - "The schoolroom was crowded, dark and cold".

10. 1 mark for any valid example, e.g.
   - The boys "were each given one stroke with the cane on the hand".

11. 1 mark for any reasonable suggestion, e.g.
   - The logbook entries make the story more interesting.
   - The logbook entries help us understand the day-to-day running of the school more clearly.

Set B — Reading Paper

Page 4 of this booklet has some really helpful points about marking — make sure you read it first.

12. 1 mark for each valid quotation and explanation, up to a maximum of 3 marks, e.g.
    - "hanging war issue blankets from the ceiling" — gives the reader the idea that materials were basic and that the school staff were doing their best with limited resources.
    - "did little to stop the noise" — emphasises to the reader how cramped the conditions were.
    - "stop the heat from … reaching the far end" — makes the reader feel sorry for the children.
    - "had to wear her outdoor coat all day to keep warm" — makes the reader empathise with Lisbeth by describing how she coped with the difficult conditions.
13. 1 mark for an appropriate choice for the purpose of the text, and 1 mark for a valid explanation. Up to a maximum of 4 marks, e.g.

	Wingrave School	*Harry Potter and the Philosopher's Stone*
Purpose of the text (circle your answer)	entertaining (informing) [circled] persuading	(entertaining) [circled] informing persuading
Give a reason for your choice	The text uses lots of factual, real-life detail about evacuation, e.g. the number of children evacuated from Tufnell Park in London.	The text uses entertaining humour to describe the school, e.g. portraits that keep going to visit each other.

Set C — Reading Paper

Page 4 of this booklet has some really helpful points about marking — make sure you read it first.

1. 1 mark for any valid phrase, e.g.
   - "seats for families — empty because no mam or dad had known what opening day meant"
   - "Borstal Boys Brass Band"
2. 1 mark for a reasonable explanation, 1 further mark for a supporting quotation, e.g.
   - The sentence is broken up into small sections which makes it seem jumpy or tense, e.g. "somebody cheered too soon; Medway bent forward; then the gun went, and I was away."
   - Words like "twitched" and "too soon" suggest tension.
   - The main information is left until the very end of the long sentence — "I was away."

3a. 1 mark for any two phrases from paragraph four that show descriptive detail of the setting, such as:
   - "smelling green grass and honeysuckle"
   - "a field bordered by the sunken lane"
   - "fenced-up copse"
   - "tongue of trees and bushes"

3b. 1 mark for a reasonable explanation, e.g.
   - It helps us to imagine the scene.
   - It seems more realistic.
   - It helps us to put ourselves into Smith's shoes.

4. A good answer could cover the points that the writer uses a lot of detail to set the scene and to help us imagine the narrator's viewpoint, the narrator's tone of voice is quite casual so it seems as if he is talking to us and the narrator seems to be an excellent runner from the description but is quite calm and detached from what he is doing until the end of the extract.

   1 or 2 marks for an answer that only partly addresses the question or that makes simple points, for example "this extract is about a boy who loves running" but does not explicitly address the writer's use of language.

   3 marks for an answer that covers all three prompts but in a simple way and gives a basic explanation of how the writer uses language but doesn't develop any significant points.

   4 or 5 marks for a fuller answer that clearly addresses and explores how the writer uses language in the extract and answers all three prompts with examples.

5. 1 mark for any two valid examples of presentational features, e.g.
   - bold font
   - numbered lists
   - bullet points
   - subheadings
   - question and answer format.

   1 further mark for a reasonable explanation, such as:
   - It makes the information easier to find.
   - It makes the information easier to digest.
   - It catches the eye of the reader.
   - It breaks up a large piece of information into smaller chunks.
6. 1 mark for a reasonable explanation, such as:
   - It makes it easier to relate to.
   - It shows a real teenager's view.
7. 1 mark for any suggestion taken from the article, e.g.
   - you should do 60 minutes of exercise a day
   - you must warm up and cool down
   - do something enjoyable
   - do something that fits your daily routine.
8. A good answer may include the fact that the language and tone are persuasive and upbeat, that it's quite light-hearted, that it's clearly organised with subheadings and that it includes an interview with someone who has an interesting sporting hobby.

   1-2 marks for a basic answer that does not cover all three prompts and doesn't clearly address how the article tries to encourage people to do more exercise.

   3 marks for an answer that covers all three prompts and attempts to develop an answer to the question, supporting some points with quotations or examples.

   4-5 marks for an answer that gives a detailed explanation covering all three prompts, makes good use of quotations or examples to support all points made and explains clearly how people are encouraged to do more exercise.
9. 1 mark for any reasonable explanation, 1 further mark for a supporting quotation, e.g.
   - It has short sentences to keep the interest up — "Some will already have competed in the UK School Games held last September in Glasgow. Some may not stay the course, but they all share a fervent desire to be Olympians. And some of them are still at school."
   - It surprises the reader with the information that the competitors of the future are of school age now — "And some of them are still at school."

Set C — Reading Paper

Page 4 of this booklet has some really helpful points about marking — make sure you read it first.

10. 1 mark for a valid answer, e.g.
   - She had to go to South Korea just before her GCSEs and then revise on the plane home.

11a. 1 mark for any two valid words or phrases, e.g.
   - demands
   - intense
   - We got up at 6.30am and went to the gym
   - hard

11b. 2 marks for a reasonable, detailed explanation such as:
   - Powerful language shows how committed they are.
   - Repetition of how difficult it is shows the reality of training.
   - The early start means they must be really dedicated.

   Award 1 mark only for a short explanation with little detail, such as:
   - It's powerful.
   - It sounds difficult.
   - They have to get up really early.

12. 1 mark for any reasonable suggestion such as:
   - They make the article more personal.
   - They make the story more believable.
   - They make the article more interesting.

13. 1 mark for each purpose, up to a maximum of 2 marks. 1 further mark for each effect on reader, up to a maximum of 2 marks. 1 further mark for each supporting quotation, up to a maximum of 2 marks. Overall, 6 marks maximum.

   A good answer may include the following points:
   - Be Active! — Purpose: To encourage people, especially teenagers, to do more exercise.
   - Be Active! — Effect on reader: The reader can understand quickly and easily how they can and should make a difference to their activity levels.
   - Be Active! — Quotation: "The best form of activity is something you enjoy and can fit into your daily routine."
   - On your marks — Purpose: To inform people about the competitors for the London Olympics.
   - On your marks — Effect on reader: The reader might be surprised and interested to learn that the future competitors are still fairly young, and the commitment they need is really high.
   - On your marks — Quotation: "Finding a balance between school and Olympic-level athletics can be daunting"

Writing Paper — Section A — Sets A, B & C

Page 4 of this booklet has some really helpful points about marking — make sure you read it first.

You can use the same mark scheme to mark any of the Section A questions for **Sentence Structure and Punctuation** and **Text Structure and Organisation**. To mark questions for **Composition and Effect**, find the correct mark scheme for the specific question on pages 14-16.

Sentence Structure and Punctuation

WHAT'S THE ANSWER LIKE?	MARK
• Only makes use of simple connectives such as "and" / "but". • Noun phrases short and simple, e.g. "narrow streets". • Little or no use of pronouns and few attempts to vary vocabulary. • Little or no variation in punctuation — uses full stops and commas.	**0** marks
• Uses some more varied connectives to link parts of sentences, e.g. "although" or "because". • Some noun phrases expanded, but in a simple way, e.g. "narrow and winding streets". • Makes some attempts to use subordinate clauses, e.g. "Harry wasn't sure what to do next, so he sat down on a park bench to think about it." • Mostly simple verbs used in the present tense. • Attempts to use a range of punctuation, although this may be limited.	**1-2** marks
• Connectives more varied and used more confidently, sometimes developing a sentence beyond simple clause and subordinate clause, e.g. "Although Harry wasn't exactly sure what he should do with the money, he did know that he was going to enjoy spending every single penny..." • Uses expanding noun phrases such as "The narrow, winding streets at the centre of town are very old, possibly medieval..." • Some attempt to vary sentence starters, such as "If I were you" / "Maybe you shouldn't". • Punctuation mostly used correctly, and some variety shown, e.g. exclamation marks, brackets.	**3-4** marks
• Good use of a range of connectives such as "on the other hand" / "however". • Sentence length and type varied for effect, e.g. includes impersonal sentences like "It is important that..." • Good use of a wide range of punctuation.	**5-6** marks
• Good range of sentence starters, such as "On the other hand..." / "Some people think..." • Uses a good range of sentence constructions, varying length of clause / subclause for effect. • Can write in an impersonal tone to increase impact of text, e.g. "Many people say that..." • Makes use of a wide range of punctuation to good effect.	**7** marks
• Secure and confident control of sentences and their structure for maximum effect. • Uses a wide range of sentence constructions, e.g. rhetorical questions, complex sentences, concise sentences. • Uses the full range of punctuation effectively.	**8** marks

Now look at the next page, and mark the piece for "Text Structure and Organisation"...

Writing Paper — Section A — Sets A, B & C

Page 4 of this booklet has some really helpful points about marking — make sure you read it first.

Text Structure and Organisation

WHAT'S THE ANSWER LIKE?	MARK
• Very limited introduction or conclusion. • Very little structure, e.g. few or no paragraphs. • Some simple linking of ideas, e.g. "and then" / "also".	**0** marks
• Some clear attempt at a beginning, middle and end. • Some use of paragraphs to divide main groups of ideas. • Topic sentences used to introduce some paragraphs, e.g. "In the city centre there is a lot more to do..." • Some topic sentences developed into further ideas, but in a limited way.	**1-2** marks
• New ideas divided into paragraphs. • Some attempt to follow a structure, e.g. "You say you're thinking about running away... but I can't believe..." • Some more varied connectives used, such as "however" / "although". • Some development of ideas within paragraphs by giving examples or more detail.	**3-4** marks
• Paragraphs consistently linked with more complicated connectives such as "In addition to the leisure centre..." / "Finally, having finished the tennis match..." • Paragraphs introduced with a strong starter sentence, e.g. "The importance of comprehensive leisure facilities cannot be overstated." • Ideas within paragraphs more fully developed, e.g. by using supporting evidence.	**5-6** marks
• Paragraphs are all well organised to make the text clear and effective. • Connectives consistently and effectively used to develop points or arguments. • Discourse markers used to show stage of argument or piece, e.g. "At last..." or "Firstly, Alex..." • Variety of well thought out sentence structures within a paragraph, that flow effectively.	**7** marks
• Suitable number of paragraphs of a suitable length to constitute a clear argument. • Each paragraph follows the previous one smoothly and logically. • Complex topic sentences direct readers' attention to argument / ideas. • Paragraph content and structure consistently, carefully and confidently controlled for maximum effect.	**8** marks

Now turn over and mark the piece for "Composition and Effect". There are different mark schemes for each paper...

Writing Paper — Section A — Set A

Page 4 of this booklet has some really helpful points about marking — make sure you read it first.

Composition and Effect — Set A, Improving the Common Room

What's the Answer Like?	Mark
• Little understanding of audience or purpose of the text. • Brief piece of writing with little detail and no developed ideas. • No attempt to explain the decisions.	**0** marks
• Attempts to organise ideas into paragraphs. • Some clear information on what has been done. • Gives some reasons for spending choices.	**1-3** marks
• Good opening paragraph which makes intentions clear. • Detailed information about several decisions with some reasons mentioned. • Appropriate choice of formal language.	**4-6** marks
• Report is well organised into distinct sections. • Describes details of spending with convincing reasons. • Clear sense of how students have benefited. • Consistent and appropriate formal tone.	**7-9** marks
• Clearly organised paragraphs which cover a variety of information. • Well-developed explanations of a range of decisions and outcomes. • Several benefits explained. • Good use of varied formal language appropriate to the audience.	**10-12** marks
• Report is well organised, with an easy-to-follow structure. • Interesting and realistic range of improvements and benefits mentioned. • Each decision / benefit is fully and clearly explained. • Confident, convincing formal tone conveys appreciation for the Parents' Association's help.	**13-14** marks

Writing Paper — Section A — Set B

Page 4 of this booklet has some really helpful points about marking — make sure you read it first.

Composition and Effect — Set B, Teen Readers

What's the Answer Like?	Mark
• Little understanding of the audience or the purpose of the task. • Brief piece of writing with few details or ideas. • No attempt to use the conventions of a report.	**0** marks
• Some attempt to tackle the purpose of the writing. • Some awareness that the report should be formal. • Some details about why teenagers might not like the library and / or how they could be encouraged to use it more.	**1-3** marks
• Fairly good opening paragraph that shows awareness of the purpose of the report. • Some good use of formal language appropriate for the purpose, e.g. "In my opinion" • Some points developed well with more detail and information, e.g. "Furthermore, Smithtown library has seen numbers rise because..." • Offers some evidence to support ideas, such as made-up quotations from teenagers.	**4-6** marks
• Clearly addresses audience and purpose of task. • Uses a consistently appropriate tone for advising, e.g. "I really believe that if we offer this we will see more teenagers coming through our doors". • Consistent use of formal language appropriate to a report for a boss. • Several detailed points and ideas with developed supporting evidence. • Clearly organised into paragraphs or sections.	**7-9** marks
• Convincing report which fulfils its objectives. • Well organised into paragraphs that follow on logically and clearly from one another, e.g. using signposts such as "In addition to these points..." • Makes confident and varied use of supporting evidence such as made-up quotations, personal stories or statistics. • Tone, style and language are appropriate and effective throughout.	**10-12** marks
• Well organised, realistic and easy-to-follow report which fulfils its objectives. • All points fully developed with a variety of supporting evidence used when appropriate. • Convincing and successful use of formal tone throughout. • Varied and interesting use of formal language appropriate for advising a boss.	**13-14** marks

Writing Paper — Section A — Set C

Page 4 of this booklet has some really helpful points about marking — make sure you read it first.

Composition and Effect — Set C, Bad Behaviour

What's the Answer Like?	Mark
• Little understanding of the audience or the purpose of the text. • Little written with few details or ideas shown. • No attempt to use conventions of a formal letter.	**0** marks
• Attempts to tackle the purpose of the writing. • Some awareness that the letter should be formal, e.g. "I understand that you have written to our head teacher..." • Some examples of persuasive writing, such as "I'm sure you agree..."	**1-3** marks
• Good opening paragraph that sets out the purpose of the letter. • Fairly good use of formal language. Not always consistent. • Some points developed well with more detail and information, e.g. "One example of the things we do for the local community is providing entertainment at the local old people's home..." • Some awareness of appropriate tone to persuade an older person.	**4-6** marks
• Clearly addresses audience and purpose of task. • Appropriate tone. • Consistent use of formal language that is respectful to the elderly lady. • Some detailed points and ideas with developed supporting evidence. • Clearly organised into paragraphs.	**7-9** marks
• Persuasive and realistic letter. • Well organised into paragraphs that follow on logically and clearly from one another, using signposts such as "Consequently..." or "However..." • Points supported by varied and persuasive evidence. • Tone, style and language appropriate and effective throughout.	**10-12** marks
• Effective, realistic and easy-to-follow letter. • Fully developed, interesting points supported with detailed evidence. • Persuasive but respectful tone throughout. • Varied and interesting use of formal language appropriate for a letter.	**13-14** marks

Writing Paper — Section B — Sets A, B & C

Page 4 of this booklet has some really helpful points about marking — make sure you read it first.

You can use the same mark scheme to mark any of the Section B questions for **Spelling** and **Sentence Structure, Punctuation and Text Organisation**. To mark questions for **Composition and Effect**, find the correct mark scheme for the specific question on pages 18-19.

Spelling

WHAT'S THE ANSWER LIKE?	MARK
• Simple words of one syllable spelt correctly. • Common words of more than one syllable spelt correctly, e.g. because. • Some words confused, e.g. here / hear. • Some words spelt as they sound, e.g. secondry instead of secondary.	**1** mark
• Most words that follow a regular pattern spelt correctly. • Some more difficult words spelt incorrectly, e.g. recieve instead of receive. • Some prefixes and suffixes spelt incorrectly, e.g. dissappeared instead of disappeared.	**2** marks
• Most words spelt correctly, including unusual words. • Some minor mistakes such as unstressed vowels missed out, e.g. diffrent instead of different. • Occasional mistakes with more difficult words.	**3** marks
• Almost every word spelt perfectly. • Any very minor slips are rare and not repeated.	**4** marks

Sentence Structure, Punctuation and Text Organisation

WHAT'S THE ANSWER LIKE?	MARK
• Makes use of only very simple connectives, such as "and". • Makes no use of pronouns (e.g. he, she, it). • Most sentences constructed correctly, but basic. • Makes little or no use of punctuation beyond full stops and commas.	**0** marks
• Sometimes uses simple subordinate clauses to extend sentences, e.g. "Though you may get slightly uncomfortable, all the money we raise will go to a good charitable cause." • Makes use of modal verbs, like "might", "may", "could" etc. • Beginning to use more complex sentences. • Sentences grouped together with the same topic. • More varied use of punctuation, but still limited.	**1-2** marks
• Longer and more complex sentences including some with several parts. • Makes use of more complex verb forms, e.g. imperatives such as "Beware!" • Sentences organised into paragraphs. • Points developed within paragraphs. • Punctuation used correctly and with some variety.	**3-4** marks
• Sustained use of complex sentences. • Sentence length and style varied for effect. • Range of connectives used effectively and confidently, both in sentences and between paragraphs — e.g. "You will need to perform for 15 minutes so make sure you have enough material." • Paragraphs clearly organised and flow smoothly. • Variety of punctuation used confidently and successfully.	**5** marks
• Able to use a range of verb forms consistently and successfully, including the passive voice to maintain an impersonal tone, where appropriate — e.g. "the changes were well received." • Points clearly and thoroughly developed. • Topic sentences used to begin paragraphs and paragraphs organised carefully for maximum effect. • Confident use of varied punctuation to good effect.	**6** marks

Writing Paper — Section B — Set A

Page 4 of this booklet has some really helpful points about marking — make sure you read it first.

Composition and Effect — Set A, Summer Fair Fundraising

What's the Answer Like?	Mark
• Little or no awareness of audience and purpose of text. • No use made of information in the prompt. • No attempt to engage interest through choice of language.	**0** marks
• Some awareness of writing for teaching staff. • Attempts to give reasons why they should volunteer. • A few attempts to sound persuasive, e.g. "You ought to volunteer"; "We need you to volunteer"; "It will be good".	**1-3** marks
• Sounds quite convincing with friendly but polite tone. • Several reasons for volunteering are given. • Vocabulary varied for persuasive effect, e.g. "this rare opportunity"; "star in the summer fair spectacular".	**4-6** marks
• Tone is light-hearted but still formal enough for staff audience. • A good range of convincing reasons to volunteer given. • Several persuasive devices used, e.g. rhetorical questions, examples, sets of three, statistics, emotive language.	**7-9** marks
• Well controlled tone of friendly persuasion, humour and the appropriate level of formality. • Intelligent use made of information in the prompt. • Uses a wide range of persuasive devices, e.g. anticipating staff response with counter-argument such as "You'll probably get wet but the water is nice and warm." • Well argued piece of writing which flows and is easy to read.	**10** marks

Writing Paper — Section B — Sets B & C

Composition and Effect — Set B, Talent Contest

What's the Answer Like?	Mark
• Little awareness shown of audience and purpose of text. • No attempt to address points suggested in the task. • Little written and little to attract readers' interest.	**0** marks
• Some awareness shown of the task's audience and purpose. • Some attempts to offer simple information relating to the talent contest. • Some use of effective vocabulary and some simple noun phrases, e.g. "The talent show will be an exciting competition."	**1-3** marks
• Good awareness of the task's audience and purpose. • Uses a range of devices to inform the audience about the talent contest and keep them interested. • Covers the ideas suggested in the task, with some developed in more detail.	**4-6** marks
• Makes an effort to catch the audience's attention from the beginning. • Well organised and informative writing. • Good use of devices, such as subheadings, to interest and inform the reader. • Appropriate use of informal language.	**7-9** marks
• Convincing and realistic leaflet that is appropriate for its audience and purpose. • Well organised and easy to follow, with varied and helpful stylistic devices. • Detailed and well developed points. • Confidently written.	**10** marks

Composition and Effect — Set C, Relaxation Area

What's the Answer Like?	Mark
• Little or no awareness of audience and purpose of text. • No attempt to provide the information requested in the task. • Little written and little attempt to describe a new relaxation area.	**0** marks
• Some awareness shown of task's audience and purpose. • Some attempts to describe the relaxation area, but little detail. • Some simple noun phrases such as, "The room should have comfortable seats. The room should have music playing in it."	**1-3** marks
• Some good awareness of the task's audience and purpose. • Suggested ideas are tackled more thoroughly, for example, "I'd like to see lilac walls with some artwork dotted around." • Uses varied language and descriptive devices. • Covers fully the requested information with some developed information where appropriate.	**4-6** marks
• Good awareness of the task's audience and purpose. • Interesting and descriptive piece of writing. • Varied use of devices such as rhetorical questions, emotive language and detail to interest the reader. • Sentences fully developed.	**7-9** marks
• Enjoyable and convincing descriptive writing, suitable for its audience and purpose. • Lots of original descriptive detail that avoids cliché. • Well organised, varied and imaginative. • Developed in an appropriate and well-controlled way.	**10** marks

Shakespeare Papers

Page 4 of this booklet has some really helpful points about marking — make sure you read it first.

1) Count up the number of separate points made to answer the essay question. On the appropriate grid, tick one box for each point (up to 6 ticks).
2) Tick one box for every one of those points that's backed up by a quote (up to 6 ticks).
3) Then tick one box for every point that's expanded with a comment (up to 6 ticks).
4) Finally count up all the ticks to give a mark out of 18.

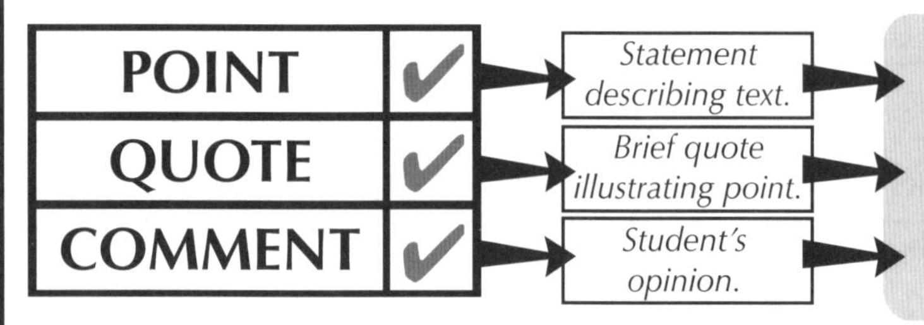

Shakespeare makes the tricksters use over-the-top language to draw Benedick in. Leonato's outburst "O God, counterfeit?" is very dramatic and out of character for him and should make the audience laugh.

Set A — Shakespeare Paper

POINT	✔					
QUOTE						
COMMENT						

Set B — Shakespeare Paper

POINT	✔					
QUOTE						
COMMENT						

Set C — Shakespeare Paper

POINT	✔					
QUOTE						
COMMENT						

English

KEY STAGE
3

LEVELS
4-7

PRACTICE PAPER
Shakespeare
Set A

Key Stage 3

English Test

Shakespeare Paper
Richard III
Set A

Instructions

- This test is **45 minutes** long.
- You will be tested on your reading and understanding of *Richard III*. There are **18 marks** for this paper.
- Check through all of your work carefully before the end of the test.
- If you're not sure what to do, ask your teacher.

First Name ____________________

Last Name ____________________

School ____________________

Exam set ER3P33

[BLANK PAGE]

Richard III

Act 1 Scene 2, lines 135 to 186
Act 4 Scene 4, lines 271 to 336

In the first extract, Richard tries to persuade Anne that he loves her; in the second he tries to persuade Queen Elizabeth to help him marry her daughter.

How do these extracts show how Richard is both dishonest and clever?

Support your ideas by referring to both of the extracts which are printed on the following pages.

(18 marks)

Richard III

Act 1 Scene 2, lines 135 to 186

In this extract, Richard tries to win over Anne. He tells her that he only killed her husband and father-in-law because he was in love with her.

RICHARD It is a quarrel most unnatural, 135
To be revenged on him that loveth thee.

ANNE It is a quarrel just and reasonable,
To be revenged on him that killed my husband.

RICHARD He that bereft thee, lady, of thy husband
Did it to help thee to a better husband. 140

ANNE His better doth not breathe upon the earth.

RICHARD He lives that loves thee better than he could.

ANNE Name him.

RICHARD Plantagenet.

ANNE Why that was he.

RICHARD The self-same name, but one of better nature.

ANNE Where is he? 145

RICHARD Here. *(She spits at him.)* Why dost thou
spit at me?

ANNE Would it were mortal poison, for thy sake!

RICHARD Never came poison from so sweet a place.

ANNE Never hung poison on a fouler toad.
Out of my sight! Thou dost infect mine eyes.

RICHARD Thine eyes, sweet lady, have infected mine. 150

ANNE Would they were basilisks to strike thee dead!

RICHARD I would they were, that I might die at once;
For now they kill me with a living death.
Those eyes of thine from mine have drawn salt tears,
Shamed their aspects with store of childish drops; 155
These eyes, which never shed remorseful tear,
No, when my father York and Edward wept
To hear the piteous moan that Rutland made
When black-faced Clifford shook his sword at him;
Nor when thy warlike father, like a child, 160
Told the sad story of my father's death,
And twenty times made pause to sob and weep

That all the standers-by had wet their cheeks
Like trees bedashed with rain. In that sad time
My manly eyes did scorn an humble tear; 165
And what these sorrows could not thence exhale
Thy beauty hath, and made them blind with weeping.
I never sued to friend nor enemy;
My tongue could never learn sweet smoothing word.
But, now thy beauty is proposed my fee, 170
My proud heart sues, and prompts my tongue to speak.

She looks scornfully at him.

Teach not thy lip such scorn for it was made
For kissing, lady, not for such contempt.
If thy revengeful heart cannot forgive,
Lo here I lend thee this sharp-pointed sword, 175
Which if thou please to hide in this true breast
And let the soul forth that adoreth thee,
I lay it naked to the deadly stroke,
And humbly beg the death upon my knee.

Kneeling he opens his shirt. She grips the sword and moves towards him as if to stab him.

Nay, do not pause: for I did kill King Henry — 180
But 'twas thy beauty that provokèd me.
Nay, now dispatch: 'twas I that stabbed young Edward —
But 'twas thy heavenly face that set me on.

She drops the sword.

Take up the sword again, or take up me.

ANNE Arise, dissembler. Though I wish thy death, 185
I will not be thy executioner.

Act 4 Scene 4, lines 271 to 336

In this extract, King Richard asks Queen Elizabeth to help him marry her daughter.

ELIZABETH Send to her, by the man that slew her brothers,
A pair of bleeding hearts. Thereon engrave
"Edward" and "York". Then haply will she weep.
Therefore present to her — as sometime Margaret
Did to thy father, steeped in Rutland's blood — 275
A handkerchief: which, say to her, did drain
The purple sap from her sweet brother's body,
And bid her wipe her weeping eyes withal.
If this inducement move her not to love,
Send her a letter of thy noble deeds. 280
Tell her thou mad'st away her uncle Clarence,
Her uncle Rivers — ay, and for her sake
Mad'st quick conveyance with her good aunt Anne.

KING RICHARD You mock me, madam. This is not the way
To win your daughter. 285

ELIZABETH There is no other way —
Unless thou couldst put on some other shape
And not be Richard that hath done all this!

KING RICHARD Say that I did all this for love of her.

ELIZABETH Nay, then indeed she cannot choose but hate thee,
Having bought love with such a bloody spoil! 290

KING RICHARD Look what is done cannot be now amended!
Men shall deal unadvisedly sometimes,
Which after-hours gives leisure to repent.
If I did take the kingdom from your sons,
To make amends I'll give it to your daughter. 295
If I have killed the issue of your womb,
To quicken your increase I will beget
Mine issue of your blood upon your daughter.
A grandam's name is little less in love
Than is the doting title of a mother. 300
They are as children but one step below,
Even of your metal, of your very blood —
Of all one pain, save for a night of groans
Endured of her, for whom you bid like sorrow.
Your children were vexation to your youth; 305

But mine shall be a comfort to your age.
The loss you have is but a son being King,
And by that loss your daughter is made Queen.
I cannot make you what amends I would,
Therefore accept such kindness as I can. 310
Dorset your son, that with a fearful soul
Leads discontented steps in foreign soil,
This fair alliance quickly shall call home
To high promotions and great dignity.
The King, that calls your beauteous daughter wife, 315
Familiarly shall call thy Dorset brother.
Again shall you be mother to a king,
And all the ruins of distressful times
Repaired with double riches of content.
What! We have many goodly days to see! 320
The liquid drops of tears that you have shed
Shall come again, transformed to orient pearl,
Advantaging their loan with interest
Of ten times double gain of happiness!
Go then, my mother — to thy daughter go. 325
Make bold her bashful years with your experience.
Prepare her ears to hear a wooer's tale.
Put in her tender heart th' aspiring flame
Of golden sovereignty! Acquaint the Princess
With the sweet silent hours of marriage joys. 330
And when this arm of mine hath chastisèd
The petty rebel, dull-brained Buckingham,
Bound with triumphant garlands will I come,
And lead thy daughter to a conqueror's bed —
To whom I will retail my conquest won, 335
And she shall be sole victoress, Caesar's Caesar!

END OF TEST

[BLANK PAGE]

English

KEY STAGE
3

LEVELS
4-7

PRACTICE PAPER
Shakespeare
Set B

Key Stage 3

English Test

Shakespeare Paper Richard III

Set B

Instructions

- This test is **45 minutes** long.
- You will be tested on your reading and understanding of *Richard III*. There are **18 marks** for this paper.
- Check through all of your work carefully before the end of the test.
- If you're not sure what to do, ask your teacher.

First Name ______________________

Last Name ______________________

School ______________________

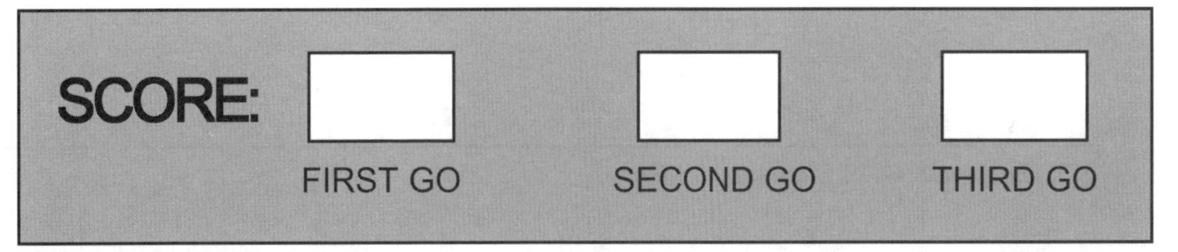

Exam set ER3P33

[BLANK PAGE]

Richard III

Act 1 Scene 2, lines 78 to 133
Act 4 Scene 4, lines 284 to 336

In these extracts, Richard attempts to persuade first Anne and then Queen Elizabeth to go along with his plans.

How does Richard use persuasive language to get both women to agree with him in these extracts?

Support your ideas by referring to both of the extracts which are printed on the following pages.

(18 marks)

Richard III

Act 1 Scene 2, lines 78 to 133

In this extract, King Richard admits murder and tries to talk his way into Anne's affections.

ANNE Vouchsafe, diffused infection of a man,
For these known evils but to give me leave
By circumstance to curse thy cursèd self. 80

RICHARD Fairer than tongue can name thee, let me have
Some patient leisure to excuse myself.

ANNE Fouler than heart can think thee, thou canst make
No excuse current but to hang thyself.

RICHARD By such despair I should accuse myself. 85

ANNE And by despairing shalt thou stand excused
For doing worthy vengeance on thyself
That didst unworthy slaughter upon others.

RICHARD Say that I slew them not?

ANNE Then say they were not slain.
But dead they are, and, devilish slave, by thee! 90

RICHARD I did not kill your husband.

ANNE Why, then he is alive.

RICHARD Nay, he is dead, and slain by Edward's hands.

ANNE In thy foul throat thou liest! Queen Margaret saw
Thy murderous falchion smoking in his blood,
The which thou once didst bend against her breast, 95
But that thy brothers beat aside the point.

RICHARD I was provokèd by her slanderous tongue
That laid their guilt upon my guiltless shoulders.

ANNE Thou wast provokèd by thy bloody mind,
That never dream'st on aught but butcheries. 100
Didst thou not kill this King?

RICHARD I grant ye.

ANNE Dost grant me, hedgehog? Then, God grant me too
Thou mayst be damnèd for that wicked deed!
O he was gentle, mild, and virtuous!

RICHARD The better for the King of Heaven, that hath him. 105

ANNE He is in heaven, where thou shalt never come.

RICHARD Let him thank me that holp to send him thither —

For he was fitter for that place than earth.

ANNE And thou unfit for any place but hell!

RICHARD Yes, one place else, if you will hear me name it. 110

ANNE Some dungeon?

RICHARD Your bed-chamber.

ANNE Ill rest betide the chamber where thou liest!

RICHARD So will it, madam, till I lie with you.

ANNE I hope so!

RICHARD I know so. But, gentle Lady Anne, 115
To leave this keen encounter of our wits,
And fall something into a slower method:
Is not the causer of the timeless deaths
Of these Plantagenets, Henry and Edward,
As blameful as the executioner? 120

ANNE Thou wast the cause and most accursed effect.

RICHARD Your beauty was the cause of that effect —
Your beauty that did haunt me in my sleep
To undertake the death of all the world
So I might live one hour in your sweet bosom. 125

ANNE If I thought that, I tell thee, homicide,
These nails should rend that beauty from my cheeks.

RICHARD These eyes could not endure that beauty's wrack:
You should not blemish it if I stood by.
As all the world is cheerèd by the sun, 130
So I by that; it is my day, my life.

ANNE Black night o'ershade thy day, and death thy life.

RICHARD Curse not thyself, fair creature — thou art both.

Act 4 Scene 4, lines 284 to 336

In this extract, King Richard asks Elizabeth to help him marry her daughter.

KING RICHARD You mock me, madam. This is not the way
To win your daughter.

ELIZABETH There is no other way — 285
Unless thou couldst put on some other shape
And not be Richard that hath done all this!

KING RICHARD Say that I did all this for love of her.

ELIZABETH Nay, then indeed she cannot choose but hate thee,
Having bought love with such a bloody spoil! 290

KING RICHARD Look what is done cannot be now amended!
Men shall deal unadvisedly sometimes,
Which after-hours gives leisure to repent.
If I did take the kingdom from your sons,
To make amends I'll give it to your daughter. 295
If I have killed the issue of your womb,
To quicken your increase I will beget
Mine issue of your blood upon your daughter.
A grandam's name is little less in love
Than is the doting title of a mother. 300
They are as children but one step below,
Even of your metal, of your very blood —
Of all one pain, save for a night of groans
Endured of her, for whom you bid like sorrow.
Your children were vexation to your youth; 305
But mine shall be a comfort to your age.
The loss you have is but a son being King,
And by that loss your daughter is made Queen.
I cannot make you what amends I would,
Therefore accept such kindness as I can. 310
Dorset your son, that with a fearful soul
Leads discontented steps in foreign soil,
This fair alliance quickly shall call home
To high promotions and great dignity.
The King, that calls your beauteous daughter wife, 315
Familiarly shall call thy Dorset brother.
Again shall you be mother to a king,
And all the ruins of distressful times
Repaired with double riches of content.
What! We have many goodly days to see! 320
The liquid drops of tears that you have shed

Shall come again, transformed to orient pearl,
Advantaging their loan with interest
Of ten times double gain of happiness!
Go then, my mother — to thy daughter go. 325
Make bold her bashful years with your experience.
Prepare her ears to hear a wooer's tale.
Put in her tender heart th' aspiring flame
Of golden sovereignty! Acquaint the Princess
With the sweet silent hours of marriage joys. 330
And when this arm of mine hath chastisèd
The petty rebel, dull-brained Buckingham,
Bound with triumphant garlands will I come,
And lead thy daughter to a conqueror's bed —
To whom I will retail my conquest won, 335
And she shall be sole victoress, Caesar's Caesar!

END OF TEST

[BLANK PAGE]

English

KEY STAGE
3

LEVELS
4-7

PRACTICE PAPER
Shakespeare
Set C

Key Stage 3

English Test

Shakespeare Paper Richard III

Set C

Instructions

- This test is **45 minutes** long.
- You will be tested on your reading and understanding of *Richard III*. There are **18 marks** for this paper.
- Check through all of your work carefully before the end of the test.
- If you're not sure what to do, ask your teacher.

First Name ______________________________

Last Name ______________________________

School ______________________________

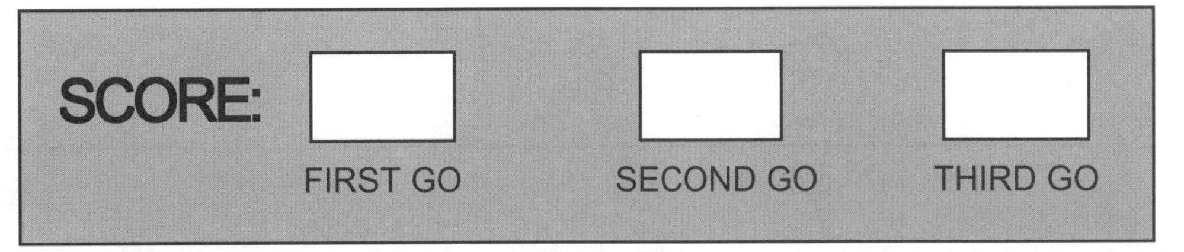

Exam set ER3P33

[BLANK PAGE]

Richard III

Act 1 Scene 2, lines 43 to 101
Act 4 Scene 4, lines 199 to 264

Imagine you're directing a school production of *Richard III*.

In the first extract, Anne accuses Richard of killing her husband and father-in-law; in the second, Richard asks Queen Elizabeth to help him marry her daughter.

How would you advise the actors playing Anne and Elizabeth to speak and behave in order to express their feelings towards Richard?

Support your ideas by referring to both of the extracts which are printed on the following pages.

(18 marks)

Richard III

Act 1 Scene 2, lines 43 to 101

In this extract, Anne accuses Richard of killing her husband and father-in-law. Richard initially denies it, but then admits that her accusations are true.

The bearers set down the coffin

ANNE What, do you tremble? Are you all afraid?
Alas, I blame you not, for you are mortal,
And mortal eyes cannot endure the devil. 45
Avaunt, thou dreadful minister of hell!
Thou hadst but power over his mortal body:
His soul thou canst not have. Therefore be gone!

RICHARD Sweet saint, for charity, be not so curst.

ANNE Foul devil, for God's sake, hence and trouble us not, 50
For thou hast made the happy earth thy hell,
Filled it with cursing cries and deep exclaims!
If thou delight to view thy heinous deeds,
Behold this pattern of thy butcheries.
O, gentlemen, see, see! Dead Henry's wounds 55
Open their congealed mouths and bleed afresh!
Blush, blush, thou lump of foul deformity,
For 'tis thy presence that exhales this blood
From cold and empty veins where no blood dwells.
Thy deeds inhuman and unnatural 60
Provokes this deluge most unnatural.
O God, which this blood mad'st, revenge his death!
O earth, which this blood drink'st, revenge his death!
Either heaven with lightning strike the murderer dead;
Or earth gape open wide and eat him quick — 65
As thou dost swallow up this good King's blood,
Which his hell-governed arm hath butcherèd.

RICHARD Lady, you know no rules of charity,
Which renders good for bad, blessing for curses.

ANNE Villain, thou knowest nor law of God nor man! 70
No beast so fierce but knows some touch of pity.

RICHARD But I know none, and therefore am no beast.

ANNE O wonderful, when devils tell the truth!

RICHARD More wonderful when angels are so angry.
Vouchsafe, divine perfection of a woman, 75
Of these supposèd crimes to give me leave
By circumstance but to acquit myself.

ANNE Vouchsafe, diffused infection of a man,
For these known evils but to give me leave

By circumstance to curse thy cursèd self. 80

RICHARD Fairer than tongue can name thee, let me have
Some patient leisure to excuse myself.

ANNE Fouler than heart can think thee, thou canst make
No excuse current but to hang thyself.

RICHARD By such despair I should accuse myself. 85

ANNE And by despairing shalt thou stand excused
For doing worthy vengeance on thyself
That didst unworthy slaughter upon others.

RICHARD Say that I slew them not?

ANNE Then say they were not slain.
But dead they are, and, devilish slave, by thee! 90

RICHARD I did not kill your husband.

ANNE Why, then he is alive.

RICHARD Nay, he is dead, and slain by Edward's hands.

ANNE In thy foul throat thou liest! Queen Margaret saw
Thy murderous falchion smoking in his blood,
The which thou once didst bend against her breast, 95
But that thy brothers beat aside the point.

RICHARD I was provokèd by her slanderous tongue
That laid their guilt upon my guiltless shoulders.

ANNE Thou wast provokèd by thy bloody mind,
That never dream'st on aught but butcheries. 100
Didst thou not kill this King?

RICHARD I grant ye.

Act 4 Scene 4, lines 199 to 264

In this extract, King Richard asks Queen Elizabeth to help him marry her daughter. Queen Elizabeth replies that her daughter would never marry Richard.

KING RICHARD Stay, madam. I must talk a word with you.

ELIZABETH I have no more sons of the royal blood 200
For thee to slaughter! For my daughters, Richard,
They shall be praying nuns, not weeping queens —
And therefore level not to hit their lives.

KING RICHARD You have a daughter called Elizabeth,
Virtuous and fair, royal and gracious. 205

ELIZABETH And must she die for this? O, let her live,
And I'll corrupt her manners, stain her beauty,
Slander myself as false to Edward's bed,
Throw over her the veil of infamy!
So she may live unscarred of bleeding slaughter, 210
I will confess she was not Edward's daughter.

KING RICHARD Wrong not her birth. She is a royal Princess.

ELIZABETH To save her life I'll say she is not so.

KING RICHARD Her life is safest only in her birth.

ELIZABETH And only in that safety died her brothers. 215

KING RICHARD Lo, at their birth good stars were opposite.

ELIZABETH No, to their lives ill friends were contrary.

KING RICHARD All unavoided is the doom of destiny.

ELIZABETH True, when avoided grace makes destiny.
My babes were destined to a fairer death, 220
If grace had blessed *thee* with a fairer life.

KING RICHARD You speak as if that I had slain my cousins.

ELIZABETH Cousins, indeed! And by their uncle cozened
Of comfort, kingdom, kindred, freedom, life!
Whose hand soever lanced their tender hearts, 225
Thy head, all indirectly, gave direction.
No doubt the murderous knife was dull and blunt
Till it was whetted on thy stone-hard heart
To revel in the entrails of my lambs!
But that still use of grief makes wild grief tame, 230
My tongue should to thy ears not name my boys
Till that my nails were anchored in thine eyes –
And I, in such a desperate bay of death,
Like a poor bark, of sails and tackling reft,
Rush all to pieces on thy rocky bosom. 235

KING RICHARD Madam, so thrive I in my enterprise
And dangerous success of bloody wars,
As I intend more good to you or yours
Than ever you or yours by me were harmed!

ELIZABETH What good is covered with the face of heaven, 240
To be discovered, that can do me good?

KING RICHARD Th' advancement of your children, gentle lady.

ELIZABETH Up to some scaffold, there to lose their heads?

KING RICHARD Unto the dignity and height of fortune,
The high imperial type of this earth's glory! 245

ELIZABETH Flatter my sorrow with report of it.
Tell me what state, what dignity, what honour,
Canst thou demise to any child of mine?

KING RICHARD Even all I have – ay, and myself and all
Will I withal endow a child of thine – 250
So in the Lethe of thy angry soul
Thou drown the sad remembrance of those wrongs
Which thou supposest I have done to thee.

ELIZABETH Be brief, lest that the process of thy kindness
Last longer telling than thy kindness' date. 255

KING RICHARD Then know, that from my soul I love thy daughter.

ELIZABETH My daughter's mother thinks it with her soul.

KING RICHARD What do you think?

ELIZABETH That thou dost love my daughter 'from' thy soul.
So from thy soul's love didst thou love her brothers, 260
And from my heart's love I do thank thee for it!

KING RICHARD Be not so hasty to confound my meaning.
I mean that with my soul I love thy daughter
And do intend to make her Queen of England.

END OF TEST

0707 - 5393

[BLANK PAGE]

English

KEY STAGE
3

LEVELS
4-7

PRACTICE PAPER
Shakespeare
Set A

CGP

Key Stage 3

English Test

Shakespeare Paper
Much Ado About Nothing
Set A

Instructions

- This test is **45 minutes** long.
- You will be tested on your reading and understanding of *Much Ado About Nothing*. There are **18 marks** for this paper.
- Check through all of your work carefully before the end of the test.
- If you're not sure what to do, ask your teacher.

First Name ______________________

Last Name ______________________

School ______________________

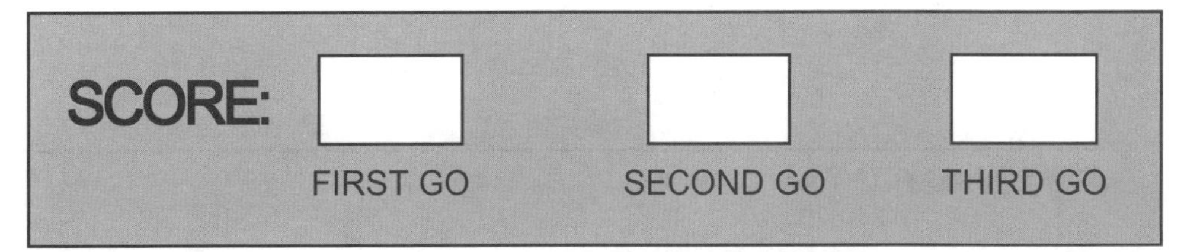

Exam set EMAP34

[BLANK PAGE]

Much Ado About Nothing

Act 4 Scene 1, lines 263 to 325
Act 5 Scene 4, lines 52 to 109

Imagine you are directing a school play of *Much Ado About Nothing.*

In the first extract, Beatrice persuades Benedrick to fight Claudio; in the second Benedick and Beatrice get married.

How would you direct the actors to speak and behave, to show the different sides of Benedick and Beatrice's relationship?

Support your ideas by referring to both of the extracts which are printed on the following pages.

(18 marks)

Much Ado About Nothing

Act 4 Scene 1, lines 263 to 325

In this extract, Benedick and Beatrice are left alone together. They admit they love each other, then Beatrice asks Benedick to kill Claudio.

BENEDICK I do love nothing in the world so well as you: is not that strange?

BEATRICE As strange as the thing I know not. It were as possible for me to say I loved nothing so well as you. (265) But believe me not; and yet I lie not. I confess nothing, nor I deny nothing. I am sorry for my cousin.

BENEDICK By my sword, Beatrice, thou lovest me.

BEATRICE Do not swear and eat it.

BENEDICK I will swear by it that you love me, and I will (270) make him eat it that says I love not you.

BEATRICE Will you not eat your word?

BENEDICK With no sauce that can be devised to it. I protest I love thee.

BEATRICE Why, then, God forgive me! (275)

BENEDICK What offence, sweet Beatrice?

BEATRICE You have stayed me in a happy hour. I was about to protest I loved *you*.

BENEDICK And do it with all thy heart.

BEATRICE I love you with so much of my heart that none (280) is left to protest.

BENEDICK Come, bid me do anything for thee.

BEATRICE Kill Claudio.

BENEDICK Ha! Not for the wide world.

BEATRICE You kill me to deny it. Farewell. (285)

BENEDICK Tarry, sweet Beatrice.

BEATRICE I am gone, though I am here. There is no love in you. Nay, I pray you, let me go.

BENEDICK Beatrice —

BEATRICE In faith, I will go. (290)

BENEDICK We'll be friends first.

BEATRICE You dare easier be friends with me than fight with mine enemy.

BENEDICK Is Claudio thine enemy?

BEATRICE Is he not approved in the height a villain, that hath slandered, scorned, dishonoured my kinswoman? O that I were a man! What, bear her in hand until they come to take hands, and then, with public accusation, uncovered slander, unmitigated rancour — O God, that I were a man! I would eat his heart in the market-place. 295 300

BENEDICK Hear me, Beatrice —

BEATRICE Talk with a man out at a window! A proper saying!

BENEDICK Nay, but, Beatrice —

BEATRICE Sweet Hero! She is wronged, she is slandered, she is undone. 305

BENEDICK Beat —

BEATRICE Princes and counties! Surely, a princely testimony, a goodly count, Count Comfect, a sweet gallant, surely! O that I were a man for his sake! Or that I had any friend would be a man for my sake! But manhood is melted into curtsies, valour into compliment, and men are only turned into tongue, and trim ones too. He is now as valiant as Hercules that only tells a lie and swears it. I cannot be a man with wishing, therefore I will die a woman with grieving. 310 315

BENEDICK Tarry, good Beatrice. By this hand, I love thee.

BEATRICE Use it for my love some other way than swearing by it.

BENEDICK Think you in your soul the Count Claudio hath wronged Hero?

BEATRICE Yea, as sure as I have a thought or a soul. 320

BENEDICK Enough, I am engaged. I will challenge him. I will kiss your hand, and so I leave you. By this hand, Claudio shall render me a dear account. As you hear of me, so think of me. Go, comfort your cousin. I must say she is dead, and so, farewell. 325

Exeunt

Act 5 Scene 4, lines 52 to 109

In this extract, Hero reveals to Claudio that she is alive, then Benedick proposes to Beatrice.

Re-enter ANTONIO, *with the ladies masked*

CLAUDIO For this I owe you. Here comes other reck'nings.
Which is the lady I must seize upon?

ANTONIO This same is she, and I do give you her.

CLAUDIO Why, then she's mine. Sweet, let me see your
face. 55

LEONATO No, that you shall not, till you take her hand
Before this Friar and swear to marry her.

CLAUDIO Give me your hand before this holy Friar.
I am your husband, if you like of me.

HERO *(unmasking)* And when I lived, I was your other wife, 60
And when you loved, you were my other husband.

CLAUDIO Another Hero!

HERO Nothing certainer.
One Hero died defiled, but I do live,
And surely as I live, I am a maid.

DON PEDRO The former Hero! Hero that is dead! 65

LEONATO She died, my lord, but whiles her slander lived.

FRIAR All this amazement can I qualify,
When after that the holy rites are ended,
I'll tell you largely of fair Hero's death.
Meantime let wonder seem familiar, 70
And to the chapel let us presently.

BENEDICK Soft and fair, friar. Which is Beatrice?

BEATRICE *(unmasking)* I answer to that name. What is
your will?

BENEDICK Do not you love me?

BEATRICE Why, no, no more than reason.

BENEDICK Why, then your uncle and the Prince and Claudio 75
Have been deceived — they swore you did.

BEATRICE Do not you love me?

BENEDICK Troth, no, no more than reason.

BEATRICE Why, then my cousin, Margaret, and Ursula
Are much deceived, for they did swear you did.

BENEDICK They swore that you were almost sick for me. 80

BEATRICE They swore that you were well-nigh dead for me.

BENEDICK 'Tis no such matter. Then you do not love me?

BEATRICE No, truly, but in friendly recompense.

LEONATO Come, cousin, I am sure you love the gentleman.

CLAUDIO And I'll be sworn upon't that he loves her, 85
For here's a paper written in his hand,
A halting sonnet of his own pure brain,
Fashioned to Beatrice.

HERO And here's another
Writ in my cousin's hand, stolen from her pocket,
Containing her affection unto Benedick. 90

BENEDICK A miracle! Here's our own hands against our
hearts. Come, I will have thee, but, by this light, I take thee
for pity.

BEATRICE I would not deny you, but, by this good day, I yield
upon great persuasion, and partly to save your life, 95
for I was told you were in a consumption.

BENEDICK Peace! I will stop your mouth. *(kisses her)*

DON PEDRO How dost thou, Benedick, the married man?

BENEDICK I'll tell thee what, Prince; a college of wit-crackers
cannot flout me out of my humour. Dost thou think I 100
care for a satire or an epigram? No. If a man will be
beaten with brains, a' shall wear nothing handsome
about him. In brief, since I do purpose to marry, I will
think nothing to any purpose that the world can say
against it, and therefore never flout at me for what I have 105
said against it, for man is a giddy thing, and this is my
conclusion. For thy part, Claudio, I did think to have beaten
thee, but in that thou art like to be my kinsman,
live unbruised and love my cousin.

END OF TEST

[BLANK PAGE]

English

KEY STAGE
3

LEVELS
4-7

PRACTICE PAPER
Shakespeare
Set B

Key Stage 3

English Test

Shakespeare Paper
Much Ado About Nothing
Set B

Instructions

- This test is **45 minutes** long.
- You will be tested on your reading and understanding of *Much Ado About Nothing*. There are **18 marks** for this paper.
- Check through all of your work carefully before the end of the test.
- If you're not sure what to do, ask your teacher.

First Name ______________________

Last Name ______________________

School ______________________

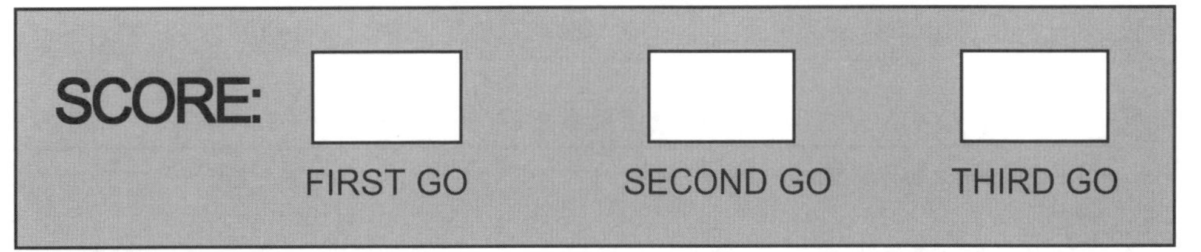

Exam set EMAP34

[BLANK PAGE]

Much Ado About Nothing

Act 4 Scene 1, lines 251 to 305
Act 5 Scene 4, lines 72 to 125

In the first extract, Beatrice asks Benedick to fight Claudio; in the second Benedick and Beatrice find out that they have been tricked into falling in love.

How does Shakespeare use language to show the different moods and feelings of the characters in these extracts?

Support your ideas by referring to both of the extracts which are printed on the following pages.

(18 marks)

Much Ado About Nothing

Act 4 Scene 1, lines 251 to 305

In this extract, Benedick and Beatrice are left alone together. They admit they love each other, then Beatrice asks Benedick to kill Claudio.

BENEDICK Lady Beatrice, have you wept all this while?

BEATRICE Yea, and I will weep a while longer.

BENEDICK I will not desire that.

BEATRICE You have no reason — I do it freely.

BENEDICK Surely I do believe your fair cousin is wronged. 255

BEATRICE Ah, how much might the man deserve of me
that would right her!

BENEDICK Is there any way to show such friendship?

BEATRICE A very even way, but no such friend.

BENEDICK May a man do it? 260

BEATRICE It is a man's office, but not yours.

BENEDICK I do love nothing in the world so well as you: is
not that strange?

BEATRICE As strange as the thing I know not. It were as
possible for me to say I loved nothing so well as you. 265
But believe me not; and yet I lie not. I confess nothing,
nor I deny nothing. I am sorry for my cousin.

BENEDICK By my sword, Beatrice, thou lovest me.

BEATRICE Do not swear and eat it.

BENEDICK I will swear by it that you love me, and I will 270
make him eat it that says I love not you.

BEATRICE Will you not eat your word?

BENEDICK With no sauce that can be devised to it.
I protest I love thee.

BEATRICE Why, then, God forgive me! 275

BENEDICK What offence, sweet Beatrice?

BEATRICE You have stayed me in a happy hour. I was
about to protest I loved *you*.

BENEDICK And do it with all thy heart.

BEATRICE I love you with so much of my heart that none 280
is left to protest.

BENEDICK Come, bid me do anything for thee.

BEATRICE Kill Claudio.

BENEDICK Ha! Not for the wide world.

BEATRICE You kill me to deny it. Farewell. 285

BENEDICK Tarry, sweet Beatrice.

BEATRICE I am gone, though I am here. There is no
love in you. Nay, I pray you, let me go.

BENEDICK Beatrice —

BEATRICE In faith, I will go. 290

BENEDICK We'll be friends first.

BEATRICE You dare easier be friends with me than fight
with mine enemy.

BENEDICK Is Claudio thine enemy?

BEATRICE Is he not approved in the height a villain, that 295
hath slandered, scorned, dishonoured my kinswoman?
O that I were a man! What, bear her in hand until they
come to take hands, and then, with public accusation,
uncovered slander, unmitigated rancour — O God, that I
were a man! I would eat his heart in the market-place. 300

BENEDICK Hear me, Beatrice —

BEATRICE Talk with a man out at a window! A proper
saying!

BENEDICK Nay, but, Beatrice —

BEATRICE Sweet Hero! She is wronged, she is
slandered, she is undone. 305

Act 5 Scene 4, lines 72 to 125

In this extract, Benedick and Beatrice find out they have been tricked into falling in love, but they agree to marry one another in the end.

BENEDICK Soft and fair, friar. Which is Beatrice?

BEATRICE *(unmasking)* I answer to that name. What is your will?

BENEDICK Do not you love me?

BEATRICE Why, no, no more than reason.

BENEDICK Why, then your uncle and the Prince and Claudio 75
Have been deceived — they swore you did.

BEATRICE Do not you love me?

BENEDICK Troth, no, no more than reason.

BEATRICE Why, then my cousin, Margaret, and Ursula
Are much deceived, for they did swear you did.

BENEDICK They swore that you were almost sick for me. 80

BEATRICE They swore that you were well-nigh dead for me.

BENEDICK 'Tis no such matter. Then you do not love me?

BEATRICE No, truly, but in friendly recompense.

LEONATO Come, cousin, I am sure you love the gentleman.

CLAUDIO And I'll be sworn upon't that he loves her, 85
For here's a paper written in his hand,
A halting sonnet of his own pure brain,
Fashioned to Beatrice.

HERO And here's another
Writ in my cousin's hand, stolen from her pocket,
Containing her affection unto Benedick. 90

BENEDICK A miracle! Here's our own hands against our hearts. Come, I will have thee, but, by this light, I take thee for pity.

BEATRICE I would not deny you, but, by this good day, I yield upon great persuasion, and partly to save your life, 95
for I was told you were in a consumption.

BENEDICK Peace! I will stop your mouth. *(kisses her)*

DON PEDRO How dost thou, Benedick, the married man?

BENEDICK I'll tell thee what, Prince; a college of wit-crackers
cannot flout me out of my humour. Dost thou think I 100

care for a satire or an epigram? No. If a man will be
beaten with brains, 'a shall wear nothing handsome
about him. In brief, since I do purpose to marry, I will
think nothing to any purpose that the world can say
against it, and therefore never flout at me for what I have 105
said against it, for man is a giddy thing, and this is my
conclusion. For thy part, Claudio, I did think to have beaten
thee, but in that thou art like to be my kinsman,
live unbruised and love my cousin.

CLAUDIO I had well hoped thou wouldst have denied 110
Beatrice, that I might have cudgelled thee out of thy
single life, to make thee a double-dealer, which, out of
question, thou wilt be, if my cousin do not look
exceeding narrowly to thee.

BENEDICK Come, come, we are friends. Let's have a 115
dance ere we are married, that we may lighten our own
hearts and our wives' heels.

LEONATO We'll have dancing afterward.

BENEDICK First, of my word! Therefore play, music.
Prince, thou art sad. Get thee a wife, get thee a wife! 120
There is no staff more reverend than one tipped with
horn.

Enter MESSENGER

MESSENGER My lord, your brother John is ta'en in flight,
And brought with armed men back to Messina.

BENEDICK Think not on him till tomorrow. I'll devise thee
brave punishments for him. Strike up, pipers. 125

Dance

Exeunt

END OF TEST

[BLANK PAGE]

English

KEY STAGE
3

LEVELS
4-7

PRACTICE PAPER
Shakespeare
Set C

Key Stage 3

English Test

Shakespeare Paper
Much Ado About Nothing
Set C

Instructions

- This test is **45 minutes** long.
- You will be tested on your reading and understanding of *Much Ado About Nothing*. There are **18 marks** for this paper.
- Check through all of your work carefully before the end of the test.
- If you're not sure what to do, ask your teacher.

First Name ______________________

Last Name ______________________

School ______________________

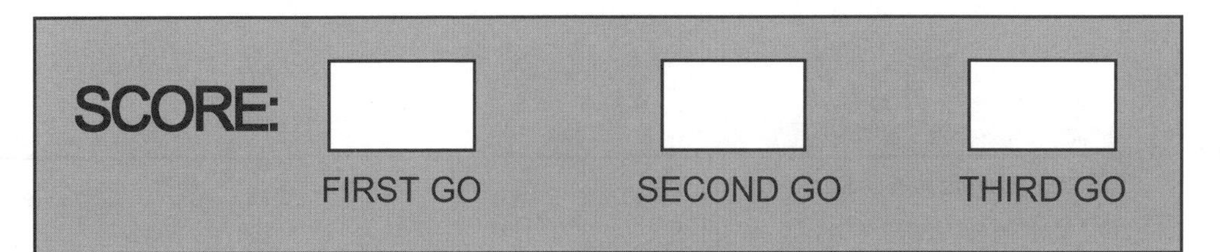

Exam set EMAP34

[BLANK PAGE]

Much Ado About Nothing

Act 4 Scene 1, lines 196 to 250
Act 5 Scene 4, lines 25 to 97

In the first extract, the Friar persuades Leonato to pretend Hero is dead; in the second Benedick and Beatrice realise that they've been fooled into falling in love.

How do these extracts show the importance of tricks in the play?

Support your ideas by referring to both of the extracts which are printed on the following pages.

(18 marks)

Much Ado About Nothing

Act 4 Scene 1, lines 196 to 250

In this extract, Friar Francis suggests that they pretend Hero is dead, so everyone will mourn her and forget the accusations against her.

FRIAR Pause awhile,
And let my counsel sway you in this case.
Your daughter here the Princes left for dead,
Let her awhile be secretly kept in,
And publish it that she is dead indeed; 200
Maintain a mourning ostentation
And on your family's old monument
Hang mournful epitaphs and do all rites
That appertain unto a burial.

LEONATO What shall become of this? What will this do? 205

FRIAR Marry, this well carried shall on her behalf
Change slander to remorse — that is some good.
But not for that dream I on this strange course,
But on this travail look for greater birth.
She dying, as it must so be maintained, 210
Upon the instant that she was accused,
Shall be lamented, pitied and excused
Of every hearer: for it so falls out
That what we have we prize not to the worth
Whiles we enjoy it, but being lacked and lost, 215
Why, then we rack the value, then we find
The virtue that possession would not show us
Whiles it was ours. So will it fare with Claudio.
When he shall hear she died upon his words,
The idea of her life shall sweetly creep 220
Into his study of imagination,
And every lovely organ of her life
Shall come apparelled in more precious habit,
More moving-delicate and full of life,
Into the eye and prospect of his soul, 225
Than when she lived indeed. Then shall he mourn,
If ever love had interest in his liver,
And wish he had not so accused her,
No, though he thought his accusation true.
Let this be so, and doubt not but success 230

Will fashion the event in better shape
Than I can lay it down in likelihood.
But if all aim but this be levelled false,
The supposition of the lady's death
Will quench the wonder of her infamy. 235
And if it sort not well, you may conceal her,
As best befits her wounded reputation,
In some reclusive and religious life,
Out of all eyes, tongues, minds and injuries.

BENEDICK Signior Leonato, let the friar advise you, 240
And though you know my inwardness and love
Is very much unto the Prince and Claudio,
Yet, by mine honour, I will deal in this
As secretly and justly as your soul
Should with your body.

LEONATO Being that I flow in grief, 245
The smallest twine may lead me.

FRIAR 'Tis well consented. Presently away;
For to strange sores strangely they strain the cure.
Come, lady, die to live. This wedding-day
Perhaps is but prolonged. Have patience and endure. 250

Exeunt all but BENEDICK *and* BEATRICE

Act 5 Scene 4, lines 25 to 97

In this extract, Benedick asks Leonato for permission to marry Beatrice, then Claudio finds out that Hero isn't dead after all.

LEONATO The sight whereof I think you had from me, 25
From Claudio and the Prince: but what's your will?

BENEDICK Your answer, sir, is enigmatical,
But, for my will, my will is your good will
May stand with ours, this day to be conjoined
In the state of honourable marriage, 30
In which, good friar, I shall desire your help.

LEONATO My heart is with your liking.

FRIAR And my help.
Here comes the Prince and Claudio.

Enter DON PEDRO *and* CLAUDIO *and two or three others*

DON PEDRO Good morrow to this fair assembly.

LEONATO Good morrow, Prince; good morrow, Claudio. 35
We here attend you. Are you yet determined
Today to marry with my brother's daughter?

CLAUDIO I'll hold my mind, were she an Ethiope.

LEONATO Call her forth, brother — here's the Friar ready.

Exit ANTONIO

DON PEDRO Good morrow, Benedick. Why, what's the matter, 40
That you have such a February face,
So full of frost, of storm and cloudiness?

CLAUDIO I think he thinks upon the savage bull.
Tush, fear not, man, we'll tip thy horns with gold
And all Europa shall rejoice at thee, 45
As once Europa did at lusty Jove,
When he would play the noble beast in love.

BENEDICK Bull Jove, sir, had an amiable low,
And some such strange bull leaped your father's cow,
And got a calf in that same noble feat 50
Much like to you, for you have just his bleat.

Re-enter ANTONIO, *with the ladies masked*

CLAUDIO For this I owe you. Here comes other reck'nings.
Which is the lady I must seize upon?

ANTONIO This same is she, and I do give you her.

CLAUDIO Why, then she's mine. Sweet, let me see your face. 55

LEONATO No, that you shall not, till you take her hand
Before this friar and swear to marry her.

CLAUDIO Give me your hand before this holy friar.
I am your husband, if you like of me.

HERO *(unmasking)* And when I lived, I was your other wife, 60
And when you loved, you were my other husband.

CLAUDIO Another Hero!

HERO Nothing certainer.
One Hero died defiled, but I do live,
And surely as I live, I am a maid.

DON PEDRO The former Hero! Hero that is dead! 65

LEONATO She died, my lord, but whiles her slander lived.

FRIAR FRANCIS All this amazement can I qualify,
When after that the holy rites are ended,
I'll tell you largely of fair Hero's death.
Meantime let wonder seem familiar, 70
And to the chapel let us presently.

BENEDICK Soft and fair, friar. Which is Beatrice?

BEATRICE *(unmasking)* I answer to that name. What is your will?

BENEDICK Do not you love me?

BEATRICE Why, no, no more than reason.

BENEDICK Why, then your uncle and the Prince and Claudio 75
Have been deceived — they swore you did.

BEATRICE Do not you love me?

BENEDICK Troth, no, no more than reason.

BEATRICE Why, then my cousin, Margaret, and Ursula
Are much deceived, for they did swear you did.

BENEDICK They swore that you were almost sick for me. 80

BEATRICE They swore that you were well-nigh dead for me.

BENEDICK 'Tis no such matter. Then you do not love me?

BEATRICE No, truly, but in friendly recompense.

LEONATO Come, cousin, I am sure you love the gentleman.

CLAUDIO And I'll be sworn upon't that he loves her, 85
For here's a paper written in his hand,
A halting sonnet of his own pure brain,
Fashioned to Beatrice.

HERO And here's another
Writ in my cousin's hand, stolen from her pocket,
Containing her affection unto Benedick. 90

BENEDICK A miracle! Here's our own hands against our hearts. Come, I will have thee, but, by this light, I take thee for pity.

BEATRICE I would not deny you, but, by this good day, I yield upon great persuasion, and partly to save your 95 life, for I was told you were in a consumption.

BENEDICK Peace! I will stop your mouth. *(kisses her)*

END OF TEST

English

KEY STAGE
3

LEVELS
4-7

PRACTICE PAPER
Shakespeare
Set A

Key Stage 3

English Test

Shakespeare Paper
The Tempest
Set A

Instructions

- This test is **45 minutes** long.
- You will be tested on your reading and understanding of *The Tempest*. There are **18 marks** for this paper.
- Check through all of your work carefully before the end of the test.
- If you're not sure what to do, ask your teacher.

First Name ______________________

Last Name ______________________

School ______________________

Exam set ETTP32

[BLANK PAGE]

The Tempest

Act 3 Scene 2, lines 40 to 108
Act 4 Scene 1, lines 194 to 250

In the first extract, Caliban persuades Stephano to kill Prospero; in the second he suggests they get on with the murder instead of stealing clothes.

What do you learn about Caliban's character from the way he behaves in these scenes?

Support your ideas by referring to both of the extracts which are printed on the following pages.

(18 marks)

The Tempest

Act 3 Scene 2, lines 40 to 108

In this extract, Caliban persuades Stephano to kill Prospero and become king of the island.

Enter ARIEL*, invisible*

CALIBAN As I told thee before, I am subject to a tyrant, 40
A sorcerer, that by his cunning hath
Cheated me of the island.

ARIEL *(in* TRINCULO's *voice)* Thou liest.

CALIBAN *(to* TRINCULO*)* Thou liest, thou jesting monkey, thou.
I would my valiant master would destroy thee. 45
I do not lie.

STEPHANO Trinculo, if you trouble him any more in's tale,
by this hand, I will supplant some of your teeth.

TRINCULO Why, I said nothing.

STEPHANO Mum, then, and no more. (*to* CALIBAN) Proceed. 50

CALIBAN I say, by sorcery he got this isle —
From me he got it. If thy greatness will
Revenge it on him — for I know *thou* dar'st,
But this thing dare not —

STEPHANO That's most certain. 55

CALIBAN Thou shalt be lord of it, and I'll serve thee.

STEPHANO How now shall this be compassed? Canst
thou bring me to the party?

CALIBAN Yea, yea, my lord, I'll yield him thee asleep,
Where thou may'st knock a nail into his head. 60

ARIEL *(in* TRINCULO's *voice)* Thou liest — thou canst not.

CALIBAN What a pied ninny's this! *(to* TRINCULO*)* Thou scurvy patch!
(to STEPHANO*)* I do beseech thy greatness, give him blows,
And take his bottle from him. When that's gone
He shall drink nought but brine, for I'll not show him 65
Where the quick freshes are.

STEPHANO Trinculo, run into no further danger. Interrupt the
monster one word further and, by this hand, I'll turn
my mercy out o'doors, and make a stockfish of thee.

TRINCULO Why, what did I? I did nothing. I'll go farther off. 70

STEPHANO Didst thou not say he lied?

ARIEL *(in* TRINCULO's *voice)* Thou liest.

STEPHANO Do I so? Take thou that! *(beats* TRINCULO*)*
As you like this, give me the lie another time!

TRINCULO I did not give the lie. Out o'your wits and hearing too? A pox o'your bottle! This can sack and drinking do. A murrain on your monster, and the devil take your fingers! 75

CALIBAN Ha, ha, ha!

STEPHANO Now, forward with your tale. 80
(to TRINCULO*)* Prithee stand further off.

CALIBAN Beat him enough — after a little time,
I'll beat him too.

STEPHANO *(to* TRINCULO*)* Stand farther.
(to CALIBAN*)* Come, proceed.

CALIBAN Why, as I told thee, 'tis a custom with him 85
I' th' afternoon to sleep. There thou mayst brain him,
Having first seized his books, or with a log
Batter his skull, or paunch him with a stake,
Or cut his wezand with thy knife. Remember
First to possess his books, for without them 90
He's but a sot, as I am, nor hath not
One spirit to command. They all do hate him
As rootedly as I. Burn but his books.
He has brave utensils — for so he calls them —
Which, when he has a house, he'll deck withal. 95
And that most deeply to consider is
The beauty of his daughter — he himself
Calls her a nonpareil. I never saw a woman
But only Sycorax my dam and she,
But she as far surpasseth Sycorax 100
As great'st does least.

STEPHANO Is it so brave a lass?

CALIBAN Ay, lord. She will become thy bed, I warrant,
And bring thee forth brave brood.

STEPHANO Monster, I will kill this man. His daughter and I will be king and queen — save our graces! — and Trinculo and thyself shall be viceroys. Dost thou like the plot, Trinculo? 105

TRINCULO Excellent.

Act 4 Scene 1, lines 194 to 250

In this extract, Trinculo and Stephano try to steal some clothes they find, but Caliban says they should get on with killing Prospero. Ariel and Prospero are watching secretly.

Enter CALIBAN, STEPHANO *and* TRINCULO, *all wet and dirty*

CALIBAN Pray you, tread softly, that the blind mole may not
Hear a foot fall — we now are near his cell. 195

STEPHANO Monster, your fairy, which you say is a
harmless fairy, has done little better than played the Jack
with us.

TRINCULO Monster, I do smell all horse-piss, at which my
nose is in great indignation.

STEPHANO So is mine. Do you hear, monster? If I 200
should take a displeasure against you, look you —

TRINCULO Thou wert but a lost monster.

CALIBAN Good my lord, give me thy favour still.
Be patient, for the prize I'll bring thee to
Shall hoodwink this mischance. Therefore speak softly. 205
All's hushed as midnight yet.

TRINCULO Ay, but to lose our bottles in the pool!

STEPHANO There is not only disgrace and dishonour in
that, monster, but an infinite loss.

TRINCULO That's more to me than my wetting, yet this is 210
your harmless fairy, monster.

STEPHANO I will fetch off my bottle, though I be o'er ears
for my labour.

CALIBAN Prithee, my king, be quiet. See'st thou here,
This is the mouth o'th' cell. No noise, and enter. 215
Do that good mischief which may make this island
Thine own for ever, and I, thy Caliban,
For aye thy foot-licker.

STEPHANO Give me thy hand. I do begin to have bloody
thoughts.

TRINCULO O King Stephano! O peer! O worthy 220
Stephano! Look what a wardrobe here is for thee!

CALIBAN   Let it alone, thou fool, it is but trash.

TRINCULO   O, ho, monster, we know what belongs to a
    frippery. O King Stephano!

They take and try on the clothes that Ariel has left.

STEPHANO   Put off that gown, Trinculo. By this hand, I'll   225
    have that gown.

TRINCULO   Thy Grace shall have it.

CALIBAN   The dropsy drown this fool! What do you mean
    To dote thus on such luggage? Let't alone,
    And do the murder first. If he awake,   230
    From toe to crown he'll fill our skins with pinches,
    Make us strange stuff.

STEPHANO   Be you quiet, monster. Mistress line, is not this
    my jerkin? Now is the jerkin under the line. Now, jerkin,
    you are like to lose your hair, and prove a bald jerkin.   235

TRINCULO   Do, do. We steal by line and level, an't like your
    grace.

STEPHANO   I thank thee for that jest — here's a garment
    for't. Wit shall not go unrewarded while I am king of this
    country. 'Steal by line and level' is an excellent pass of
    pate — there's another garment for't.   240

TRINCULO   Monster, come, put some lime upon your
    fingers, and away with the rest.

CALIBAN   I will have none on't. We shall lose our time,
    And all be turned to barnacles, or to apes
    With foreheads villainous low.   245

STEPHANO   Monster, lay-to your fingers — help to bear this
    away where my hogshead of wine is, or I'll turn you out
    of my kingdom. Go to, carry this.

TRINCULO   And this.

STEPHANO   Ay, and this.   250

A noise of hunters is heard.
Enter SPIRITS, *in the shape of hounds,*
chasing CALIBAN, STEPHANO *and* TRINCULO *about.*
PROSPERO *and* ARIEL *are urging them on.*

END OF TEST

[BLANK PAGE]

English

KEY STAGE
3

LEVELS
4-7

PRACTICE PAPER
Shakespeare
Set B

Key Stage 3

English Test

Shakespeare Paper
The Tempest
Set B

Instructions

- This test is **45 minutes** long.
- You will be tested on your reading and understanding of *The Tempest*. There are **18 marks** for this paper.
- Check through all of your work carefully before the end of the test.
- If you're not sure what to do, ask your teacher.

First Name ______________________

Last Name ______________________

School ______________________

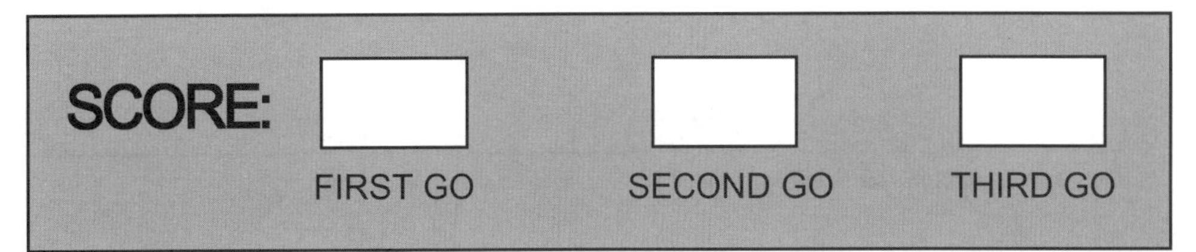

Exam set ETTP32

[BLANK PAGE]

The Tempest

Act 3 Scene 2, lines 1 to 50
Act 4 Scene 1, lines 194 to 253

In the first extract, Caliban, Stephano and Trinculo are drunk; in the second they try on some fancy clothes.

How does Shakespeare use language to create a humorous effect in these extracts?

Support your ideas by referring to both of the extracts which are printed on the following pages.

(18 marks)

The Tempest

Act 3 Scene 2, lines 1 to 50

In this extract, Caliban, Stephano and Trinculo are drunk. Trinculo is nasty to Caliban, then Ariel imitates him, tricking the others into thinking that he is still being nasty.

Enter CALIBAN, STEPHANO, *and* TRINCULO

STEPHANO Tell not me — when the butt is out we will drink water; not a drop before. Therefore bear up, and board 'em. Servant-monster, drink to me.

TRINCULO Servant-monster! The folly of this island! They say there's but five upon this isle: we are three of them. If the other two be brained like us, the state totters. 5

STEPHANO Drink, servant-monster, when I bid thee — thy eyes are almost set in thy head.

TRINCULO Where should they be set else? He were a brave monster indeed, if they were set in his tail. 10

STEPHANO My man-monster hath drowned his tongue in sack. For my part, the sea cannot drown me. I swam, ere I could recover the shore, five and thirty leagues, off and on. By this light, thou shalt be my lieutenant, monster, or my standard. 15

TRINCULO Your lieutenant, if you list. He's no standard.

STEPHANO We'll not run, Monsieur Monster.

TRINCULO Nor go neither, but you'll lie like dogs, and yet say nothing neither.

STEPHANO Mooncalf, speak once in thy life, if thou be'st a good mooncalf. 20

CALIBAN *(very drunk)* How does thy honour? Let me lick thy shoe. I'll not serve him — he is not valiant.

TRINCULO Thou liest, most ignorant monster: I am in case to jostle a constable. Why, thou deboshed fish, thou, was there ever man a coward that hath drunk so much sack as I today? Wilt thou tell a monstrous lie, being but half a fish and half a monster? 25

CALIBAN Lo, how he mocks me! Wilt thou let him, my lord?

TRINCULO 'Lord', quoth he! That a monster should be such a natural! 30

CALIBAN Lo, lo again! Bite him to death, I prithee.

STEPHANO Trinculo, keep a good tongue in your head. If you prove a mutineer — the next tree! The poor monster's my subject, and he shall not suffer indignity. 35

CALIBAN   I thank my noble lord. Wilt thou be pleased to
hearken once again to the suit I made to thee?

STEPHANO   Marry will I — kneel and repeat it. I will stand,
and so shall Trinculo.

Enter ARIEL, *invisible*

CALIBAN   As I told thee before, I am subject to a tyrant,   40
A sorcerer, that by his cunning hath
Cheated me of the island.

ARIEL   *(in* TRINCULO's *voice)* Thou liest.

CALIBAN   (*to* TRINCULO) 'Thou liest', thou jesting monkey, thou.
I would my valiant master would destroy thee.   45
I do not lie.

STEPHANO   Trinculo, if you trouble him any more in's tale,
by this hand, I will supplant some of your teeth.

TRINCULO   Why, I said nothing.

STEPHANO   Mum, then, and no more. (*to* CALIBAN) Proceed.   50

Act 4 Scene 1, lines 194 to 253

In this extract, Trinculo and Stephano try on some fancy clothes. Caliban says they should get on with killing Prospero, but then they are driven away by spirits in the form of dogs.

Enter CALIBAN, STEPHANO *and* TRINCULO, *all wet and dirty*

CALIBAN Pray you, tread softly, that the blind mole may not
Hear a foot fall — we now are near his cell. 195

STEPHANO Monster, your fairy, which you say is a
harmless fairy, has done little better than played the Jack
with us.

TRINCULO Monster, I do smell all horse-piss, at which my nose
is in great indignation.

STEPHANO So is mine. Do you hear, monster? If I 200
should take a displeasure against you, look you —

TRINCULO Thou wert but a lost monster.

CALIBAN Good my lord, give me thy favour still.
Be patient, for the prize I'll bring thee to
Shall hoodwink this mischance. Therefore speak softly. 205
All's hushed as midnight yet.

TRINCULO Ay, but to lose our bottles in the pool!

STEPHANO There is not only disgrace and dishonour in that,
monster, but an infinite loss.

TRINCULO That's more to me than my wetting, yet this is your 210
harmless fairy, monster.

STEPHANO I will fetch off my bottle, though I be o'er ears for
my labour.

CALIBAN Prithee, my king, be quiet. See'st thou here,
This is the mouth o'th' cell. No noise, and enter. 215
Do that good mischief which may make this island
Thine own for ever, and I, thy Caliban,
For aye thy foot-licker.

STEPHANO Give me thy hand. I do begin to have bloody
thoughts.

TRINCULO O King Stephano! O peer! O worthy 220
Stephano! Look what a wardrobe here is for thee!

CALIBAN Let it alone, thou fool, it is but trash.

TRINCULO O, ho, monster, we know what belongs to a frippery.
O King Stephano!

They take and try on the clothes that Ariel has left.

STEPHANO Put off that gown, Trinculo. By this hand, I'll have that gown. 225

TRINCULO Thy Grace shall have it.

CALIBAN The dropsy drown this fool! What do you mean
To dote thus on such luggage? Let't alone,
And do the murder first. If he awake, 230
From toe to crown he'll fill our skins with pinches,
Make us strange stuff.

STEPHANO Be you quiet, monster. Mistress line, is not this my jerkin? Now is the jerkin under the line. Now, jerkin, you are like to lose your hair, and prove a bald jerkin. 235

TRINCULO Do, do. We steal by line and level, an't like your grace.

STEPHANO I thank thee for that jest — here's a garment for't. Wit shall not go unrewarded while I am king of this country. 'Steal by line and level' is an excellent pass of pate — there's another garment for't. 240

TRINCULO Monster, come, put some lime upon your fingers, and away with the rest.

CALIBAN I will have none on't. We shall lose our time,
And all be turned to barnacles, or to apes
With foreheads villainous low. 245

STEPHANO Monster, lay-to your fingers — help to bear this away where my hogshead of wine is, or I'll turn you out of my kingdom. Go to, carry this.

TRINCULO And this.

STEPHANO Ay, and this. 250

A noise of hunters is heard.
Enter SPIRITS, *in the shape of hounds,*
chasing CALIBAN, STEPHANO *and* TRINCULO *about.*
PROSPERO *and* ARIEL *are urging them on.*

PROSPERO Hey, Mountain, hey!

ARIEL Silver! There it goes, Silver!

PROSPERO Fury, Fury! There, Tyrant, there! Hark, hark!

CALIBAN, STEPHANO *and* TRINCULO *are driven out.*

END OF TEST

[BLANK PAGE]

English

KEY STAGE
3

LEVELS
4-7

PRACTICE PAPER
Shakespeare
Set C

CGP

Key Stage 3

English Test

Shakespeare Paper
The Tempest
Set C

Instructions

- This test is **45 minutes** long.
- You will be tested on your reading and understanding of *The Tempest*. There are **18 marks** for this paper.
- Check through all of your work carefully before the end of the test.
- If you're not sure what to do, ask your teacher.

First Name ______________________

Last Name ______________________

School ______________________

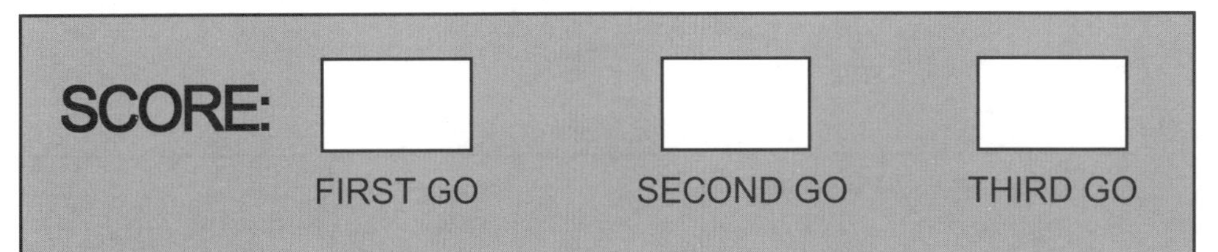

Exam set ETTP32

[BLANK PAGE]

The Tempest

Act 3 Scene 2, lines 85 to 149
Act 4 Scene 1, lines 164 to 206

Imagine you're directing these extracts for a school performance.

In the first extract, Ariel leads the plotters away; in the second Ariel and Prospero make a plan to catch them.

How would you direct the actor playing Ariel to behave and speak in these extracts?

Support your ideas by referring to both of the extracts which are printed on the following pages.

(18 marks)

The Tempest

Act 3 Scene 2, lines 85 to 149

> In this extract, Caliban persuades Stephano to kill Prospero, then Caliban, Stephano and Trinculo are led away, following Ariel's music.

CALIBAN Why, as I told thee, 'tis a custom with him 85
I'th' afternoon to sleep. There thou mayst brain him,
Having first seized his books, or with a log
Batter his skull, or paunch him with a stake,
Or cut his wezand with thy knife. Remember
First to possess his books, for without them 90
He's but a sot, as I am, nor hath not
One spirit to command. They all do hate him
As rootedly as I. Burn but his books.
He has brave utensils — for so he calls them —
Which, when he has a house, he'll deck withal. 95
And that most deeply to consider is
The beauty of his daughter — he himself
Calls her a nonpareil. I never saw a woman
But only Sycorax my dam and she,
But she as far surpasseth Sycorax 100
As great'st does least.

STEPHANO Is it so brave a lass?

CALIBAN Ay, lord. She will become thy bed, I warrant,
And bring thee forth brave brood.

STEPHANO Monster, I will kill this man. His daughter and I
will be king and queen — save our graces! — and 105
Trinculo and thyself shall be viceroys. Dost thou like the
plot, Trinculo?

TRINCULO Excellent.

STEPHANO Give me thy hand — I am sorry I beat thee, but
while thou liv'st, keep a good tongue in thy head. 110

CALIBAN Within this half hour will he be asleep.
Wilt thou destroy him then?

STEPHANO Ay, on mine honour.

ARIEL *(aside)* This will I tell my master.

CALIBAN Thou mak'st me merry. I am full of pleasure.
Let us be jocund — will you troll the catch 115
You taught me but whilere?

STEPHANO At thy request, monster, I will do reason, any
reason. Come on, Trinculo, let us sing.

(They sing) Flout 'em and scout 'em,
And scout 'em and flout 'em; 120
Thought is free.

CALIBAN That's not the tune.

ARIEL *plays the tune on a tabor and pipe*

STEPHANO What is this same?

TRINCULO This is the tune of our catch, played by the
picture of Nobody. 125

STEPHANO If thou be'st a man, show thyself in thy
likeness. If thou be'st a devil, take't as thou list.

TRINCULO O, forgive me my sins!

STEPHANO He that dies pays all debts. I defy thee.
Mercy upon us! 130

CALIBAN Art thou afeard?

STEPHANO No, monster, not I.

CALIBAN Be not afeard. The isle is full of noises,
Sounds, and sweet airs, that give delight, and hurt not.
Sometimes a thousand twangling instruments
Will hum about mine ears, and sometimes voices, 135
That, if I then had waked after long sleep,
Will make me sleep again, and then, in dreaming,
The clouds methought would open and show riches
Ready to drop upon me, that, when I waked,
I cried to dream again. 140

STEPHANO This will prove a brave kingdom to me, where I
shall have my music for nothing.

CALIBAN When Prospero is destroyed.

STEPHANO That shall be by and by. I remember the story.

TRINCULO The sound is going away. Let's follow it, and 145
after do our work.

STEPHANO Lead, monster — we'll follow. I would I could
see this taborer. He lays it on.

TRINCULO Wilt come? I'll follow, Stephano.

Exeunt

Act 4 Scene 1, lines 164 to 206

In this extract, Ariel tells Prospero about what he did to Caliban, Stephano and Trinculo. Ariel and Prospero make a plan to catch the three plotters.

PROSPERO *(calling* ARIEL*)* Come, with a thought. *(to* FERDINAND
and MIRANDA*)* I thank thee. Ariel, come.

Enter ARIEL

ARIEL Thy thoughts I cleave to. What's thy pleasure? 165

PROSPERO Spirit, we must prepare to meet with Caliban.

ARIEL Ay, my commander. When I presented Ceres
I thought to have told thee of it, but I feared
Lest I might anger thee.

PROSPERO Say again, where didst thou leave these varlets? 170

ARIEL I told you, sir, they were red-hot with drinking,
So full of valour that they smote the air
For breathing in their faces, beat the ground
For kissing of their feet, yet always bending
Towards their project. Then I beat my tabor, 175
At which like unbacked colts they pricked their ears,
Advanced their eyelids, lifted up their noses
As they smelt music, so I charmed their ears,
That calf-like they my lowing followed, through
Toothed briers, sharp furzes, pricking gorse and thorns, 180
Which entered their frail shins. At last I left them
I'th' filthy mantled pool beyond your cell,
There dancing up to th' chins, that the foul lake
O'erstunk their feet.

PROSPERO This was well done, my bird.
Thy shape invisible retain thou still. 185
The trumpery in my house, go bring it hither
For stale to catch these thieves.

ARIEL I go, I go.

Exit

PROSPERO A devil, a born devil, on whose nature
Nurture can never stick, on whom my pains,
Humanely taken, all, all lost, quite lost, 190
And as with age his body uglier grows,
So his mind cankers. I will plague them all,
Even to roaring.

Re-enter ARIEL*, loaded with shiny clothing, etc.*

Come, hang them on this line.

PROSPERO and ARIEL remain, invisible
Enter CALIBAN, STEPHANO and TRINCULO, all wet and dirty

CALIBAN Pray you, tread softly, that the blind mole may not
Hear a foot fall — we now are near his cell. 195

STEPHANO Monster, your fairy, which you say is a
harmless fairy, has done little better than played the Jack
with us.

TRINCULO Monster, I do smell all horse-piss at which my nose is
in great indignation.

STEPHANO So is mine. Do you hear, monster? If I 200
should take a displeasure against you, look you —

TRINCULO Thou wert but a lost monster.

CALIBAN Good my lord, give me thy favour still.
Be patient, for the prize I'll bring thee to
Shall hoodwink this mischance. Therefore speak softly. 205
All's hushed as midnight yet.

END OF TEST

0707 - 5394

[BLANK PAGE]

Maths

KEY STAGE

3

LEVELS

5-8

PRACTICE PAPER

1A

Key Stage 3

Mathematics Test

Practice Paper 1A

Calculator NOT allowed

Read this page, but don't open the booklet until your teacher says you can start. Write your name and school in the spaces below.

First Name ______________________________

Last Name ______________________________

School ______________________________

Remember

- The test is one hour long.
- Make sure you have these things with you before you start: pen, pencil, rubber, ruler, angle measurer or protractor and pair of compasses.
  You may use tracing paper.
- There are some formulas you might need on page 2.
- The easier questions are at the start of the test.
- Try to answer all of the questions.
- Don't use any rough paper — write all your answers and working in this test paper.
- Check your work carefully before the end of the test.
- If you're not sure what to do, ask your teacher.

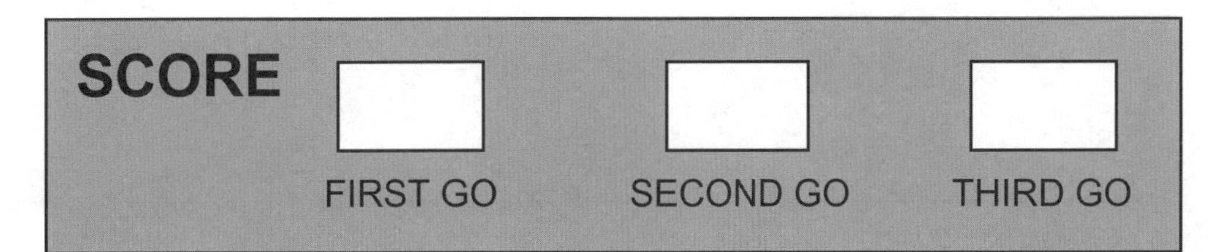

Exam Set MHGP31

Instructions

This means write down your answer or show your working and your answer.

You may not use a calculator in this test.

Formulas

Trapezium

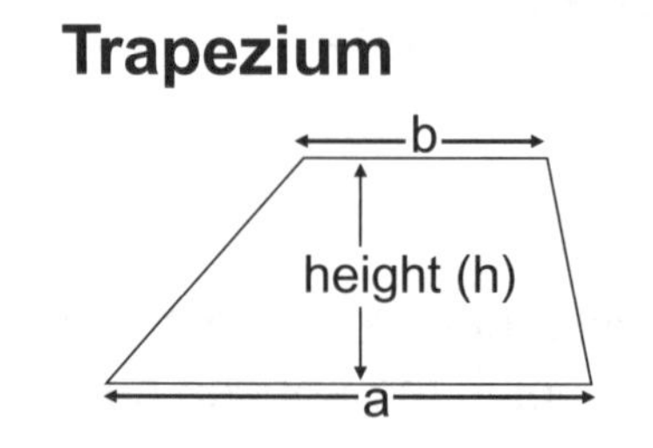

$$\text{Area} = \frac{(a + b)}{2} \times h$$

Prism

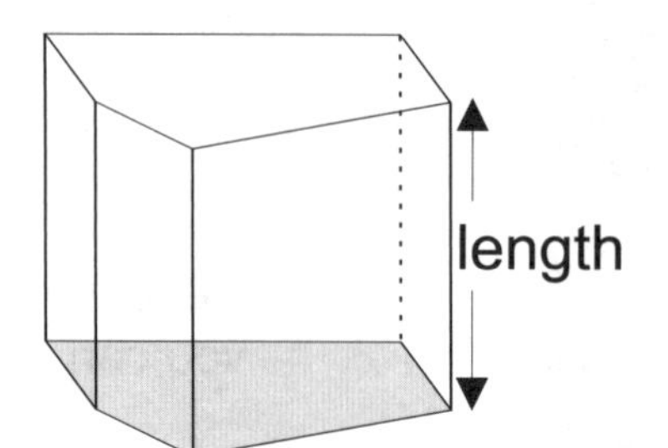

Volume = area of cross-section × length

1. ABCD is a rhombus. Angle A is 53°.

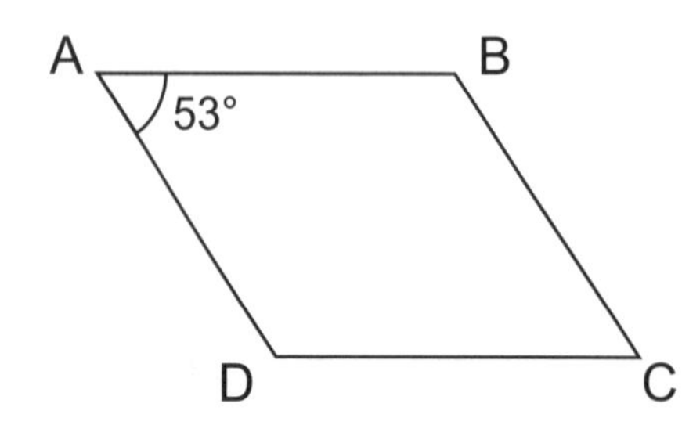

(DIAGRAM NOT TO SCALE)

(a) Write down the size of angle C.

C = ... °

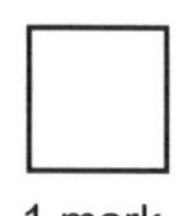

1 mark

(b) Work out the size of angle B.

B = ... °

2 marks

2. Complete the following statements.

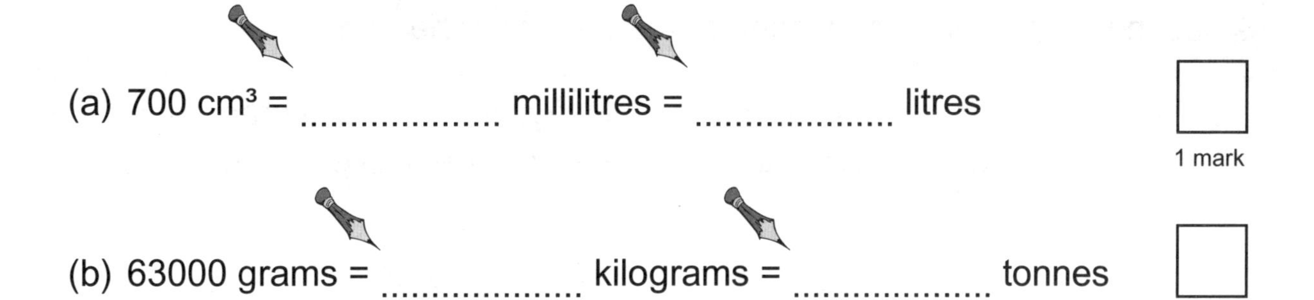

(a) 700 cm³ = ... millilitres = ... litres

1 mark

(b) 63000 grams = ... kilograms = ... tonnes

1 mark

3. Enlarge the shape below by a scale factor of ½, about centre of enlargement (0,0).

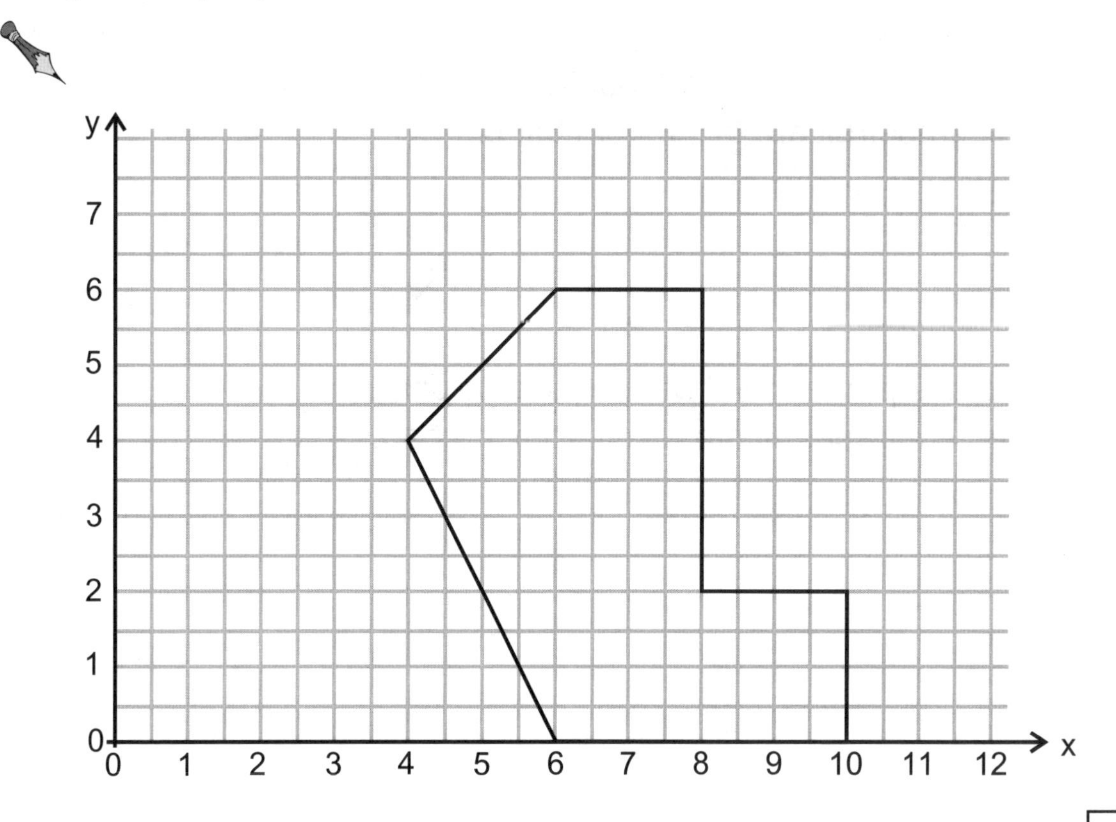

2 marks

4. There are 4 pink grapefruit and 7 red grapefruit in a bag.
A grapefruit is taken at random from the bag and not replaced.
A second grapefruit is then taken at random from the bag.

(a) This tree diagram shows the different ways in which two grapefruit can be taken from the bag. Write the four missing probabilities on the diagram.

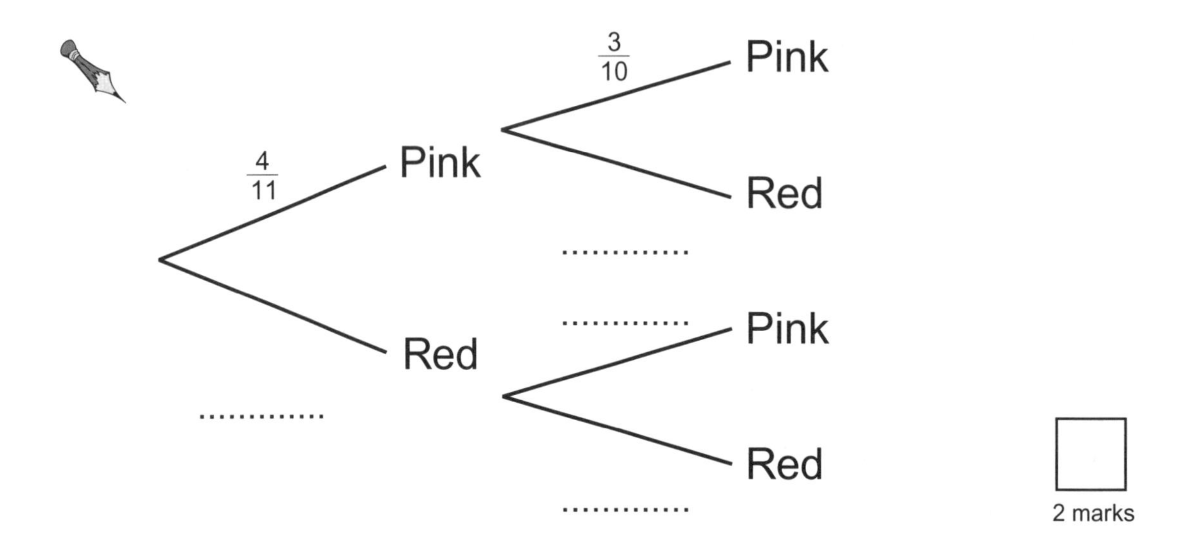

2 marks

(b) Use the tree diagram to work out the probability that two pink grapefruit are taken from the bag.

1 mark

(c) Work out the probability that one pink grapefruit and one red grapefruit are taken from the bag.

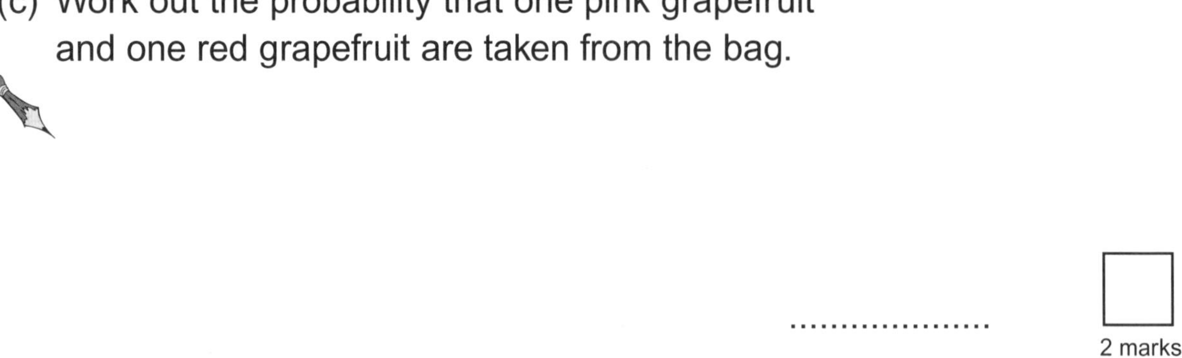

2 marks

5. The diagram below shows the position of Ann's house **A**, Brenda's house **B** and the school **S**.

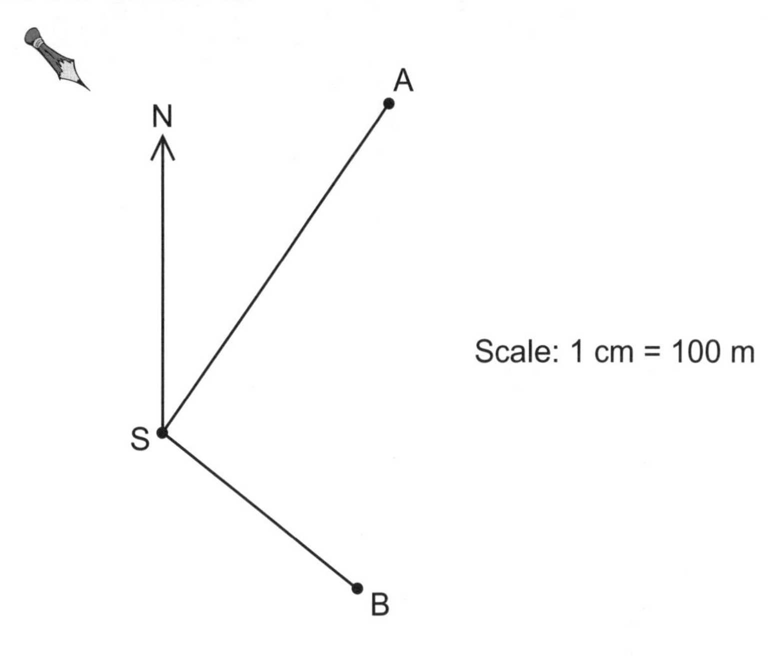

(a) Measure and write down the bearing from the school to Ann's house.

1 mark

(b) Carol's house is positioned 500 m from the school and on a bearing of 320° from the school.

Mark the position of Carol's house on the diagram with a letter **C**.

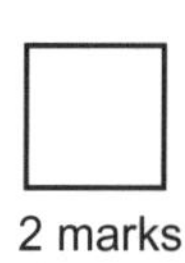

2 marks

6. The diagram below shows a multiplication cross.
Opposite squares multiply together to give the answer in the middle square.

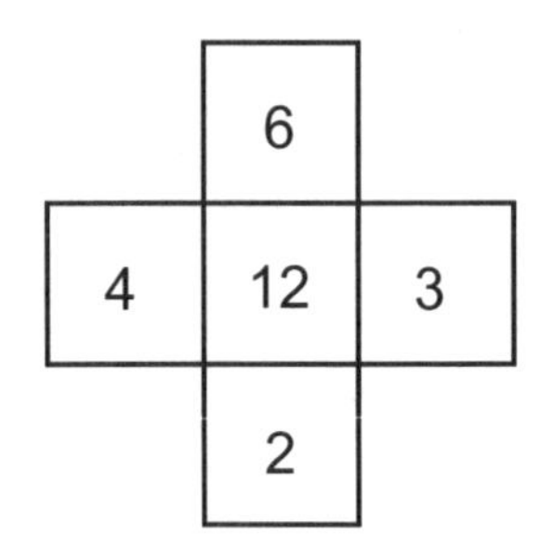

Complete the multiplication crosses below.

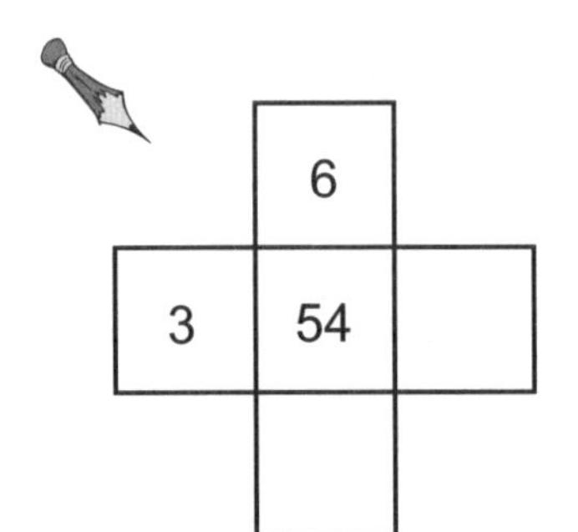

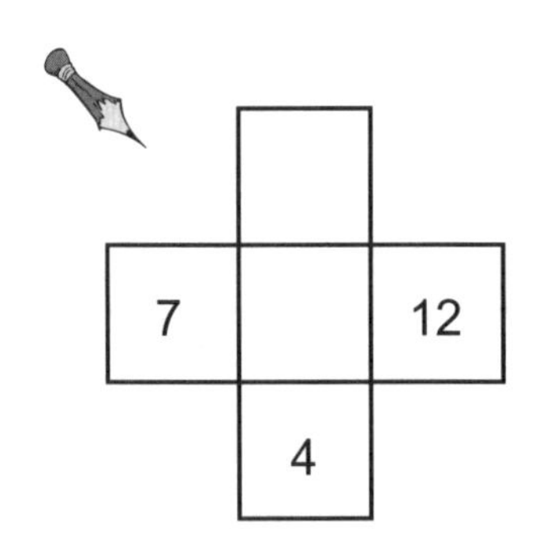

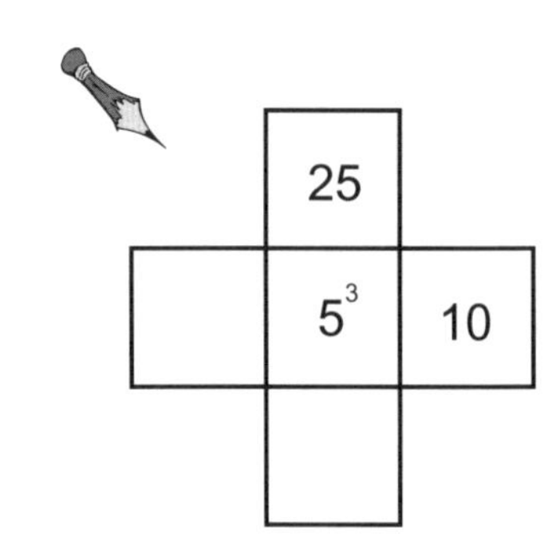

4 marks

7. Eleanor pays 14p per minute for a phone call to Morocco.
The total cost of the phone call is £8.96.

Work out the length of the call in minutes.

.... minutes

2 marks

8. Solve these equations:

(a) $\frac{3x}{9} = -2$

x = ...

1 mark

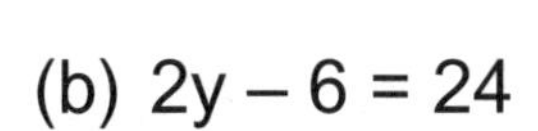

(b) $2y - 6 = 24$

y = ...

1 mark

(c) $3z - 7 = 29 + z$

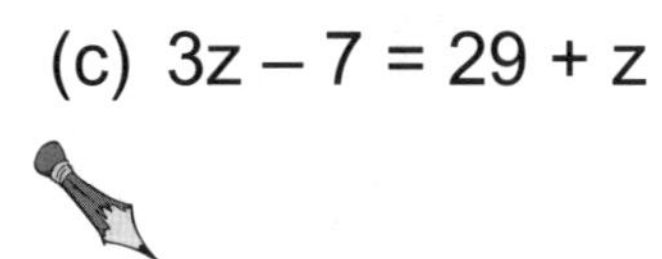

z = ...

2 marks

9. A survey was conducted to find out how many people were registered with a National Health Service dentist, a private dentist or no dentist. The pie chart shows the results.

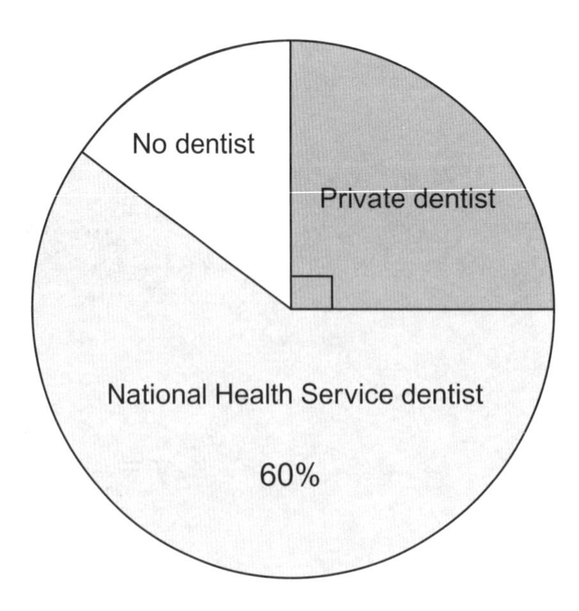

(a) The angle on the pie chart for the people registered with a private dentist is 90°. What percentage of the people is this?

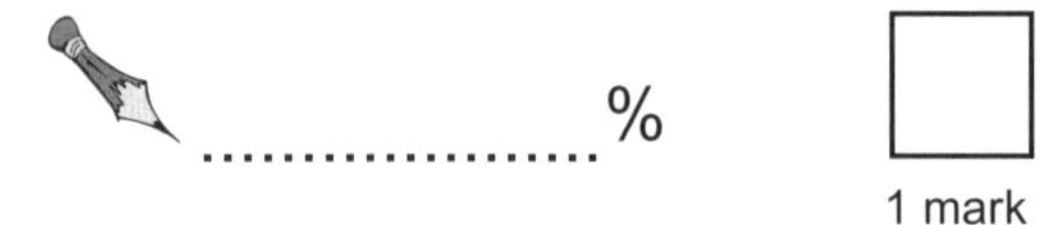

.... %

1 mark

(b) Work out the angle on the pie chart for the people registered with a National Health Service dentist.

.... °

2 marks

(c) 300 people were not registered with a dentist. Work out how many people took part in the survey.

....

2 marks

10. Look at these fractions:

$$\frac{3}{4} \qquad \frac{1}{2} \qquad \frac{5}{8}$$

(a) Work out the range of the fractions.

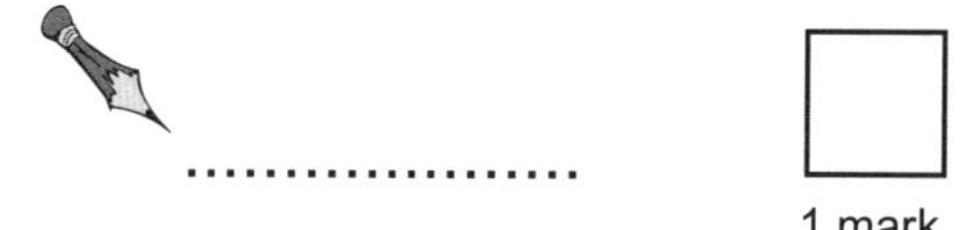

.... 1 mark

(b) Work out the mean of the fractions.

.... 2 marks

11. On a school trip the ratio of teachers to pupils was 2 : 7.
108 people went on the trip.

How many teachers and how many pupils went on the trip?

.... teachers and .... pupils

3 marks

12. In the year 2010, Josie will be x years old.
Her mum will be exactly four times Josie's age.
Josie's Nanna is 30 years older than her Mum.
Josie's Nanna will be 78 years old in 2010.

(a) Use this information to form an algebraic expression and solve it to find x. You must show your working.

x = ...

2 marks

(b) In what year was Josie born?

....

1 mark

13. Here is the graph of the straight line $y = -2x + 3$.

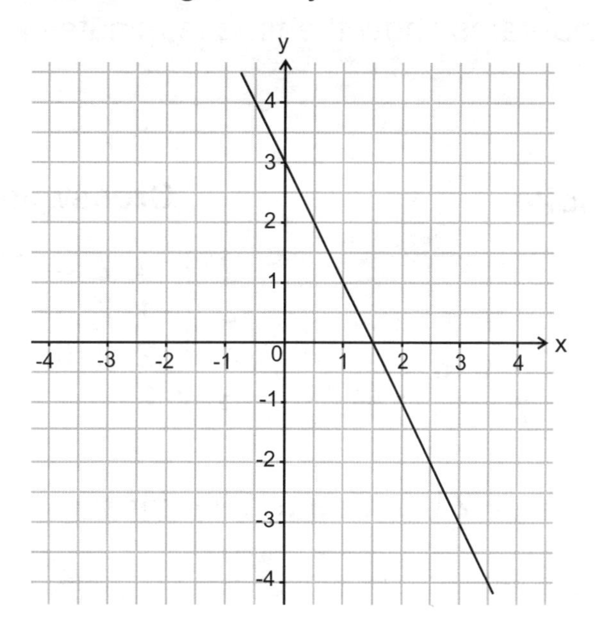

(a) A point on the line $y = -2x + 3$ has an x-coordinate of 25.
What is the y-coordinate of the point?

1 mark

(b) A point on the line $y = -2x + 3$ has a y-coordinate of -31.
What is the x-coordinate of the point?

1 mark

(c) Using an algebraic method, find the point that lies on both the straight lines $y = -2x + 3$ and $y = 6x - 17$.
You must show your working.

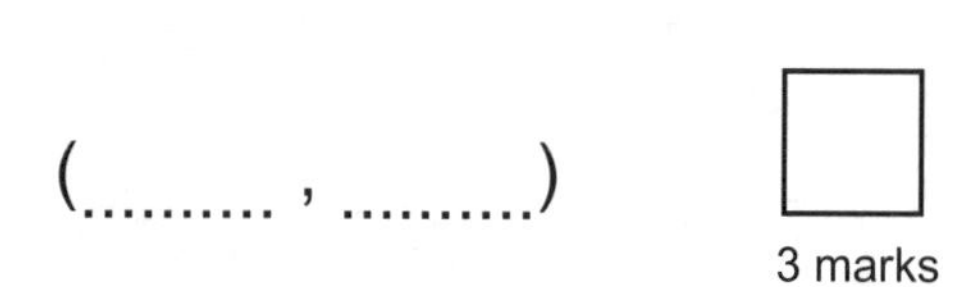

(.......... , ...)

3 marks

14. 15 students were asked to solve a sudoku puzzle and a crossword puzzle. The stem and leaf diagrams show the time in minutes it took them to solve each puzzle.

Sudoku

2	4 9
3	2 2 4 6 9
4	1 4 5 6 8
5	0 2 7

Crossword

2	0 2 4 6 8
3	1 3 3 7
4	2 2 5 7 7
5	3

Key: 2 | 9 means 29 minutes

(a) Use the diagrams to fill in the missing numbers in the sentence below.

The least time taken to solve the Sudoku puzzle was

.... minutes and .... students took more than 35 minutes.

1 mark

(b) Work out the range of times for solving the crossword puzzle.

.... minutes

1 mark

(c) What is the difference in the median times for the two puzzles?

.... minutes

1 mark

15. In a school 75% of the pupils have fillings.
20% of the pupils with fillings also have braces.

Work out the percentage of pupils in the school with fillings and braces.

16. (a) Rearrange the equation $2d + 6 = e$ to make d the subject.

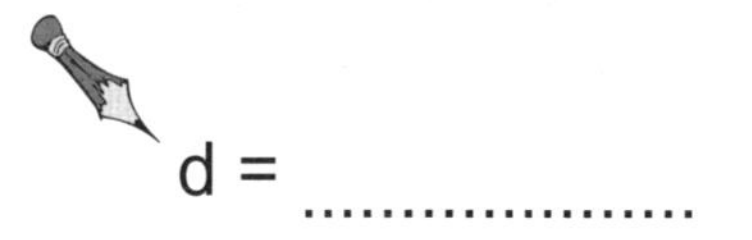

1 mark

(b) Rearrange the equation $8 + 5f^2 = 3g$ to make f the subject.

$f =$ ....

2 marks

17. These two kites are similar:

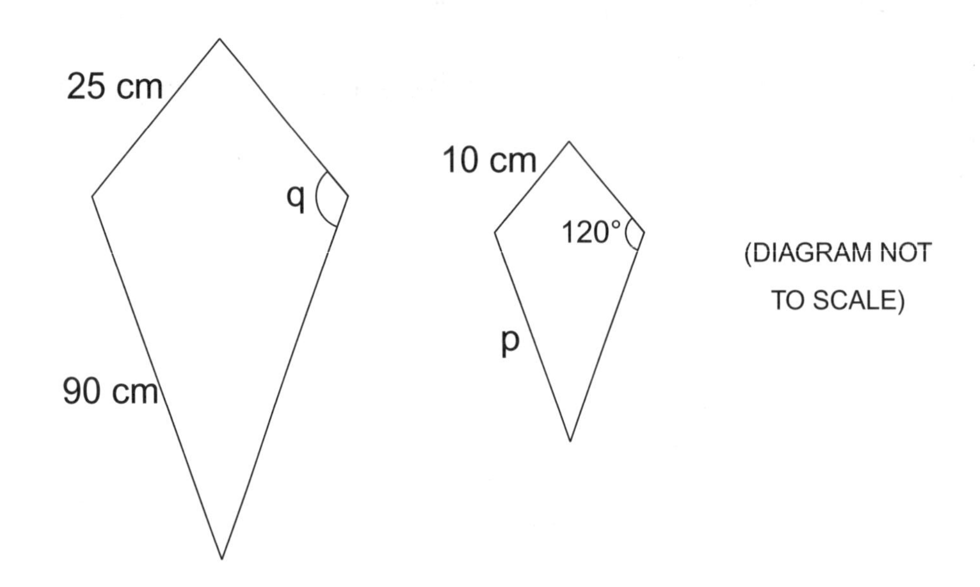

(a) Work out the length of side p in the smaller kite.

p = ... cm

2 marks

(b) What is the size of angle q in the larger kite?

q = ... °

1 mark

18. There are 500 sheets of paper in a ream.
There are 5 reams in a carton.

(a) Find the number of sheets of paper in a carton.
Give your answer in standard form.

....

2 marks

(b) A stationery supplier sells 5×10^8 sheets of paper in a month.
How many cartons of paper is this?
Give your answer in standard form.

....

2 marks

[Blank Page]

Coordination Group Publications

Key Stage 3 **Mathematics**

Mental Mathematics Tests
Questions to Read Out

SATS Practice Papers Levels 5-8

1) In this pack there are 3 mental mathematics tests.

2) To do a test, get someone else to read these questions out loud.

3) The sheets where you write the answers are on the backs of the calculator tests.

KS3 Levels 5-8
Mental Mathematics Test 1 — Questions **1**

Read each question out twice, then allow the right amount of time to write down the answer. Read out all the instructions.

"For this first group of questions, you will get 5 seconds to answer each question."

1. How many centimetres are there in two hundred and thirty millimetres?
2. Write the number three and a half million in figures.
3. How many degrees do the angles around a point add up to?
4. Divide minus twenty-eight by four.
5. Look at the spinner on your answer sheet. It has five equal sections. What is the probability of spinning an even number?
6. Write a fraction that is equivalent to two thirds.
7. Look at the expression on your answer sheet. Write it as simply as possible.
8. I am one hundred and sixty-five centimetres tall to the nearest centimetre. What is the maximum height I could be?

"For the next group of questions, you will get 10 seconds to answer each question."

9. If n equals ten, what is the value of n cubed minus one?
10. Look at the grid on your answer sheet. Put a cross on the grid to show the point with coordinates three, minus two.
11. I am waiting for the bus. The probability that the bus arrives early is nought point two five. The probability that the bus arrives on time is nought point four. What is the probability that the bus will arrive late?
12. Look at the numbers on your answer sheet. What is the mode?
13. Simplify the expression on your answer sheet.
14. Double fifty-seven.
15. Three sisters are aged eight, fifteen and nineteen years old. Work out their mean age.
16. What is the value of one point one squared?
17. Look at the numbers on your answer sheet. Put them in order of size starting with the smallest.
18. I am counting down in equal steps, nineteen, thirteen, seven. Write down the next two numbers.
19. Look at the equation on your answer sheet. Find the value of y when x equals minus two.
20. Work out the area of the triangle on your answer sheet.
21. Write the number twenty thousand in standard index form.
22. Mike runs at an average speed of six miles per hour. How far does he run in three and a half hours?

"For this next group of questions, you will get 15 seconds to answer each question."

23. What is five-twelfths of eighty-four?
24. Thirty percent of a number is twenty-seven. What is the number?
25. Look at the diagram on your answer sheet. Work out the size of angle p.
26. Look at the graph on your answer sheet. The gradient of the line marked A is two. What is the equation of this line?
27. I mix cranberry juice and water in the ratio one to four. I want to make two litres of this drink. How many millilitres of cranberry juice should I use?
28. In a sale, the price of a CD costing ten pounds and fifty pence is reduced by one third. What is the new price of the CD?
29. Look at the rectangle on your answer sheet. The rectangle is enlarged by a scale factor of three. Work out the perimeter of the enlarged rectangle.
30. x squared equals sixteen. What are the two possible values of ten minus x?

"Put your pens down. The test is finished."

KS3 Levels 5-8
Mental Mathematics Test 2 — Questions

2

Read out each question twice, then allow the right amount of time to write down the answer. Read out all the instructions.

"For this first group of questions, you will get 5 seconds to answer each question."

1. What is the square root of forty-nine?
2. Your answer sheet shows three angles. Circle the acute angle.
3. What number is nine more than minus five?
4. How many days are there in twenty weeks?
5. Round three hundred and fifty to one significant figure.
6. What number is the arrow pointing to on the number line?
7. Look at the numbers on your answer sheet. Circle the number that is closest to two-thirds.
8. What is the gradient of the line with equation y equals minus three x plus 4?

"For the next group of questions, you will get 10 seconds to answer each question."

9. Write ten minutes to midnight as a twenty-four hour clock time.
10. Look at the diagram on your answer sheet. Mark on another angle that is the same size as angle p. Label it q.
11. Nicky got thirty-five out of fifty in a test. What percentage did she get?
12. The bar chart shows the number of boys and girls in a school play. There are eight boys. How many girls are there?
13. There are twenty coloured balls in a bag. The probability that I pick a red ball is nought point seven. How many red balls are there in the bag?
14. What is the total cost of five cinema tickets at three pounds and fifty pence each?
15. The diagram shows a box plot. What value is the arrow pointing to? Circle the correct answer.
16. An architect's plan uses the scale one centimetre to five metres. How tall is a building that is nineteen centimetres on the plan?
17. What is the total cost of three shirts at nineteen pounds and ninety-nine pence each?
18. Multiply two point nought five by ten thousand.
19. I am thinking of a number. I call it x. I square my number and subtract three. Write an expression to show the result.
20. I am counting up in equal steps, one point three, one point six, one point nine. Write down the next two numbers.
21. The grid shows three points marked A, B and C. Circle the point which lies on the line $y = x$.

"For this next group of questions, you will get 15 seconds to answer each question."

22. The stem and leaf diagram shows the marks of fifteen pupils in a Maths test. What is the modal mark?
23. Write the number nought point two five in standard form.
24. An mp3 player costs fifty-six pounds. Its price is increased by ten percent. What is the new price of the mp3 player?
25. I asked sixty people whether they watched the football last night. The pie chart shows the results. What is the size of the angle that represents the people who said yes?
26. On any given day, the probability that James does his homework is two fifths. What is the probability that James will do his homework both today and tomorrow?
27. Write an approximate answer to the calculation on your answer sheet.
28. The radius of a circle is nine centimetres. Taking π to be three, calculate the area of the circle.
29. Three pencils cost ninety-nine pence. How much would seven pencils cost?
30. Look at the right-angled triangle on your answer sheet. What is the value of sin a? Circle the correct answer.

"Put your pens down. The test is finished."

KS3 Levels 5-8
Mental Mathematics Test 3 — Questions

3

Read out each question twice, then allow the right amount of time to write down the answer. Read out all the instructions.

"For this first group of questions, you will get 5 seconds to answer each question."

1. Subtract fifty from one hundred and thirty.
2. What do cubic metres measure? Circle the correct answer.
3. What is fifty percent of two hundred and forty?
4. How many seconds are there in ten minutes?
5. What is the cube root of one hundred and twenty five?
6. Round the number five point two eight to one decimal place.
7. The probability that I will pass my driving test is sixty-five percent. What is the probability that I will fail my driving test?

"For the next group of questions, you will get 10 seconds to answer each question."

8. What is one quarter of four hundred and twenty?
9. Look at the numbers on your answer sheet. Circle the median number.
10. Look at your answer sheet. Write down the coordinates of the point marked P.
11. Write down a number between thirty and forty which is a multiple of four and also a multiple of six.
12. Your answer sheet shows some temperatures recorded in winter. What is the range of temperatures?
13. The diagram on your answer sheet shows an isosceles triangle. What is the size of angle a?
14. What number multiplied by minus two gives the answer sixteen?
15. I am thinking of a shape. It is a quadrilateral with no parallel sides and one line of symmetry. What is the mathematical name of the shape?
16. The length of a swimming pool is twenty-five metres. Jack swims eight hundred metres. How many lengths is this?
17. Solve the equation x minus three tenths equals seven tenths.
18. The tally chart shows the number of houses on my street. How many houses are there?
19. What fraction of a right angle is thirty degrees?
20. Town P lies to the west of town Q. What is the bearing of town P from town Q?
21. The diameter of a circle is ten n plus four. Write an expression for the radius of the circle in its simplest terms.
22. What must I multiply k by to get seven k cubed?

"For this next group of questions, you will get 15 seconds to answer each question."

23. Your answer sheet shows the nth term of a sequence. What is the eighth term of the sequence?
24. Ann buys six ice creams at seventy-five pence each. How much change does she receive from five pounds?
25. The mean of three numbers is twenty. Two of the numbers are sixteen and nineteen. What is the third number?
26. The table shows the number of cakes eaten by twenty children at a party. How many cakes were eaten altogether?
27. Ben has two pounds in ten pence coins and two pounds in five pence coins. How many coins does he have altogether?
28. In a recipe the ratio of flour to sugar is four to three. If I use three hundred and sixty grams of flour, how much sugar do I need?
29. Look at the right-angled triangle on your answer sheet. Circle the expression that represents the length of the hypotenuse.
30. What is three-quarters squared?

"Put your pens down. The test is finished."

Maths

EY STAGE

3

EVELS

5-8

RACTICE PAPER

1B

Key Stage 3

Mathematics Test

Practice Paper 1B

Calculator allowed

Read this page, but don't open the booklet until your teacher says you can start. Write your name and school in the spaces below.

First Name ______________________________

Last Name ______________________________

School ______________________________

Remember

- The test is one hour long.
- Make sure you have these things with you before you start: pen, pencil, rubber, ruler, calculator, angle measurer or protractor and pair of compasses.
  You may use tracing paper.
- There are some formulas you might need on page 2.
- The easier questions are at the start of the test.
- Try to answer all of the questions.
- Don't use any rough paper — write all your answers and working in this test paper.
- Check your work carefully before the end of the test.
- If you're not sure what to do, ask your teacher.

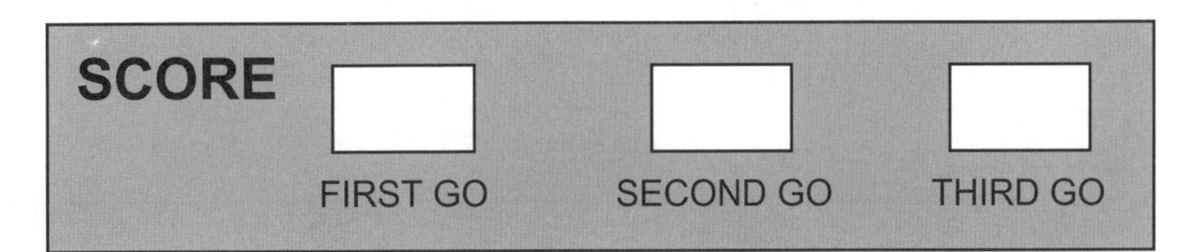

Instructions

This means write down your answer or show your working and your answer.

You may use a calculator in this test.

Formulas

Trapezium

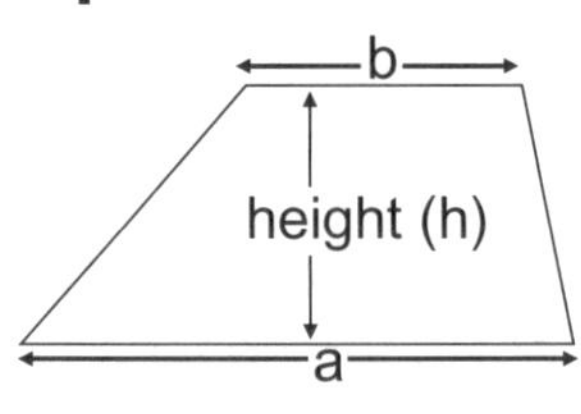

$$\text{Area} = \frac{(a + b)}{2} \times h$$

Prism

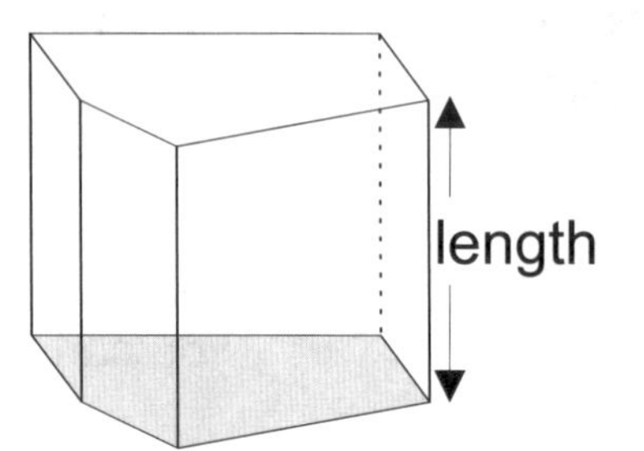

Volume = area of cross-section × length

1. (a) Use your calculator to find the answer to $\sqrt{15200} \div 3.2^4$.
Write down the full answer displayed on your calculator.

....

1 mark

(b) Round your answer to part (a) to three decimal places.

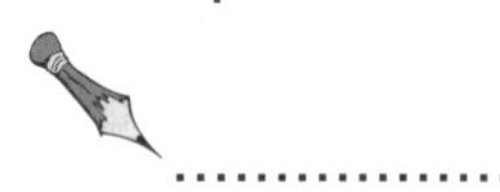

....

1 mark

(c) Use your calculator to find the answer to

$$\frac{151 - 39}{90 - 55} = \text{....................}$$

1 mark

2. (a) Shade in four tenths of this shape:

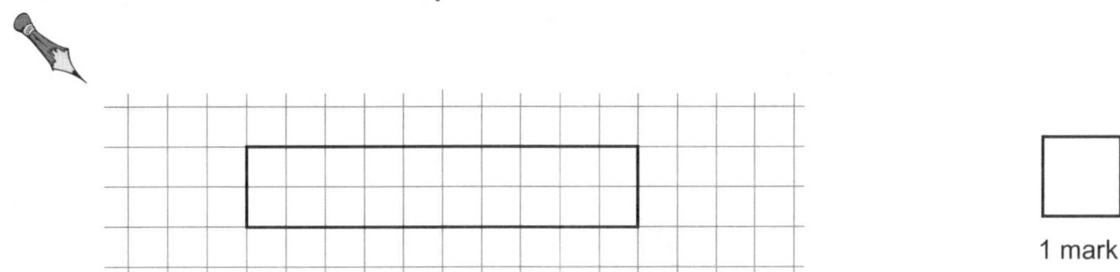

1 mark

(b) What proportion of this shape is shaded?
Give your answer as a decimal number.

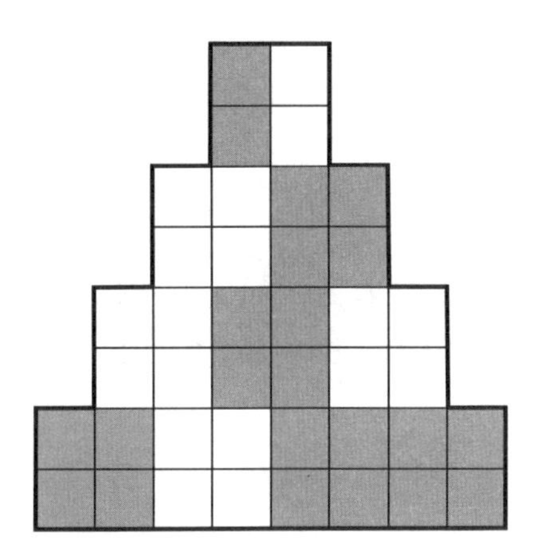

1 mark

(c) What percentage of this diagram is shaded?

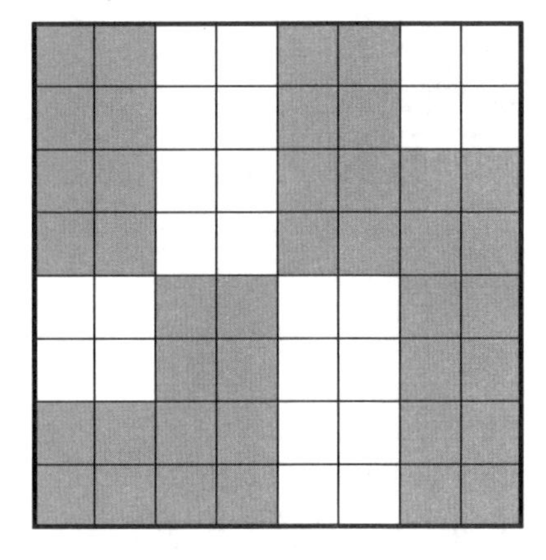

.... %

1 mark

3. (a) This diagram has four small squares shaded in.

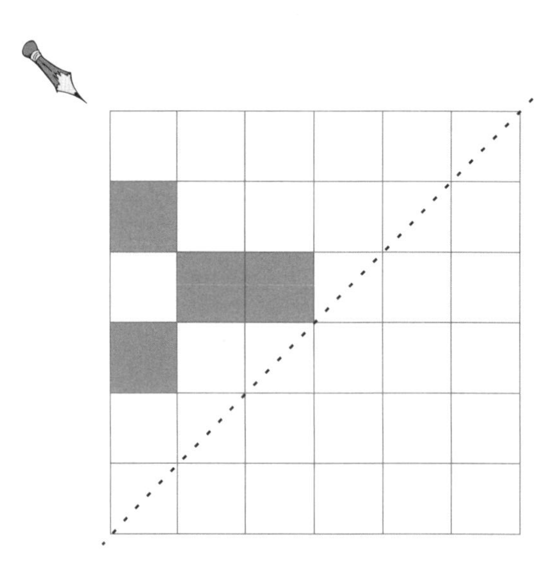

Shade in four more small squares to make a pattern that has a line of symmetry along the dotted line.

2 marks

(b) Here is another diagram with four small squares shaded in.

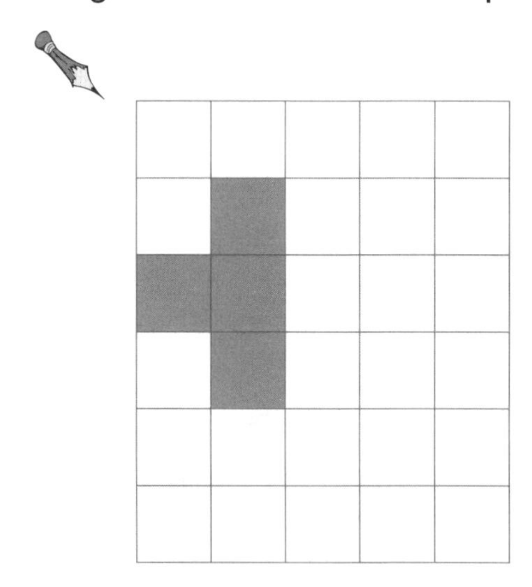

Shade in four more small squares to make a pattern that has rotational symmetry of order two.

2 marks

4. This table shows the number of students in a school who are learning to play a musical instrument:

	Boys	**Girls**
Guitar	15	3
Clarinet	2	11
Keyboard	4	5

A student is chosen at random.

(a) Find the probability that the student chosen will be a boy.

....

1 mark

(b) Find the probability that the student chosen will play the keyboard.

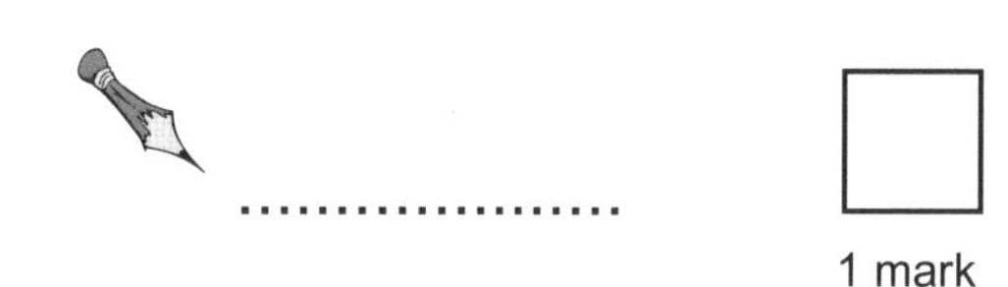

1 mark

(c) A guitarist is chosen at random.

Find the probability that the guitarist is a girl.

1 mark

5. Shops A and B both sell cans of cola.

Cola only 36p per can

Shop A

SPECIAL DEAL
Pack of 6 cans of Cola
only £2.19

Shop B

(a) How much does it cost to buy 8 cans of Cola from shop A?

£ ....

1 mark

(b) Abigail wants to buy 18 cans of Cola.
Which shop would be cheaper and by how much?
You must show your working.

2 marks

6. Mr Smith is on a diet. He weighs 105 kg. His target weight is 77 kg.

If he loses 1.4 kg each week, how many weeks will it take him to reach his target weight?

.... weeks

2 marks

7. Simplify these expressions:

(a) $6 - 3s + 5s - 2$

....

1 mark

(b) $9t^2 + 3t + 2t^2$

....

1 mark

(c) $6u \times 3u$

....

1 mark

(d) $\dfrac{16v^3}{4v}$

....

1 mark

8. The table shows the speed in miles per hour of a tennis player's serve during a match.

Speed (s) in mph	**frequency (f)**	**midpoint (x)**	**fx**
$90 < s \leq 100$	12	95	1140
$100 < s \leq 110$	18	....	....
$110 < s \leq 120$	28	....	....
$120 < s \leq 130$	7	....	....
Total	65	-	7125

(a) Complete the table.

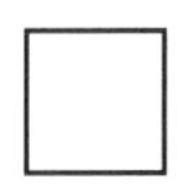

2 marks

(b) Work out an estimate of the mean speed of the tennis player's serve.

.... mph

1 mark

9. The diagram shows the trapezium ABCD.
Angle A measures 130° and angles B and C are both right angles.

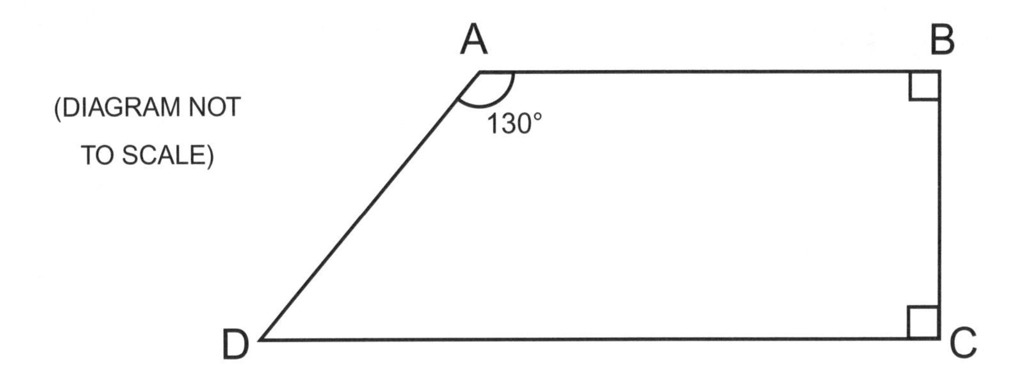

The trapezium is cut into two shapes labelled P and Q.

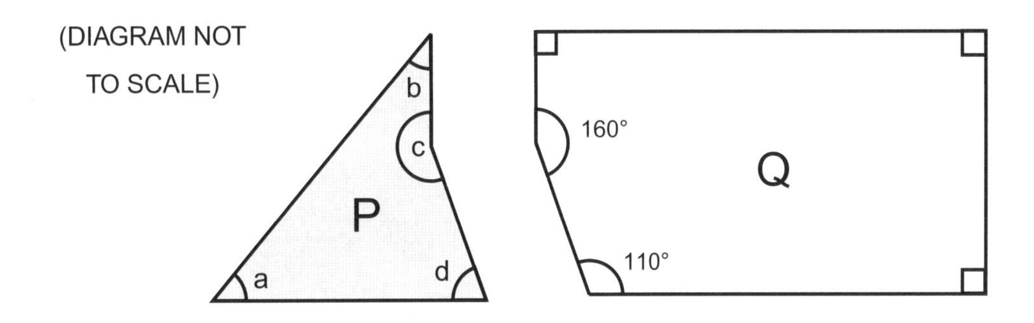

Work out the sizes of angles a, b, c and d.

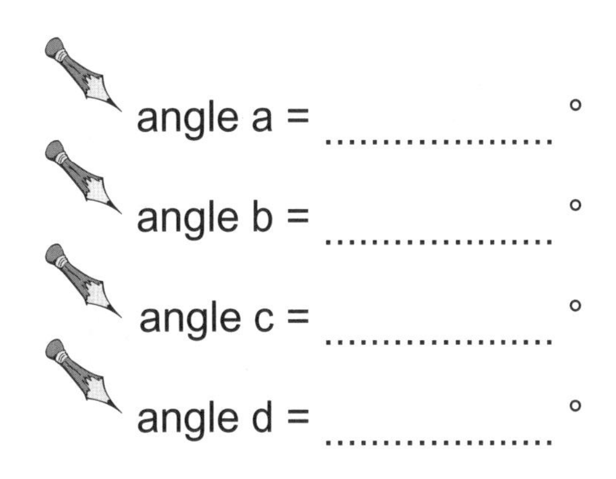

angle a = ... °

angle b = ... °

angle c = ... °

angle d = ... °

4 marks

10. In a sale, the price of a digital camera is reduced by 18%.
The new price of the camera is £287.

(a) Work out the price of the camera before the sale.

£....................

2 marks

(b) Jenny takes 120 photographs with her digital camera.
She prints off 54 photographs and discards the rest.

Work out the percentage of the photographs that are discarded.

.... %

2 marks

11. A glass tumbler is a cylinder with a radius of 3 cm and a height of 12 cm.

3 cm

12 cm

(DIAGRAM NOT TO SCALE)

Calculate the volume of the glass tumbler.

.... cm^3

2 marks

12.

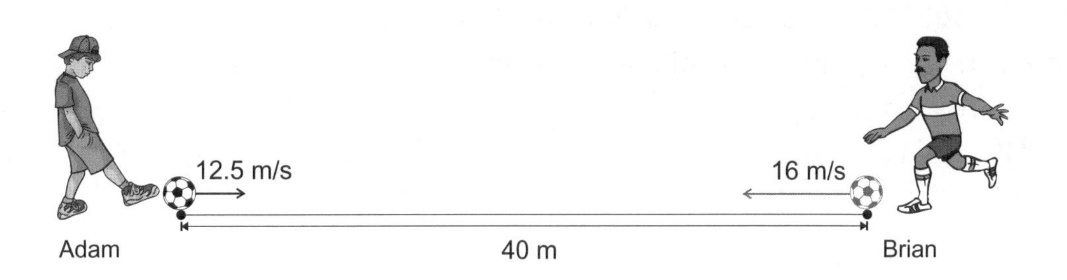

Adam and Brian are standing 40 metres apart.

Adam kicks a ball to Brian at an average speed of 12.5 m/s.

Brian kicks the ball back to Adam at an average speed of 16 m/s.

Work out the total time, in seconds, that the ball takes to travel from Adam to Brian and back again.

.... seconds

2 marks

13. In one week, Andy delivered 114 newspapers.

He delivered the same number of newspapers on Monday, Tuesday and Wednesday.

On Thursday he delivered half the number of papers he had delivered on Monday.

He delivered 10 newspapers each day on Friday, Saturday and Sunday.

How many newspapers did he deliver on Tuesday?

....

3 marks

14. Multiply out the brackets in this expression.
Write your answer as simply as possible.

$(x + 7)(x - 4)$

....

2 marks

15. A survey was carried out to find the ages of people who visited a gardening show.

The youngest person that attended the show was 19 years old and the oldest person was 78 years old.

The median age was 47 years.

The inter-quartile range of ages was 35 years.

A quarter of the people surveyed were over the age of 60.

Using this information, draw what the box plot would look like.

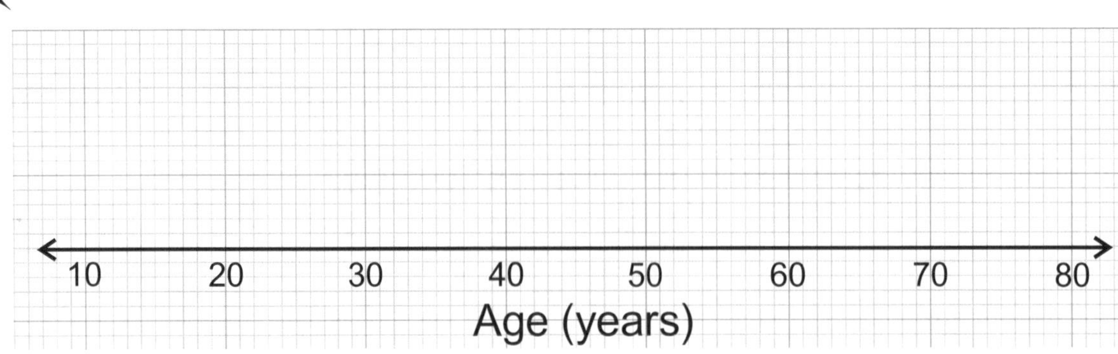

4 marks

16. Body mass index is a number used to identify possible weight problems in adults. The table below shows how it can be interpreted.

Body mass index (b)	**Weight Status**
$b < 20$	Underweight
$20 \le b < 25$	Normal
$25 \le b < 30$	Overweight
$b \ge 30$	Obese

A person's body mass index is calculated using the formula

$$\mathbf{b} = \frac{\mathbf{w}}{\mathbf{h}^2}$$

where b = body mass index, w = weight in kg and h = height in metres.

(a) Adam weighs 70 kilograms and is 1.75 metres tall.
Work out his body mass index and find his weight status.

Body mass index = ... Weight status = ...

2 marks

(b) Jodie has a body mass index of 19 and weighs 55 kilograms.
Work out how tall she is. Give your answer correct to 2 decimal places.

.... m

2 marks

(c) Daniel is 1.64 metres tall and has a body mass index of 28.
How much weight must he lose to achieve a body mass index of 24?
Give your answer to the nearest kilogram.

.... kg

3 marks

17. The diagram shows the cross-section of a dry ski slope.

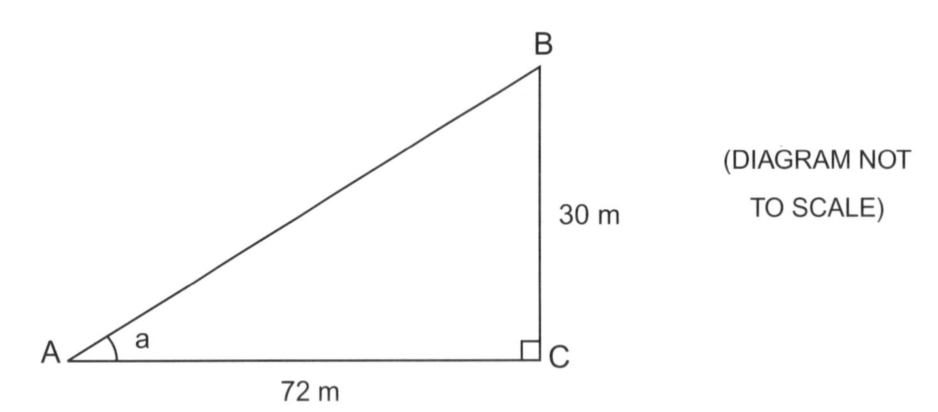

The ski slope AB stands on horizontal ground AC of length 72 m.
The height of the ski slope is 30 m.

(a) Work out the length of the ski slope AB.

.... m

2 marks

(b) The ski slope makes an angle of a° with the horizontal.
Work out the size of angle a. Give your answer correct to 1 decimal place.

.... °

2 marks

18. On any given day in June, the probability that the pollen count will be high is 0.6.

(a) What is the probability that the pollen count will not be high?

....

1 mark

(b) On how many days would you expect the pollen count not to be high in June?

....

1 mark

(c) Find the probability that the pollen count will be high on each of the first three days in June.

....

1 mark

Key Stage 3 Mathematics **Levels 5-8**

Mental Arithmetic Practice Test 1

First Name ____________________

Last Name ____________________

School ____________________

Score: [ ] 1st GO [ ] 2nd GO [ ] 3rd GO

Time: 5 seconds

1	cm	
2		
3	°	
4		-28
5		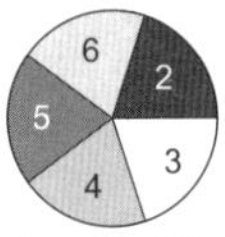
6		
7		3y × 2y
8	cm	165 cm

Time: 10 seconds

9		$n^3 - 1$
10	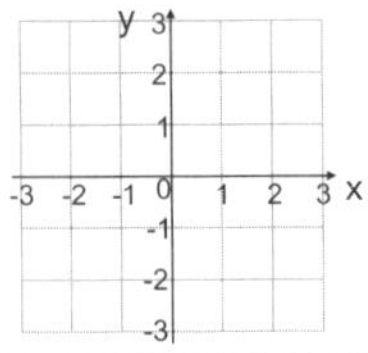	
11		0.25 0.4
12		22, 23, 28, 23, 26, 28, 23
13		3a + 4b – 2a + 6b
14		
15		8, 15, 19
16		1.1
17		$\frac{1}{4}$, 0.3, 15%
18		19, 13, 7
19		y = 3x + 5
20	cm^2	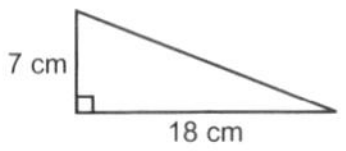
21		20 000
22	miles	6 mph

Time: 15 seconds

23		$\frac{5}{12}$ 84
24		30% is 27
25	°	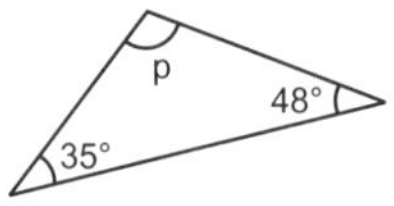
26		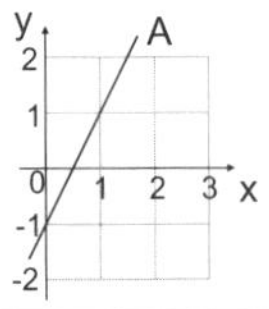
27	ml	1:4 2 litres
28	£	£10.50 $\frac{1}{3}$
29	cm	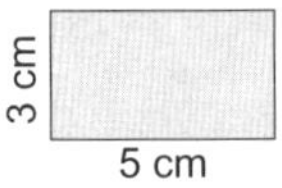 3
30	&	$x^2 = 16$, 10 – x

Maths

EY STAGE

3

EVELS

5-8

RACTICE PAPER

2A

Key Stage 3

Mathematics Test

Practice Paper 2A

Calculator NOT allowed

Read this page, but don't open the booklet until your teacher says you can start. Write your name and school in the spaces below.

First Name ____________________

Last Name ____________________

School ____________________

Remember

- The test is one hour long.
- Make sure you have these things with you before you start: pen, pencil, rubber, ruler, angle measurer or protractor and pair of compasses.
  You may use tracing paper.
- There are some formulas you might need on page 2.
- The easier questions are at the start of the test.
- Try to answer all of the questions.
- Don't use any rough paper — write all your answers and working in this test paper.
- Check your work carefully before the end of the test.
- If you're not sure what to do, ask your teacher.

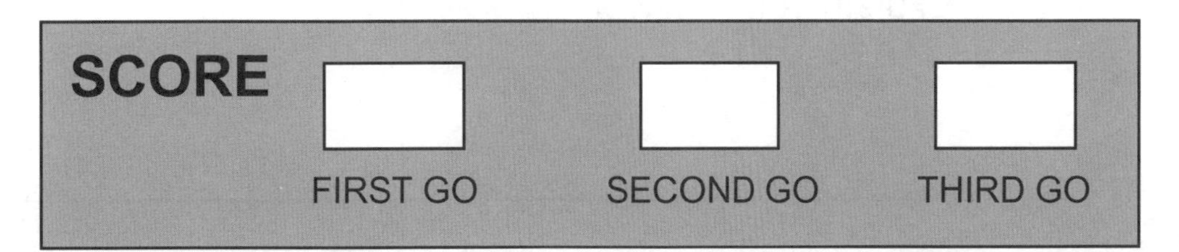

Instructions

This means write down your answer or show your working and your answer.

You may not use a calculator in this test.

Formulas

Trapezium

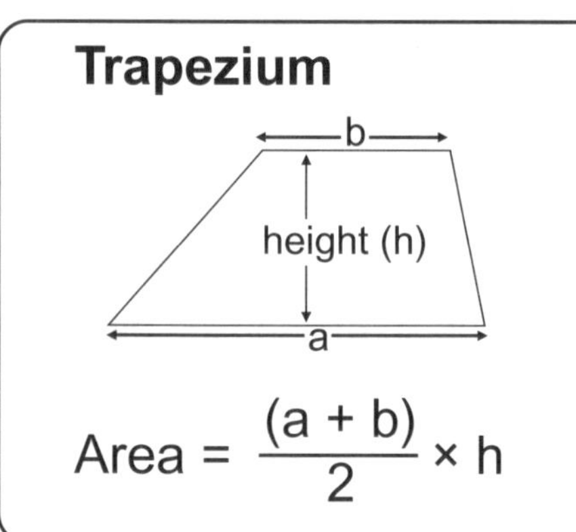

$$\text{Area} = \frac{(a + b)}{2} \times h$$

Prism

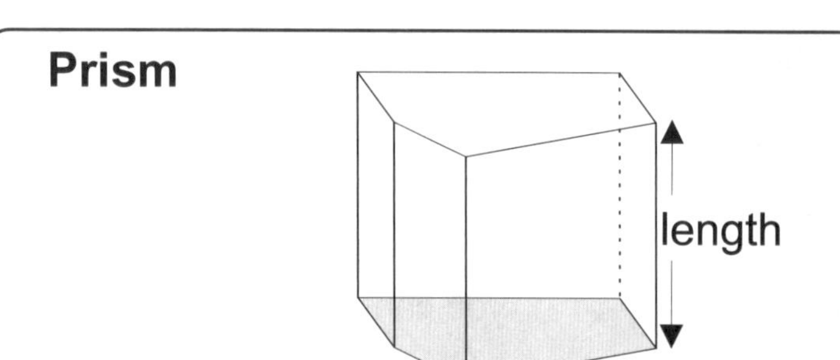

Volume = area of cross-section × length

1. A bag of fruit sweets contains 5 strawberry flavour, 4 raspberry flavour and 6 blackberry flavour.

Debbie chooses a sweet at random. Find the probability that it is:

(a) raspberry flavour

....

1 mark

(b) not blackberry flavour

....

1 mark

(c) Steve has another bag of fruit sweets. Half of them are strawberry flavour. Tick the correct box to show who has the most strawberry sweets.

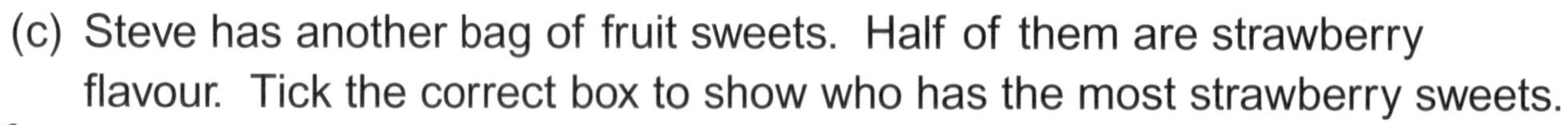

☐ Debbie

☐ Steve

☐ Cannot tell

Explain your answer.

1 mark

2. (a) Construct this triangle accurately in the space below.

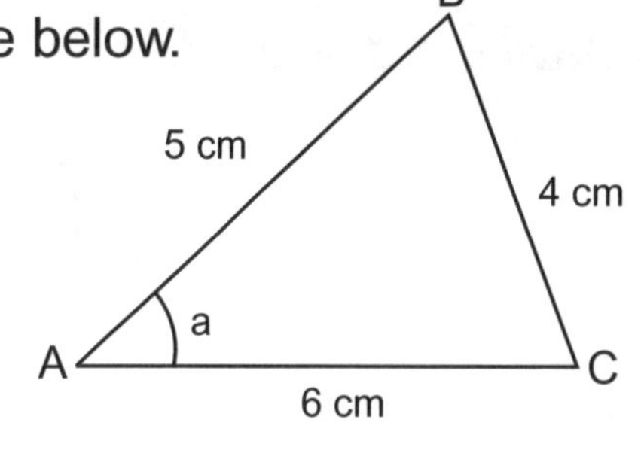

(DIAGRAM NOT TO SCALE)

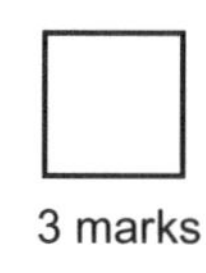

3 marks

(b) Measure the size of angle a.

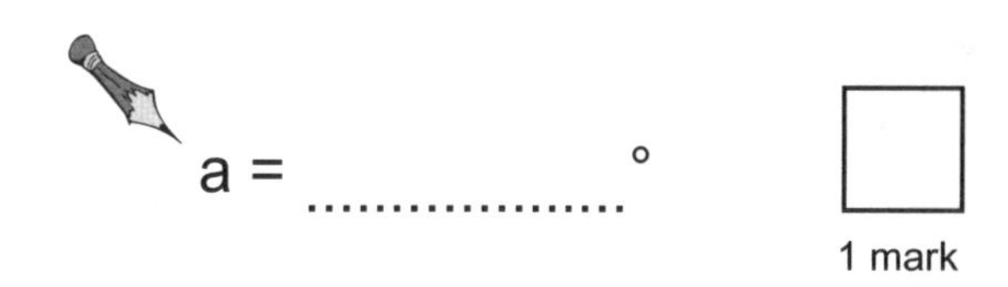

a = ... °

1 mark

3. Mr. Wardell ordered 52 calculators for the Maths department.
Each calculator cost £2.32.

Estimate how much Mr. Wardell spent on calculators.

£.....................

2 marks

4. The diagram shows how to work out the cost of hiring a cement mixer and having it delivered.

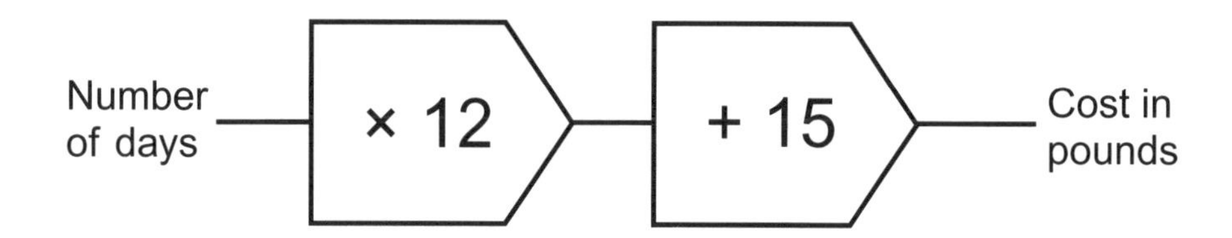

(a) How much would it cost to hire the cement mixer for 7 days?

£ ....

1 mark

(b) Marlon paid £147.
How many days did he have the cement mixer for?

....

2 marks

(c) The 12 in the diagram above represents the daily charge for hiring the cement mixer.

What does the 15 represent?

....

1 mark

5. Solve the following equations:

(a) $3x + 7 = 25$

$x =$ ....

1 mark

(b) $4(x - 2) = 30$

$x =$ ....

1 mark

(c) $2x - 9 = 5x + 3$

$x =$ ....

1 mark

6. Fill in the gaps to complete these calculations correctly:

(a) $7 +$ .... $= 2$

1 mark

(b) $5 -$ .... $= 8$

1 mark

(c) $-2 \times$ .... $= -8$

1 mark

(d) .... $\div -4 = -3$

1 mark

7. The cuboid below is made of 2 cm cubes.

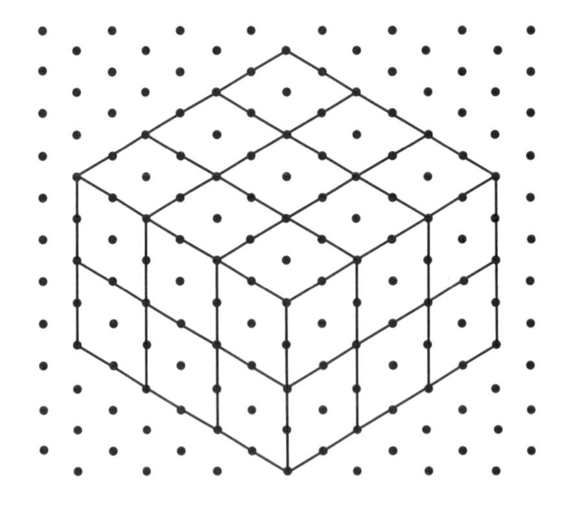

(DIAGRAM NOT TO SCALE)

(a) What is the volume of the cuboid?

.... cm^3

1 mark

(b) What is the surface area of the cuboid?

.... cm^2

2 marks

(c) The diagram shows a 2 cm cube. Add more 2 cm cubes to form a cuboid with a volume of 48 cm^3.

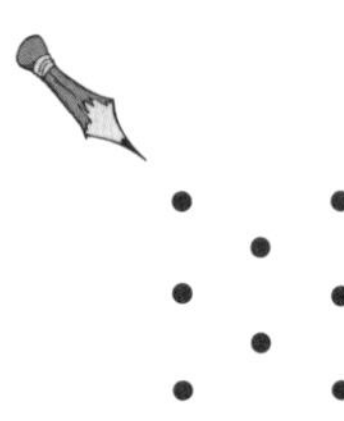

(DIAGRAM NOT TO SCALE)

2 marks

8. Roop was studying the birds at a wildlife sanctuary.
She noticed that the ratio of ducks to geese to swans was 3 : 5 : 2.

(a) What percentage of the birds were swans?

.... %

1 mark

(b) She counted 18 ducks. How many geese and swans were there?

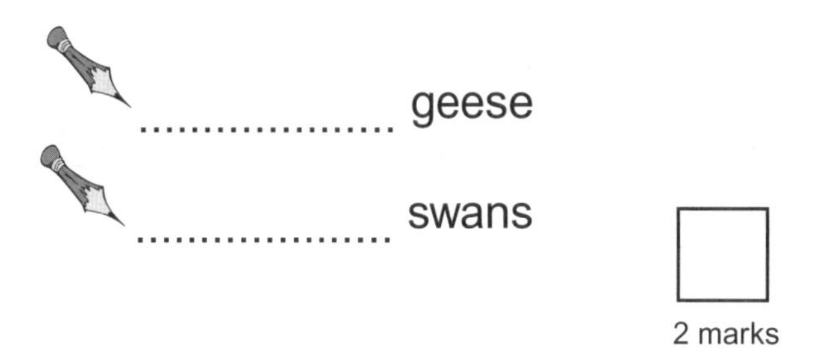

.... geese

.... swans

2 marks

9. 120 Year 9 students were being taken on a school trip.
They could choose between a day at a theme park or the seaside.

41 boys wanted to go to the theme park.

14 girls wanted to go to the seaside.

56 of the students were girls.

Complete the table to show where the students decided to go.

	Theme Park	Seaside	Total
Boys	41	....	....
Girls	....	14	56
Total	....	....	120

2 marks

10. The diagram shows a kite ABCD.

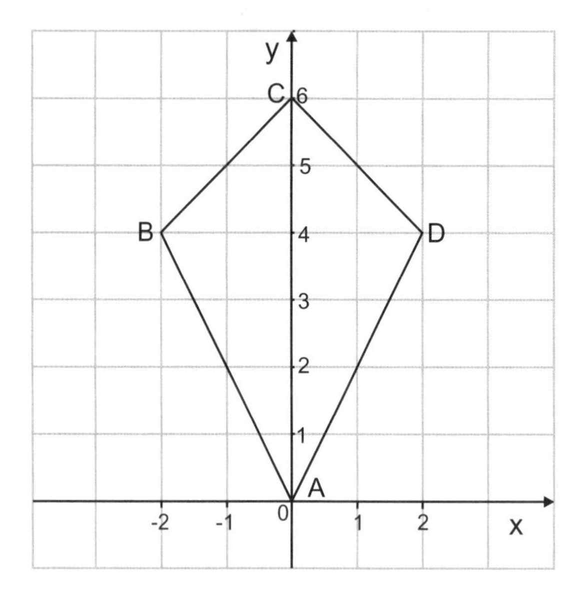

Write down the equations of the following lines.

(a) The line passing through A and D.

....

1 mark

(b) A line perpendicular to the line passing through A and D.
(There are many possible lines.)

1 mark

(c) The line passing through C and D.

1 mark

(d) A line parallel to the line passing through C and D.
(There are many possible lines.)

1 mark

11. The formula for converting temperature in Celsius (C) to Fahrenheit (F) is

$$F = \frac{9C}{5} + 32$$

(a) Convert 10°C into Fahrenheit.

.... °F

1 mark

(b) Convert -20°C into Fahrenheit.

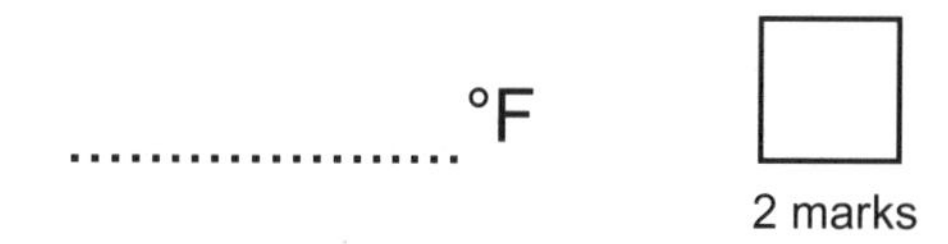

.... °F

2 marks

(c) Rearrange the formula so that it can be used to convert Fahrenheit into Celsius.

C = ...

2 marks

12. Look at the triangle below.

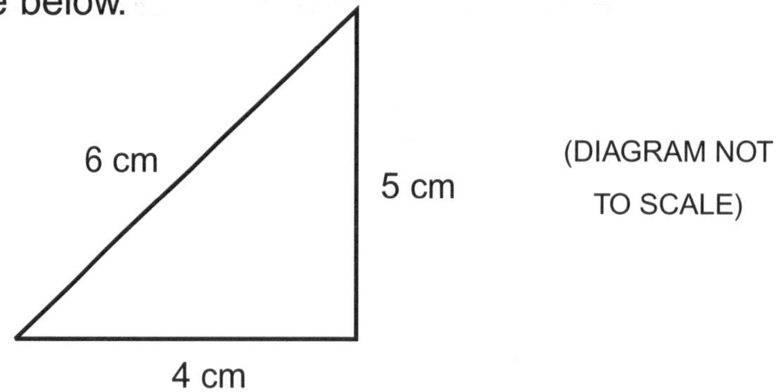

Is this a right-angled triangle? Explain how you know.

2 marks

13. Expand and simplify the following expression.

$$(x + 5)(x + 4)$$

....

2 marks

14. Pat is playing a game with two spinners. She works out her score by multiplying the two numbers she spins together.

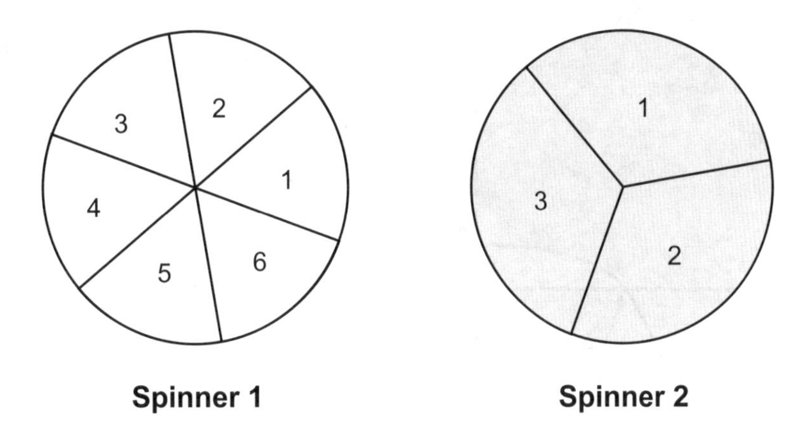

(a) Complete the table to show all her possible scores.

Spinner 1

Spinner 2	1	2	3	4	5	6
1	1	2	....	....	....	....
2	2	4	....	....	....	....
3	3	6	....	....	....	....

2 marks

(b) Use your table to work out the probability that Pat's score is an odd number.

....

1 mark

15. The diagram shows part of the graph $y = x^3 + 8$.

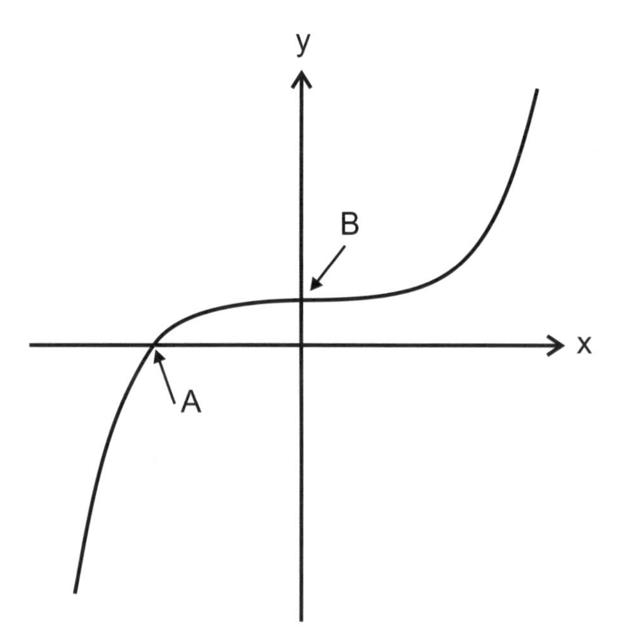

Write down the co-ordinates of points A and B.

A = (.......... , ...)

B = (.......... , ...)

2 marks

16. The box plot shows the hand spans in cm of the girls in a Year 9 class.

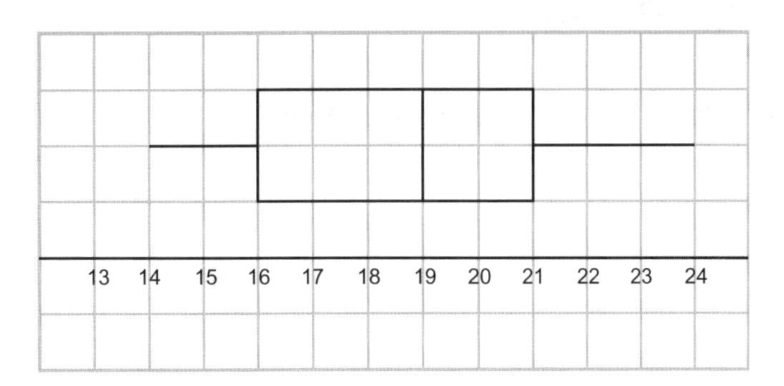

(a) What is the shortest hand span?

.... cm

1 mark

(b) What is the median hand span?

.... cm

1 mark

(c) Work out the inter-quartile range for the girls' hand spans.

.... cm

1 mark

(d) The boys also measured their hand spans.

The median was 1 cm longer than for the girls.
The lower and upper quartiles were the same as for the girls.
The longest and shortest hand spans were 1 cm longer than for the girls.

Draw a box plot showing the hand spans of the boys.

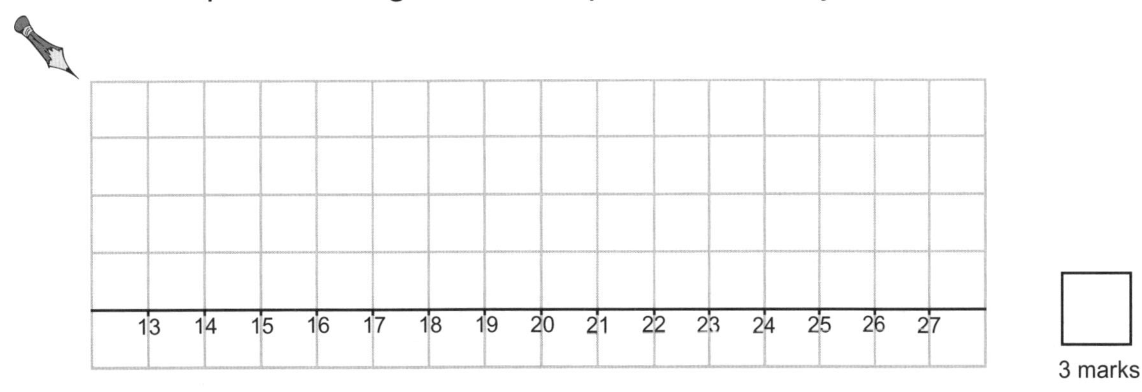

3 marks

17. The highest mountain in the world is Mount Everest.
Its height in feet is 2.903×10^4.

(a) Write 2.903×10^4 as an ordinary number.

....

1 mark

(b) The highest mountain in the UK is Ben Nevis.
Its height in feet is 4.41×10^3.

How much higher is Mount Everest than Ben Nevis?
Give your answer in standard form.

.... feet

2 marks

18. Find the value of y in each of the equations below.

(a) $6^y = 1$

y = ...

1 mark

(b) $3^y = 81$

y = ...

1 mark

(c) $72 = y^3 \times 3^2$

y = ...

1 mark

[Blank Page]

Maths
EY STAGE
3
EVELS
5-8
RACTICE PAPER
2B

Key Stage 3

Mathematics Test

Practice Paper 2B

Calculator allowed

Read this page, but don't open the booklet until your teacher says you can start. Write your name and school in the spaces below.

First Name ____________________

Last Name ____________________

School ____________________

Remember

- The test is one hour long.
- Make sure you have these things with you before you start: pen, pencil, rubber, ruler, calculator, angle measurer or protractor and pair of compasses.
  You may use tracing paper.
- There are some formulas you might need on page 2.
- The easier questions are at the start of the test.
- Try to answer all of the questions.
- Don't use any rough paper — write all your answers and working in this test paper.
- Check your work carefully before the end of the test.
- If you're not sure what to do, ask your teacher.

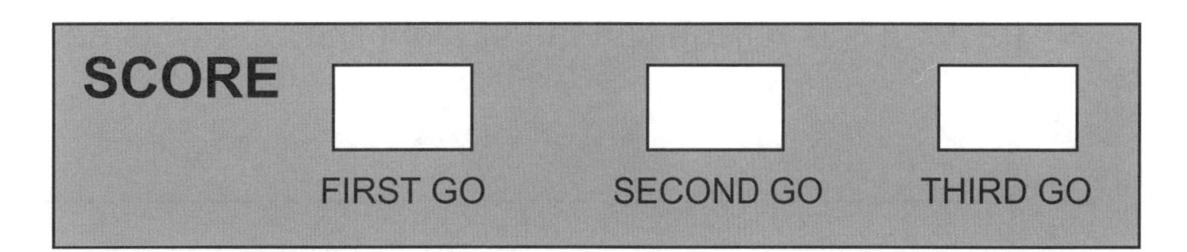

Exam Set MHGP31

Instructions

This means write down your answer or show your working and your answer.

You may use a calculator in this test.

Formulas

Trapezium

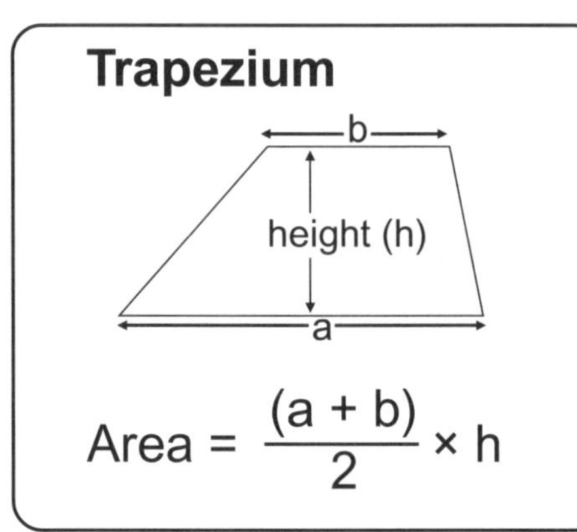

$$\text{Area} = \frac{(a + b)}{2} \times h$$

Prism

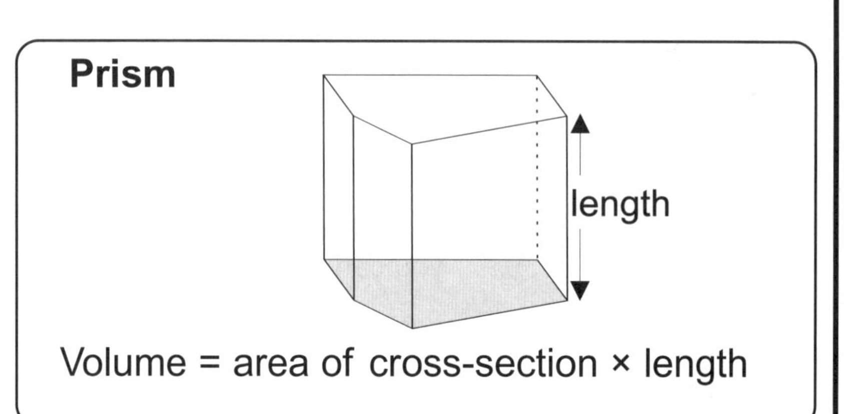

Volume = area of cross-section × length

1. The diagram shows two flags and a straight line.

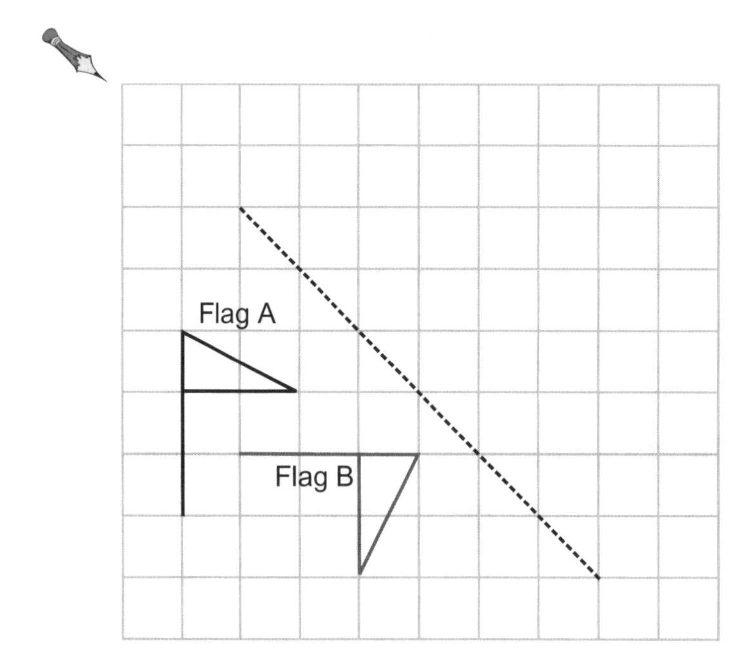

(a) Flag A has been rotated 90° clockwise to give Flag B.
Mark the centre of rotation with a cross.

1 mark

(b) Flag B is reflected in the straight line. Draw its new position.

1 mark

2. Jeff wants to buy a bottle of water from a vending machine.
The bottle costs 45p. Jeff only has 5p, 10p and 20p coins.

Complete the table to show all the ways he can pay exactly 45p.

Number of 5p coins	Number of 10p coins	Number of 20p coins
1	0	2
....	....	....
....	....	....
....	....	....
....	....	....
....	....	....
....	....	....
....	....	....
....	....	....

3 marks

3. (a) Shade $\frac{4}{7}$ of this shape:

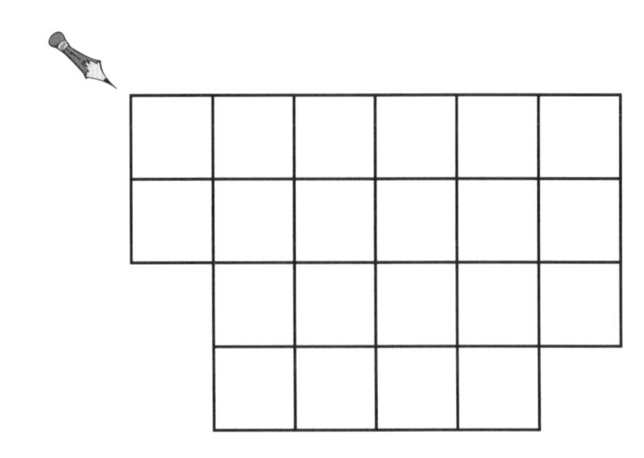

1 mark

(b) Shade 0.3 of this shape:

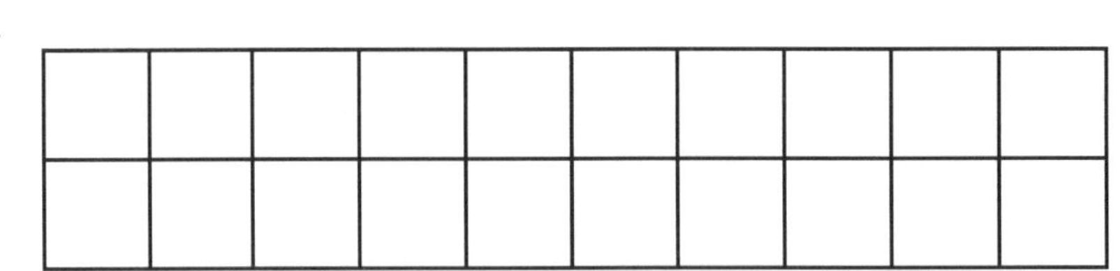

1 mark

(c) Shade 45% of this shape:

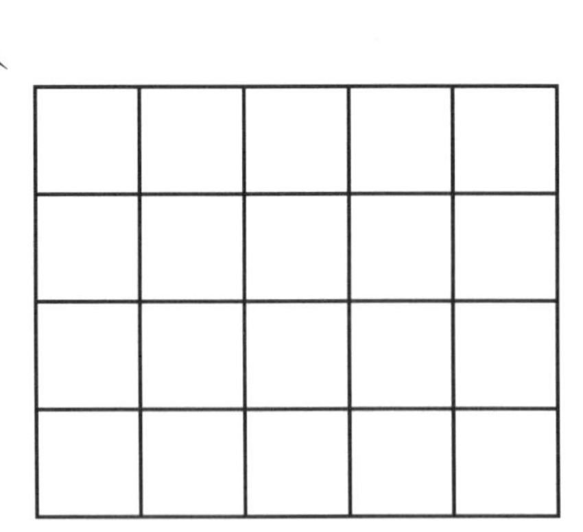

1 mark

4. Peter timed how long it took him to do his last five sets of Maths homework.

Set	Time to do homework (minutes)
1	17
2	26
3	52
4	31
5	43

(a) What is the range of the times taken?

.... minutes

1 mark

(b) What was the median time taken?

.... minutes

1 mark

(c) Pattie timed how long it took her to do the same five sets of homework.

The range of her times was 20 minutes.
The median of her times was 25 minutes.

Write down a set of times that Pattie might have taken.

2 marks

5. Helen drew two pie charts to show what pets are owned by students in classes 9A and 9B.

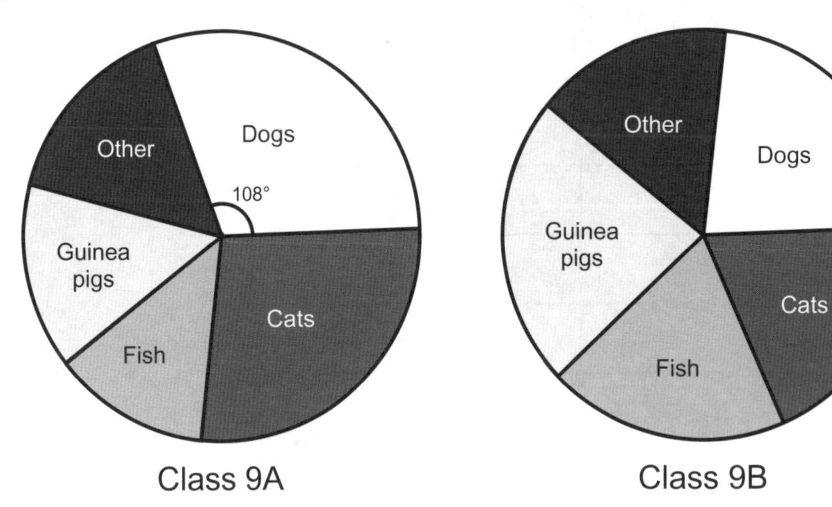

(a) In class 9A, the section for dogs represents 9 students.
How many students are in class 9A?

(b) Tick the box to say which class has the most dog owners.

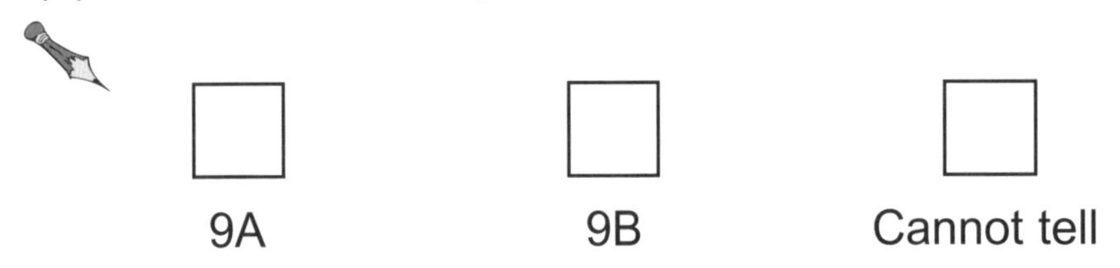

Explain your answer.

1 mark

6. (a) Write down three pairs of coordinates that fit the rule **x + y = 7**.

(.......... , ...), (.......... , ...), (.......... , ...)

2 marks

(b) Draw the graph of x + y = 7 on the grid below.

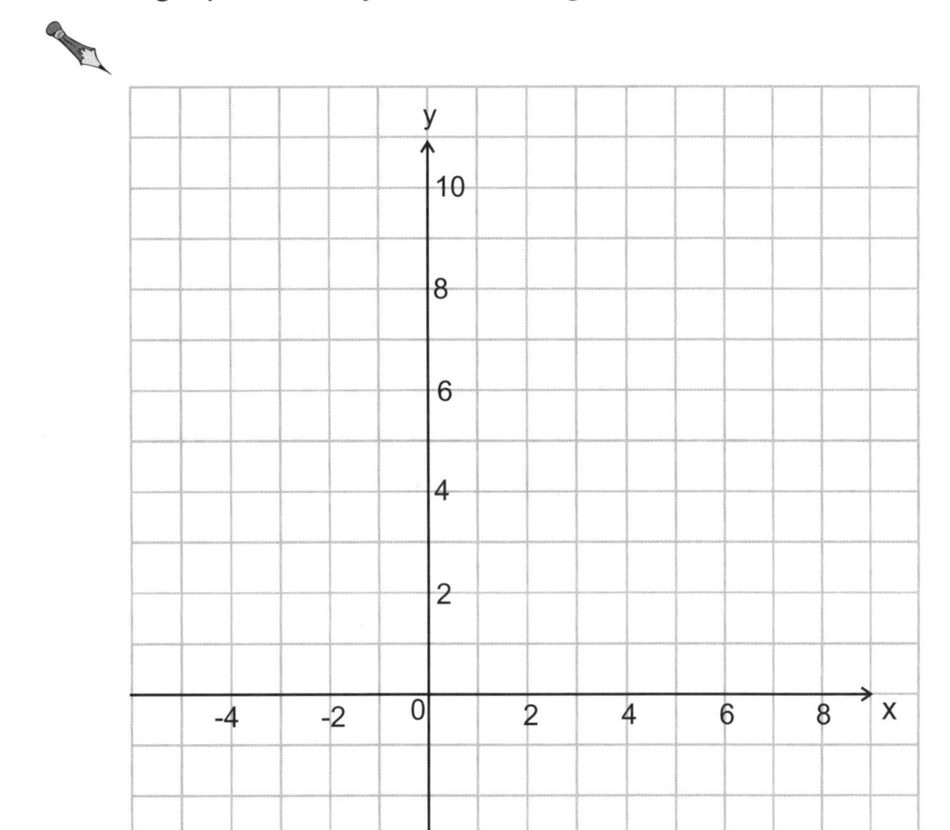

2 marks

7. The diagram shows part of Bekani's garden.
The crosses represent the positions of two trees.
He wants to lay a path so that it is equidistant from the two trees.

Construct the locus that the path should take.

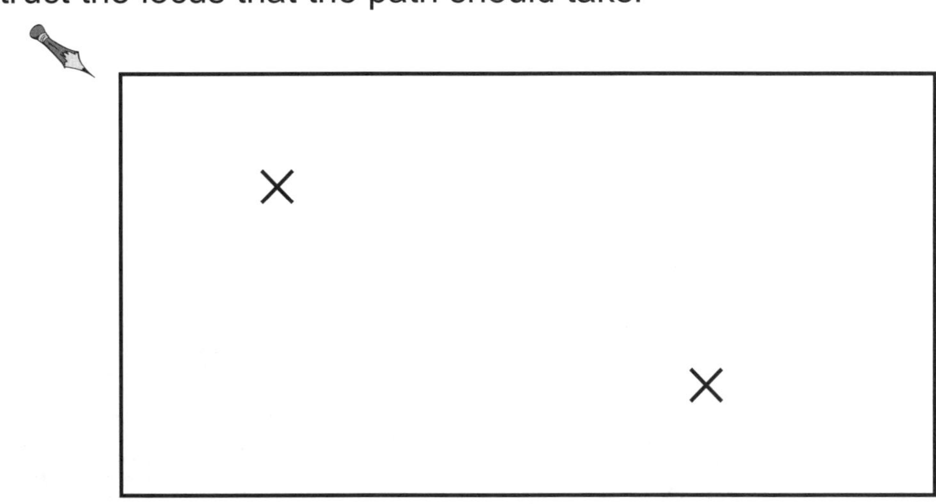

2 marks

8. In 2005 Gail's annual salary was £32 200.
In 2006 her salary was increased to £35 800.

(a) What was the percentage increase in her salary?

.... %

2 marks

(b) In 2006 Mark's annual salary was increased by 7% from his 2005 salary.
His salary after the increase was £28 400.

What was Mark's salary in 2005 to the nearest pound?

£ ....

2 marks

9. Miss Singleton asked her Year 9 form group how much time they had spent watching television over the weekend.

The answers are shown in the graph below.

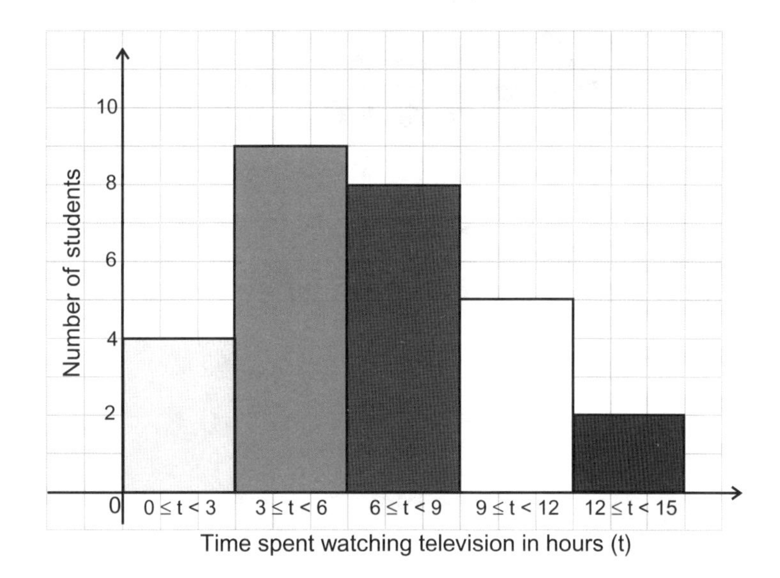

(a) How many students did she ask?

....

1 mark

(b) Calculate an estimate of the mean time spent watching television.
Give your answer in hours and minutes to the nearest 10 minutes.

.... hours and .... minutes

3 marks

10. The wheels on Dominic's toy truck have a diameter of 2 cm.

(a) He pushes the truck forward 65 cm.
How many complete revolutions do the wheels make?

....

2 marks

(b) What is the area of the cross section of a wheel on the truck?

.... cm^2

2 marks

The toy is a scale model of a real truck.
The cross sectional area of a wheel on the real truck is 0.58 m^2.

(c) Find the scale factor of the enlargement that would transform the toy truck into a truck the same size as the real truck.

....

3 marks

11. The diagram shows part of the edge of a regular polygon.

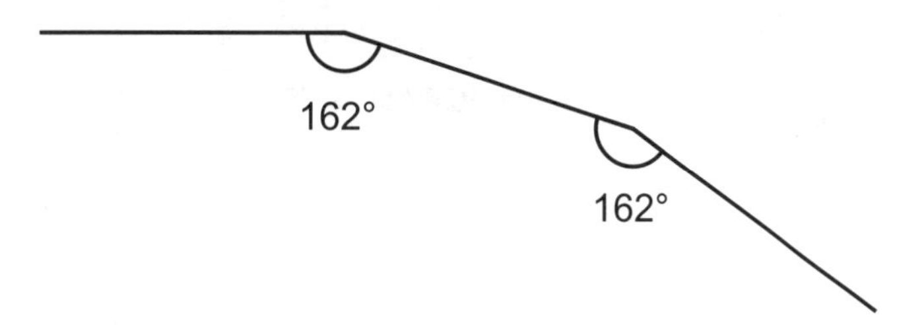

(a) What size are the exterior angles of the polygon?

.... °

1 mark

(b) How many sides does the polygon have?

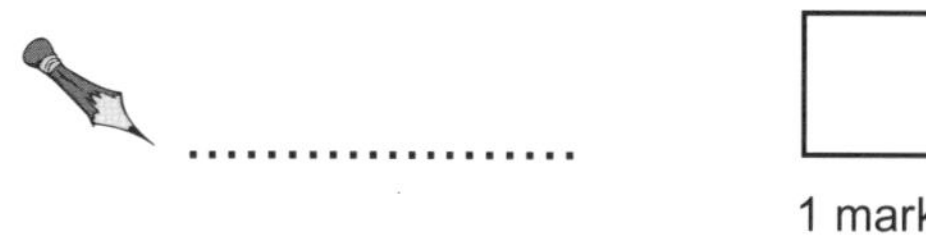

....

1 mark

12. Louise travels 18 miles to work.

(a) One day the journey took 35 minutes.
What was her average speed?

.... mph

1 mark

(b) If she drove at an average speed of 38 miles per hour,
how long would it take her to get to work?

.... minutes

1 mark

(c) Clarissa took 25 minutes to drive to work.
Her average speed during the journey was 40 miles per hour.
How long was her journey?

.... miles

1 mark

13. Find the missing side x in each of the following right-angled triangles.

(a)

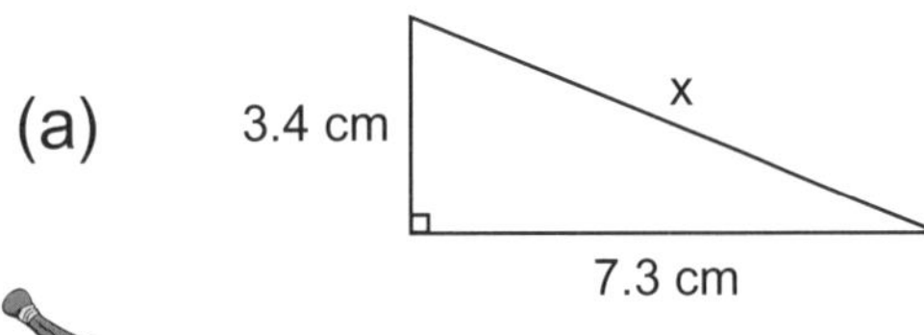

(DIAGRAM NOT TO SCALE)

x = ... cm

2 marks

(b)

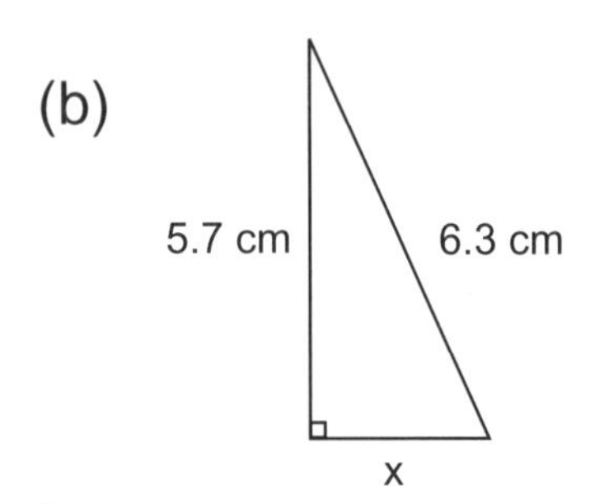

(DIAGRAM NOT TO SCALE)

x = ... cm

2 marks

14. The formula for the volume, V, of a sphere of radius r is $V = \frac{4}{3}\pi r^3$.

(a) Find the volume of a sphere with radius 3.6 cm.

.... cm^3

2 marks

(b) Find the radius of a sphere with a volume of 28.3 cm^3.

.... cm

2 marks

15. (a) Find the size of angle a in the right-angled triangle below.

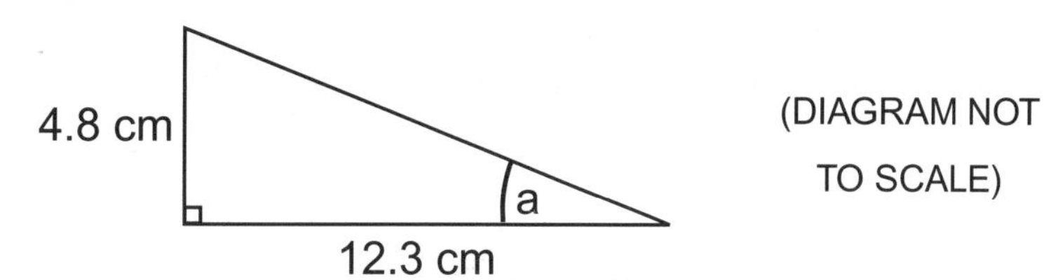

a = ... °

2 marks

(b) Find the length of side b in this right-angled triangle:

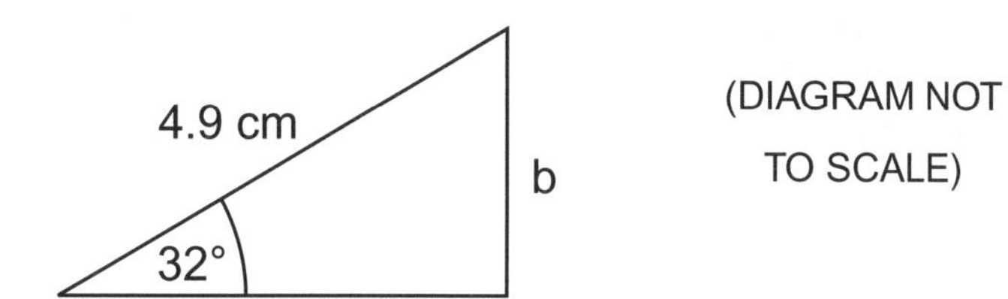

b = ... cm

2 marks

16. The Clewes family and the Bleach family visited the Italian Gardens.

The Clewes family consisted of 3 adults and 2 children and they were charged £31.

The Bleach family consisted of 2 adults and 5 children and they were charged £39.

(a) Using **a** to represent the adult cost and **c** to represent the child cost, write down 2 equations.

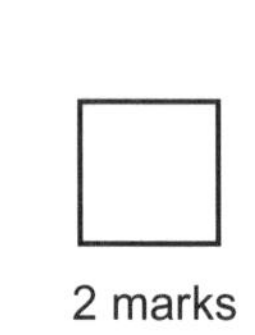

(b) Solve your equations to find the cost of entry for adults and children. You must show an algebraic method.

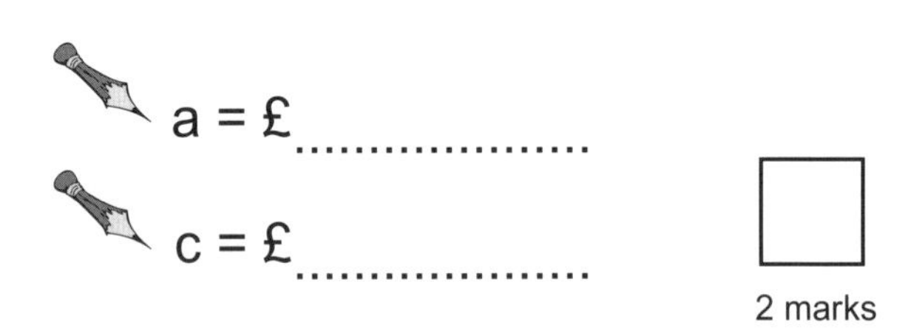

17. The diagram shows three similar rectangles — A, B and C.

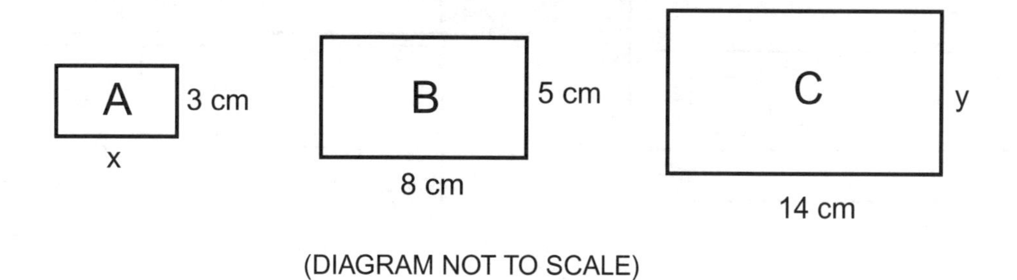

(DIAGRAM NOT TO SCALE)

(a) Find the missing lengths x and y.

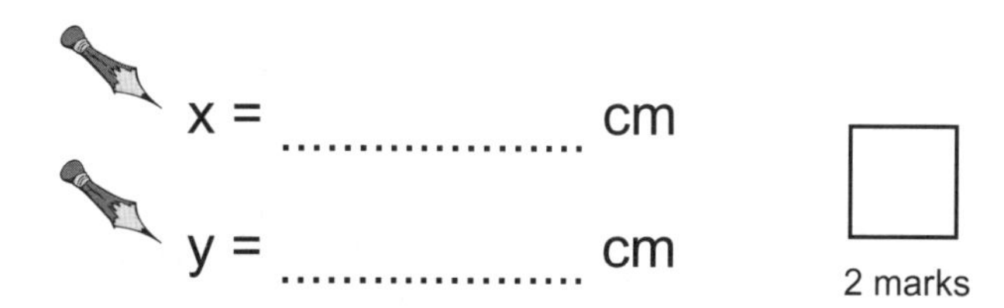

(b) What is the scale factor of the enlargement that would transform C to A?

Key Stage 3 Mathematics **Levels 5-8**

Mental Arithmetic Practice Test 2

First Name ______________________

Last Name ______________________

School ______________________

Score: ☐ 1st GO ☐ 2nd GO ☐ 3rd GO

Time: 5 seconds

1		
2	85° 95° 105°	
3		-5
4		
5		350
6		
7	0.5 0.6 0.7 0.8	
8		y = -3x + 4

Time: 10 seconds

9		
10	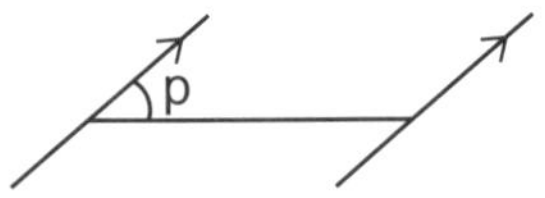	
11	%	35 out of 50
12		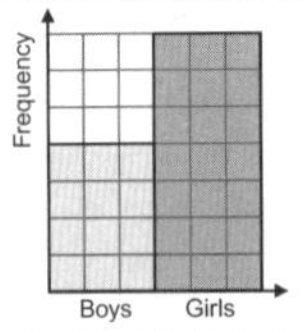 8
13		20 0.7
14	£	£3.50
15	mean median mode range	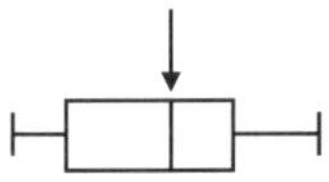
16	m	1 cm : 5 m
17	£	£19.99
18		2.05
19		
20		1.3, 1.6, 1.9
21	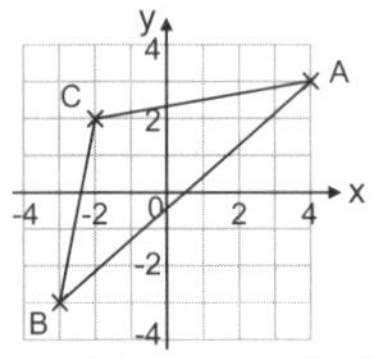	

Time: 15 seconds

22		4 | 2 3 5 8 5 | 0 0 0 1 4 4 6 | 1 3 5 5 7 KEY: 4|2 = 42
23		0.25
24	£	£56 10%
25	°	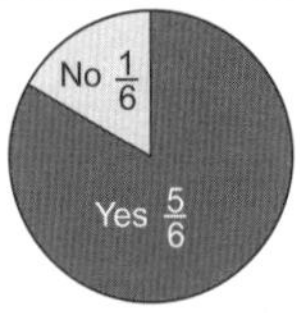
26		$\frac{2}{5}$
27		$\frac{707}{9.7 - 2.5}$
28	cm^2	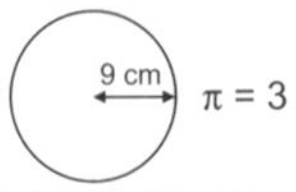
29	£	99p
30	$\frac{3}{5}$ $\frac{4}{5}$ $\frac{4}{3}$ $\frac{5}{3}$ $\frac{3}{4}$	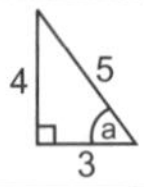

Maths

EY STAGE

3

EVELS

5-8

RACTICE PAPER

3A

CGP

Key Stage 3

Mathematics Test

Practice Paper 3A

Calculator NOT allowed

Read this page, but don't open the booklet until your teacher says you can start. Write your name and school in the spaces below.

First Name ______________________

Last Name ______________________

School ______________________

Remember

- The test is one hour long.
- Make sure you have these things with you before you start: pen, pencil, rubber, ruler, angle measurer or protractor and pair of compasses. You may use tracing paper.
- There are some formulas you might need on page 2.
- The easier questions are at the start of the test.
- Try to answer all of the questions.
- Don't use any rough paper — write all your answers and working in this test paper.
- Check your work carefully before the end of the test.
- If you're not sure what to do, ask your teacher.

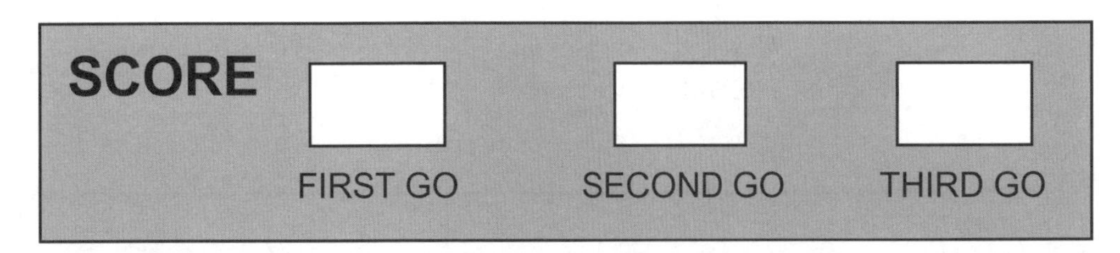

Exam Set MHGP31

Instructions

This means write down your answer or show your working and your answer.

You may not use a calculator in this test.

Formulas

Trapezium

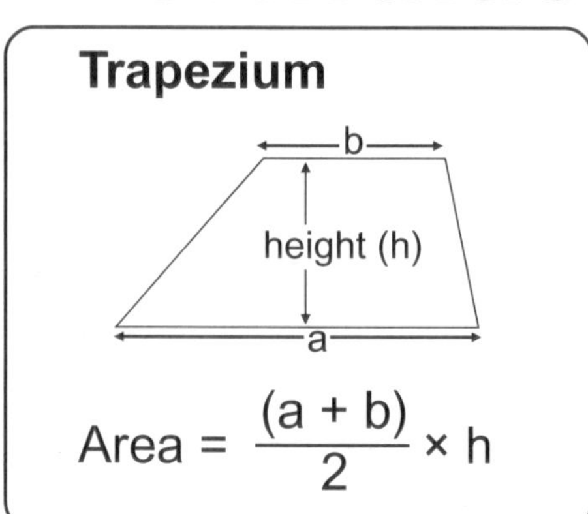

$$\text{Area} = \frac{(a + b)}{2} \times h$$

Prism

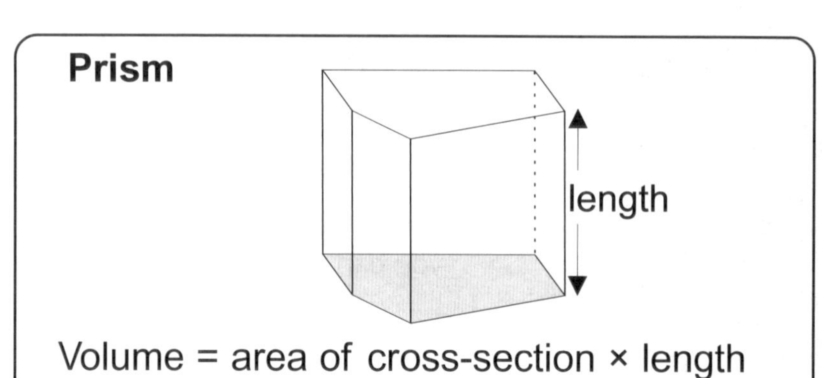

Volume = area of cross-section × length

1. (a) Show that $8 \times 37 = 296$.

1 mark

(b) What is 32×37? You can use part (a) to help you.

....

2 marks

2. David is d years old.
His younger sister Katya is k years old.
Their father is three times as old as David.

Write down expressions for each of the following:

(a) David's age in 10 years time.

....

1 mark

(b) Katya's age 7 years ago.

....

1 mark

(c) Their father's age.

....

1 mark

(d) The difference between their father's age and David's age.
Simplify your answer as much as possible.

....

1 mark

(e) David's age, when Katya is as old as he is now.
Simplify your answer as much as possible.

....

2 marks

3. (a) Solve this inequality: $3x + 2 \leq 17$

....

1 mark

(b) Solve this inequality: $4 - 6y \geq -8$

....

1 mark

4. (a) I am thinking of a number. My number is a multiple of 3.

Anish says: "Because 3 is an odd number, your number must be odd."

Is Anish correct? Explain your answer.

2 marks

(b) I am thinking of a different number. It is a multiple of 12.

Tick all the statements from the list below that must be true.

☐ It is greater than 12

☐ It is a multiple of 3

☐ It is divisible by 6

☐ It is not divisible by 11

☐ It is a factor of 24

2 marks

5. Look at this sequence of patterns made with crosses:

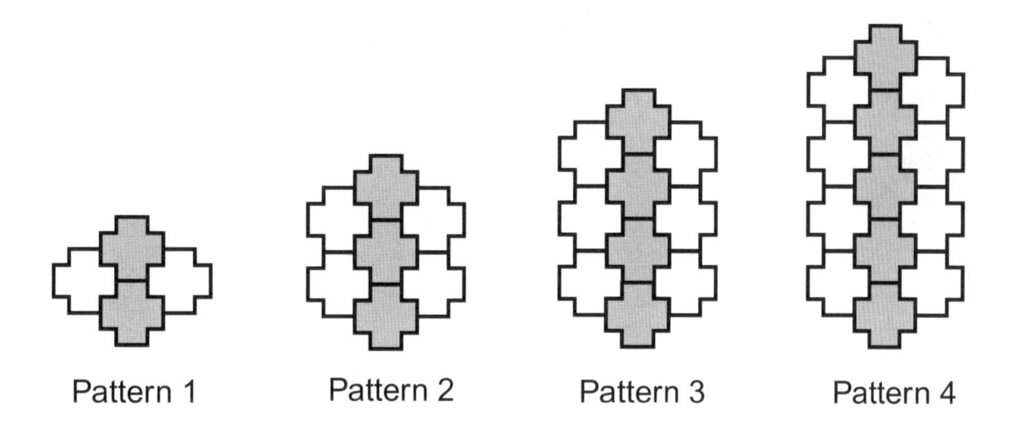

(a) How many grey crosses will there be in the 10th pattern?

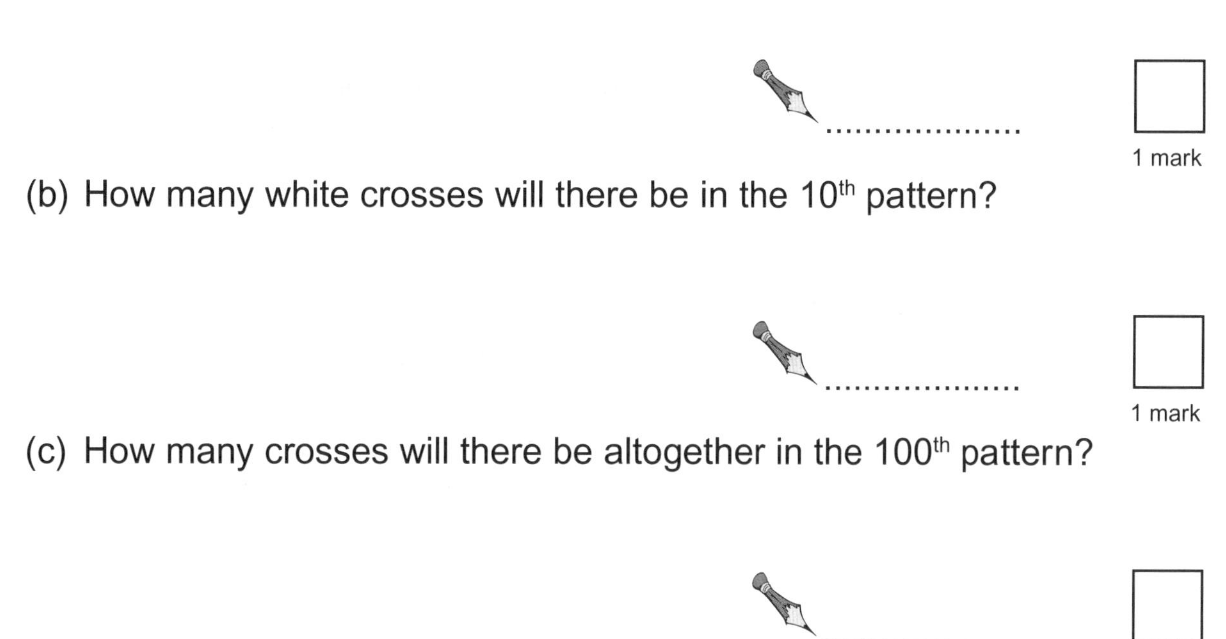

....

1 mark

(b) How many white crosses will there be in the 10th pattern?

....

1 mark

(c) How many crosses will there be altogether in the 100th pattern?

....

1 mark

6. Fill in the missing fraction in each of the sums below.

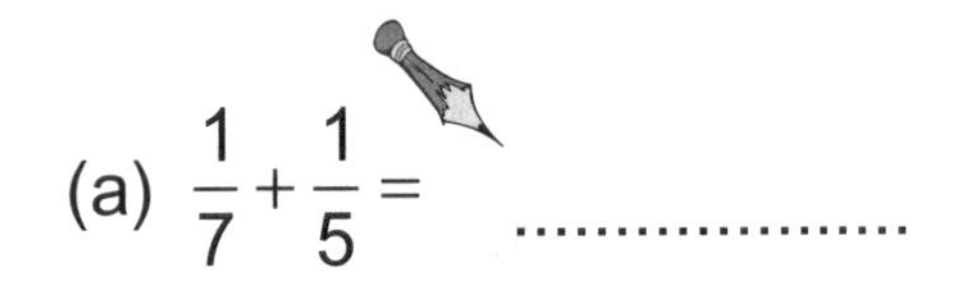

(a) $\frac{1}{7} + \frac{1}{5} =$ ....

1 mark

(b) $\frac{2}{13} - \frac{2}{39} =$ ....

1 mark

7. Solve these simultaneous equations using an algebraic method:

$5x + 6y = 28$
$3x - y = 3$

You must show your working.

$x =$ ....

$y =$ ....

3 marks

8. The diagram shows two common sizes of paper, called A4 and A3.
A3 paper is an enlargement of A4 paper.
One A3 sheet is exactly the same size as two A4 sheets next to each other.

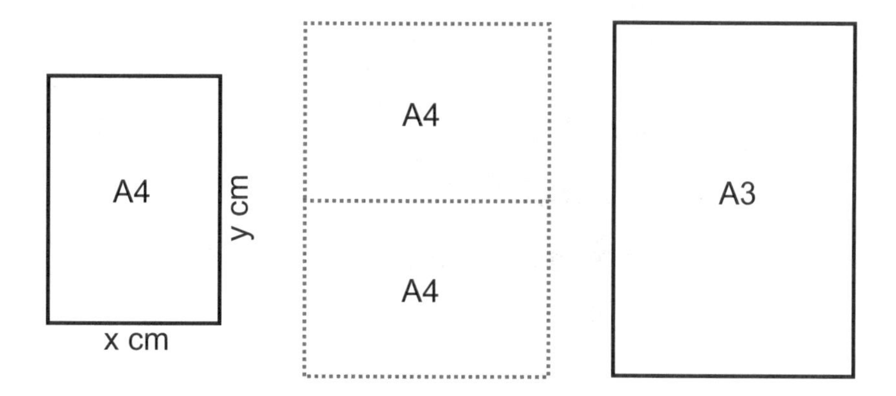

A4 paper is x cm wide and y cm long.

(a) Use the second diagram to write down the width and length of A3 paper.

Width = ... cm

Length = ... cm

1 mark

(b) Explain why $\frac{2x}{y} - \frac{y}{x}$.

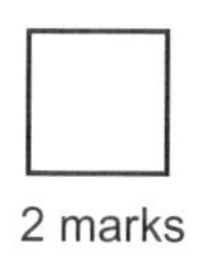

2 marks

(c) Sophie says "That means y = 2x". Sophie is not correct.
Write down a correct version of her statement.

y = ...

1 mark

9. The diagram shows a circle with diameter AB, which contains the triangle ABC. The circle has an area of 4π cm^2.

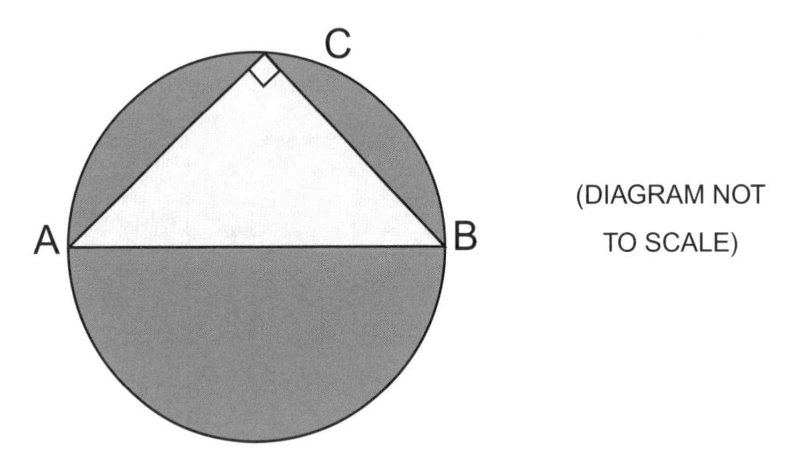

(a) Find the radius of the circle.

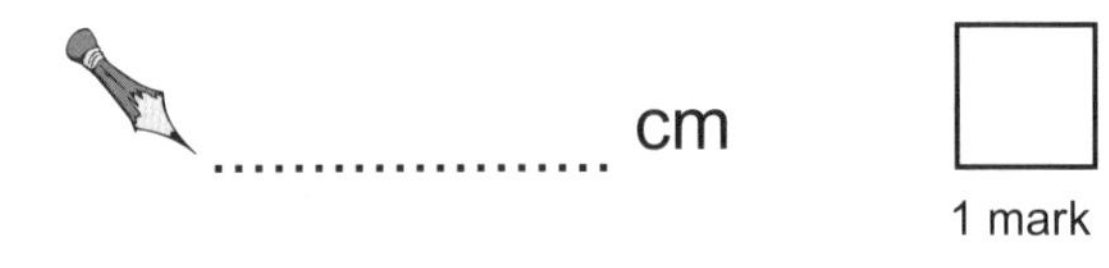
.... cm

1 mark

(b) The side BC of the right-angled triangle is $\sqrt{8}$ cm.
Show that the triangle is isosceles.

2 marks

(c) Find the area of the triangle.

.... cm^2

1 mark

10. At a party there are:

25 three-year olds

20 four-year olds

two mothers, aged 28 and 32

three fathers, aged 30, 31 and 33

one grandmother, aged 68

(a) Put the following in order, from smallest to largest.
(You do not need to do any calculations.)

mean age **median age** **modal age**

1. ....

2. ....

3. ....

1 mark

(b) Explain how you know which was the largest without working it out.

1 mark

11. In my Gran's cupboard, she has tins of peaches, pineapple and pears.
The tins are either large or small.
The table shows the numbers of each type of tin Gran has.

	Large tins	Small tins
Peaches	4	3
Pineapple	8	4
Pears	2	3

(a) Gran chooses a tin at random.
What is the probability it is a small tin of pears?

1 mark

(b) My younger sister takes the labels off all of the tins.
Gran wants a tin of peaches.

Which size tin should Gran open to have the best chance of getting a tin of peaches? Explain your answer, including any calculations.

3 marks

12. Look at the triangle below.

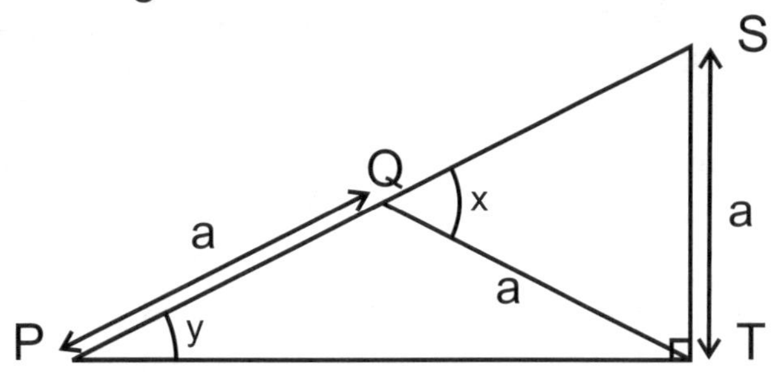

(DIAGRAM NOT TO SCALE)

(a) Explain carefully why $x = 2y$.

2 marks

(b) Find the value of y.

$y =$ .... °

2 marks

13. (a) Calculate 10% of £200.

£....................

1 mark

(b) Use your answer to (a) to find 2½% of £200.

1 mark

(c) In Meanland, there is a tax of 22½% on every item that is sold.
A television costs £220 before tax.

Work out how much it costs including the tax.

£....................

2 marks

14. Factorise these expressions:

(a) $x^2 + 8x - 20$

....

2 marks

(b) $x^2 - 100$

1 mark

15. I have a list of five numbers.
The mean of the numbers is 4.
The mode of the numbers is 2.
The median of the numbers is 3.

Write down one possibility for my list of numbers.

2 marks

16. (a) Find the area of the trapezium below.

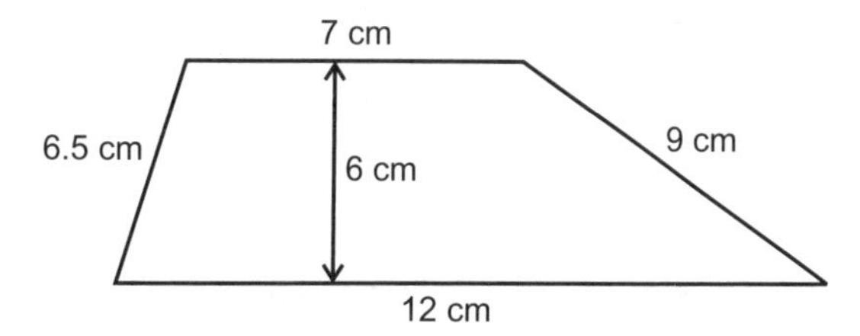

.... cm^2

2 marks

(b) This prism has the trapezium from part (a) as its cross-section.

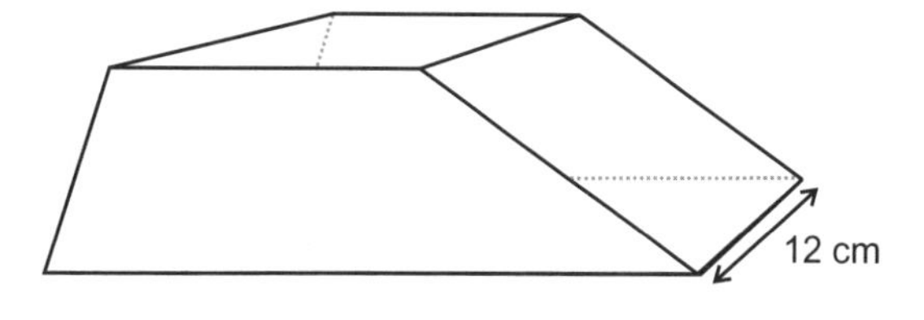

Find its volume.

.... cm^3

2 marks

17. In a science experiment, Sabiha investigated the relationship between temperature and time taken for a chemical reaction to finish.

She plotted a graph of her results.

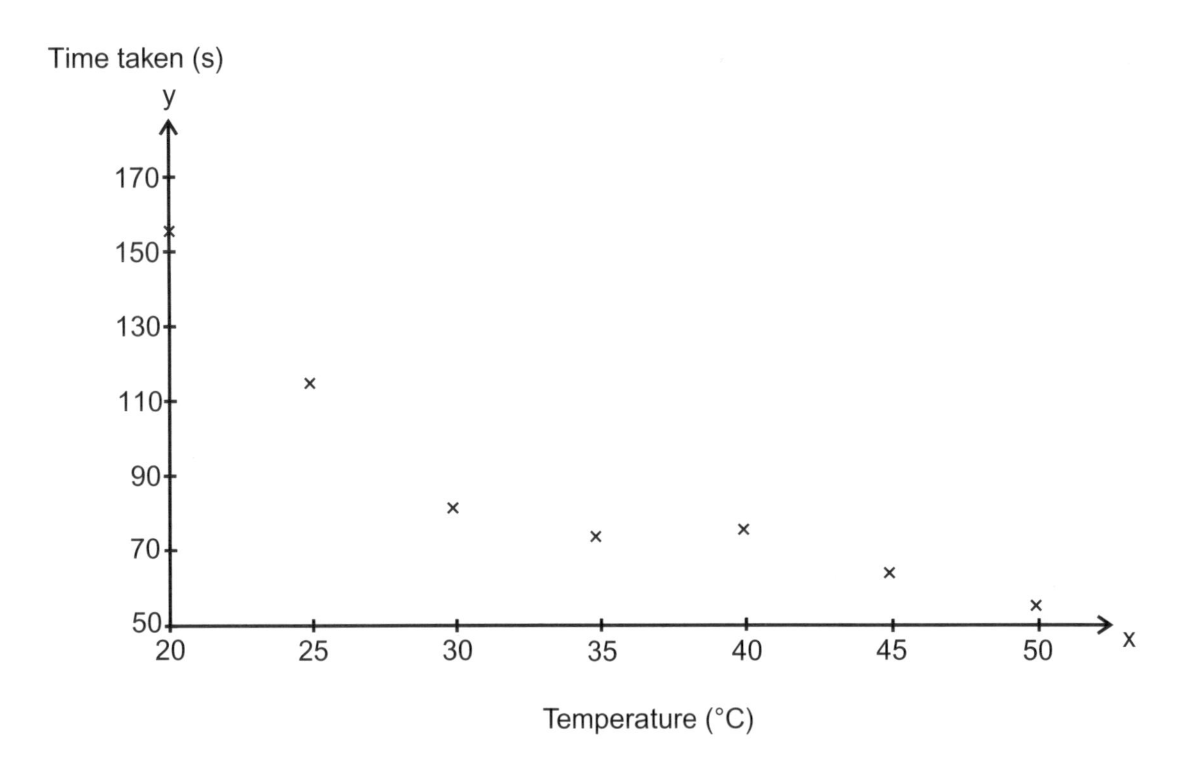

(a) What type of correlation does the graph show?

1 mark

(b) Sabiha thought the equation of the line of best fit was $y = 3x + 20$.

Give two reasons why this cannot be correct.

2 marks

18. (a) Write 5020 in standard form.

....

1 mark

(b) If $a = 3.5 \times 10^3$ and $b = 4 \times 10^{-6}$, find $a \times b$.
Give your answer in standard form.

....

2 marks

[Blank Page]

Maths

EY STAGE

3

EVELS

5-8

RACTICE PAPER

3B

Key Stage 3

Mathematics Test

Practice Paper 3B

Calculator allowed

Read this page, but don't open the booklet until your teacher says you can start. Write your name and school in the spaces below.

First Name ______________________________

Last Name ______________________________

School ______________________________

Remember

- The test is one hour long.
- Make sure you have these things with you before you start: pen, pencil, rubber, ruler, calculator, angle measurer or protractor and pair of compasses.
  You may use tracing paper.
- There are some formulas you might need on page 2.
- The easier questions are at the start of the test.
- Try to answer all of the questions.
- Don't use any rough paper — write all your answers and working in this test paper.
- Check your work carefully before the end of the test.
- If you're not sure what to do, ask your teacher.

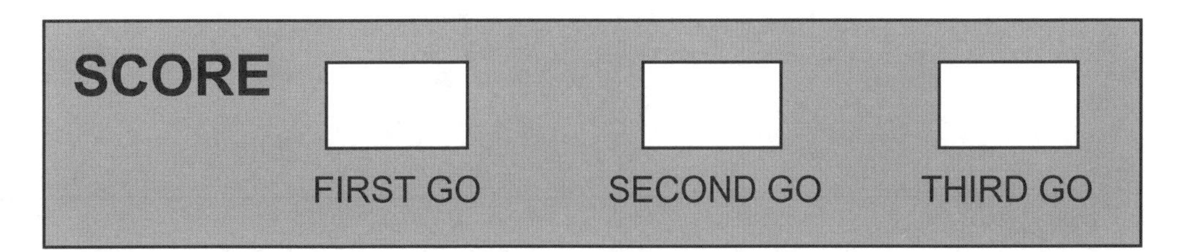

Exam Set MHGP31

Instructions

This means write down your answer or show your working and your answer.

You may use a calculator in this test.

Formulas

Trapezium

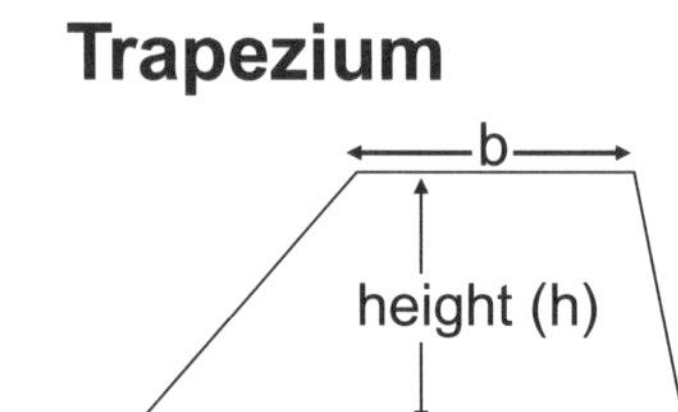

$$\text{Area} = \frac{(a + b)}{2} \times h$$

Prism

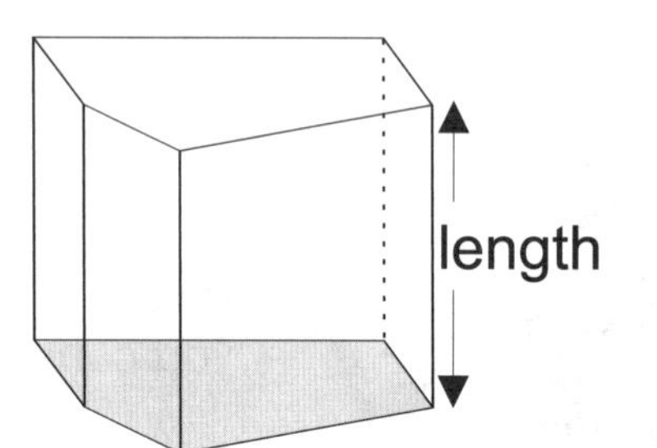

Volume = area of cross-section × length

1. Calculate the value of each of the expressions below when x = -2.

(a) $4 + x =$ ....

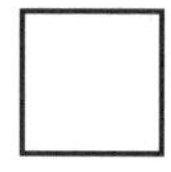

1 mark

(b) $5x =$ ....

1 mark

(c) $2x^2 =$ ....

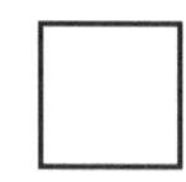

1 mark

2. I am going on holiday and need to buy some euros.

BetaTravel offers 82 euros for £60

BestXchange offers 100 euros for £72

(a) Which gives the better value for money?
You must show your working.

....

2 marks

(b) Calculate how many euros I would get for £100 at BestXChange.

.... euros

1 mark

3. Look at the diagram. The lines marked with arrows are parallel.
PQ and QR are the same length.

(DIAGRAM NOT TO SCALE)

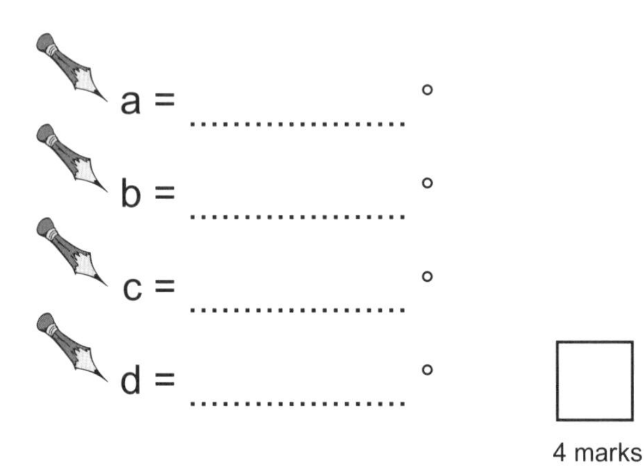

Work out the size of the angles a, b, c and d.

a = ... °

b = ... °

c = ... °

d = ... °

4 marks

4. (a) Write down the nth term for this number sequence:

1, 4, 9, 16, 25, ...

....

1 mark

Use your answer to work out the nth term for these number sequences:

(b) **2, 5, 10, 17, 26, ...**

....

1 mark

(c) **3, 12, 27, 48, 75, ...**

....

1 mark

(d) **3, 9, 19, 33, 51, ...**

....

1 mark

5. A goat has a rope attached to its collar.
The length of the rope is 6 metres.
The other end of the rope is attached to the outside of the shed as shown.

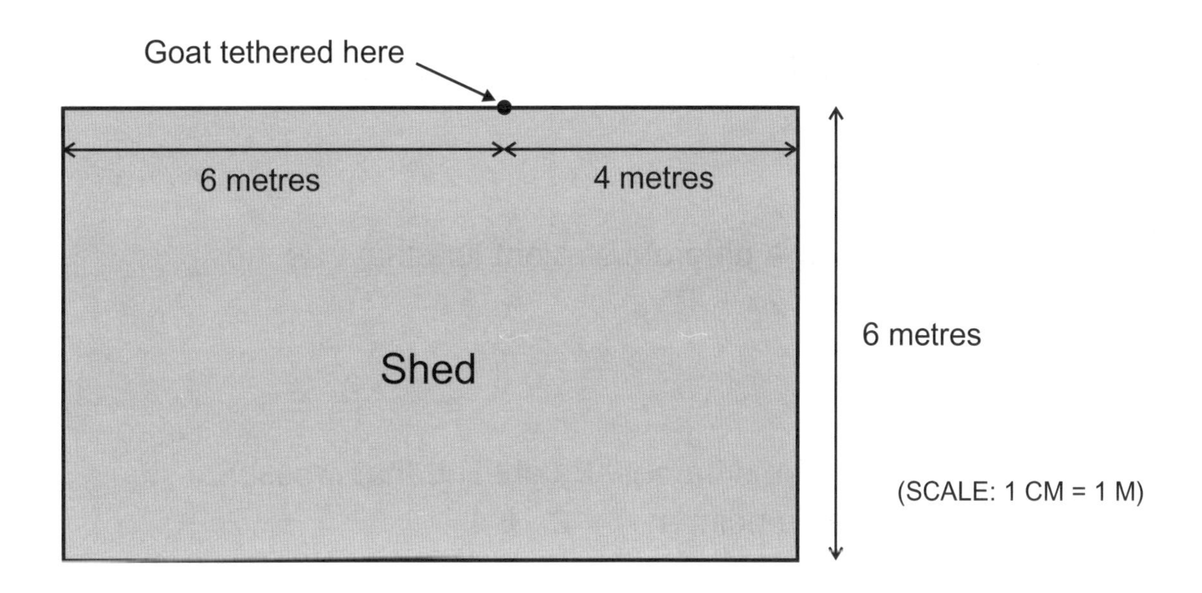

Show accurately on the diagram the region where the goat could be.
Label the region R.

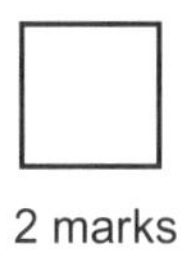

2 marks

6. The graph shows the straight-line equation $y = 2x + 4$.

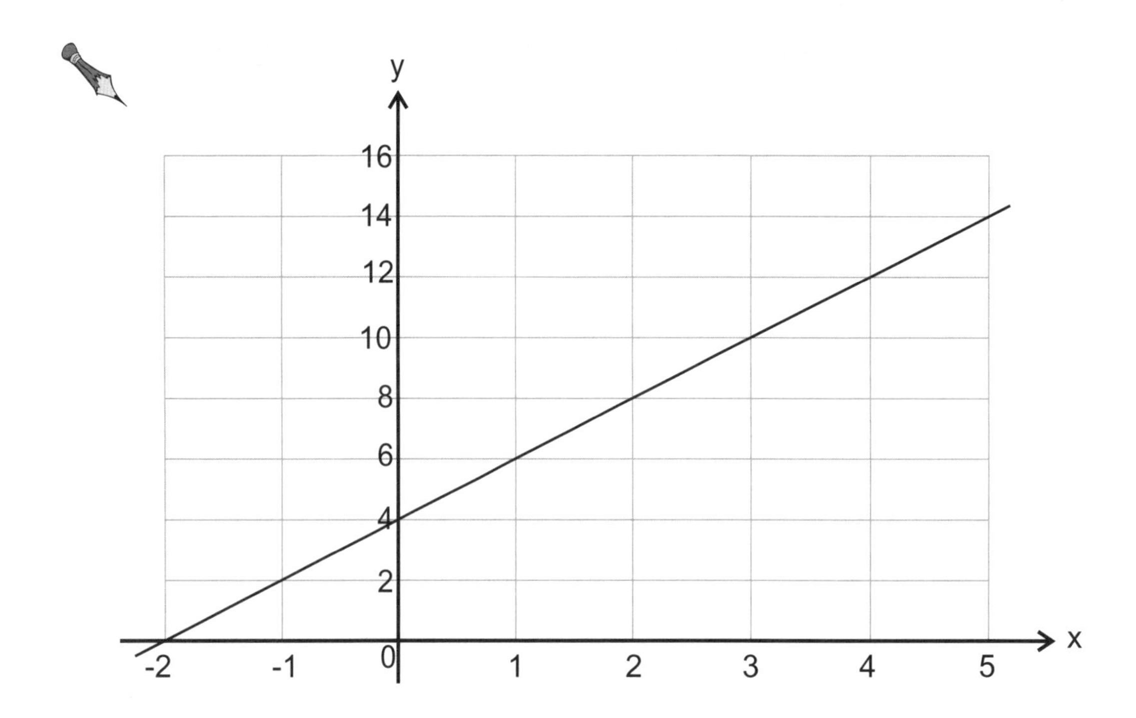

(a) Write the equation of a different straight line that has the same gradient as $y = 2x + 4$.

$y =$ ....

1 mark

(b) Write the equation of a different straight line that crosses the y-axis at the same point as $y = 2x + 4$.

$y =$ ....

1 mark

(c) Another straight line has gradient -2 and passes through the point (0, 14). Draw this straight line on the diagram above.

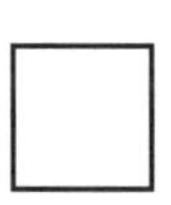

2 marks

7. I have three coins — a 2p, a 5p and a 10p.

The 2p and 5p coins are equally likely to show a head or a tail.

The 10p coin is biased so it is twice as likely to show a head as a tail.

I throw all three coins.

What is the probability I get the same on all of them?

....

3 marks

8. Harry has started weight-training.

Since he started, his weight has increased by $\frac{1}{16}$.
He now weighs 76.5 kg.

How much did he weigh before he started?

.... kg

2 marks

9. Look at the triangle below.

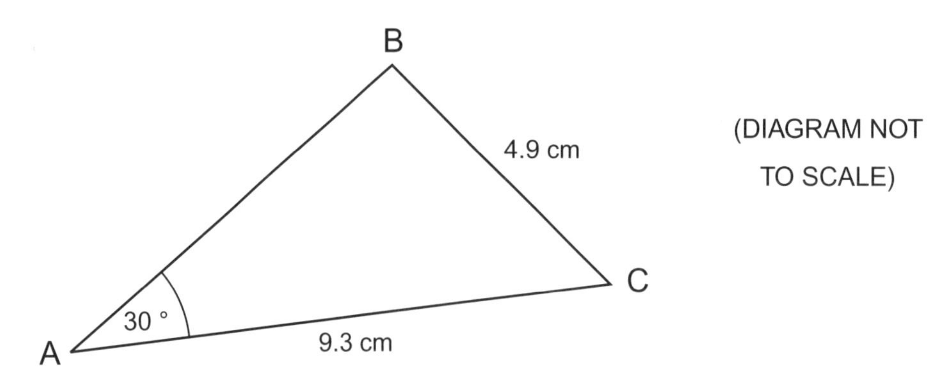

(DIAGRAM NOT TO SCALE)

Use trigonometry to show that angle ABC cannot be a right angle.

2 marks

10. Multiply out the expressions below.
Write your answers as simply as possible.

(a) $3(x - 3) - 2(3 - 2x)$

....

2 marks

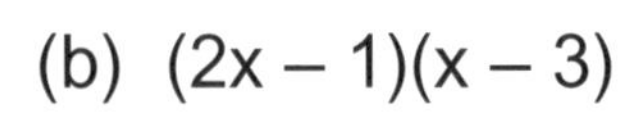

(b) $(2x - 1)(x - 3)$

....

2 marks

11. Anjum, Billie and Catie are eating sweets.

The ratio of the number Anjum eats to the number Billie eats is 3 : 5.
The ratio of the number Billie eats to the number Catie eats is 4 : 7.
Catie eats 70 sweets.

How many sweets do the three children eat altogether?

....

2 marks

12. Fill in the missing numbers:

(a) 150 mm is the same as .... m.

1 mark

(b) 150 mm^2 is the same as .... m^2.

1 mark

(c) The length of a piece of wood is 150 mm to the nearest 10 mm.

The actual length lies between .... mm and .... mm.

1 mark

13. A class of 31 pupils did a test. Their marks were out of 60.
The stem-and-leaf diagram shows all 31 results.

Stem	Leaf
0	9
1	0 1 6 8
2	0 5 5 8 9
3	1 1 2 3 7 8
4	0 4 5 6 6 7 8 9
5	0 1 2 2 2 4 7

Key: 1 | 6 represents 16

(a) Find the range of the marks.

 ....

1 mark

(b) Find the median mark.

 ....

1 mark

(c) Pupils who got less than 40% of the marks had to do a retest.
What percentage of pupils had to do a retest?

....................%

2 marks

14. Some exam-markers get paid £2 for each paper they mark.

Anna takes 20 minutes to mark each paper.
David takes 15 minutes to mark each paper.

(a) Work out how much Anna and David earn per hour.

Anna earns £.................... per hour

David earns £.................... per hour

1 mark

(b) Use your answers to part (a) to plot two points on the grid below.
By plotting at least two more points, draw a graph to show the relationship between amount earned per hour and the time taken to mark each paper.

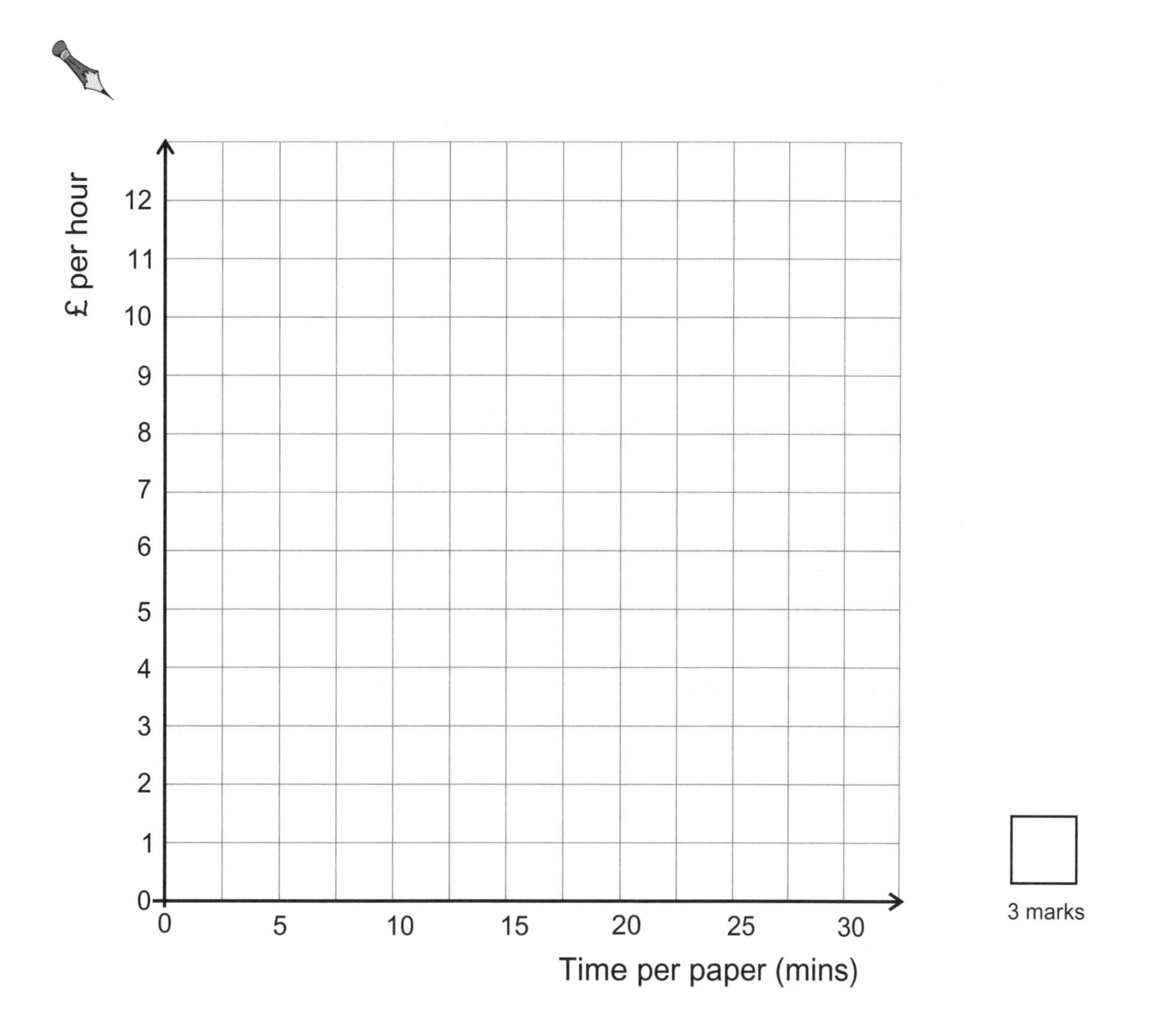

3 marks

15. (a) In a test, Jamie answered 40% of the questions.
He got 50% of the questions he answered right.
Manjinder answered 50% of the questions and got 40% of them right.
Manjinder said "That means we got the same mark."

Is Manjinder right or wrong? Explain your answer.

2 marks

(b) In a sale, a shop reduced all its prices by 10%.
After the sale, the shop manager increased the prices by 10%.
A customer said "That means the prices are now the same as they were before the sale."

Is the customer right or wrong? Explain your answer.

2 marks

(c) At Mary's local garage, the price of a litre of petrol rose by 20% in April, then by another 20% in May.
Mary said "That's a 40% rise in two months."

Is Mary right or wrong? Explain your answer.

2 marks

16. David reads in the paper that the dice produced at one factory are more likely to land on a six than on any of the other numbers.

To investigate this he buys 20 dice.
He throws all 20 dice together 12 times.
He counts the number of sixes he gets each time.

The table shows his results.

Throw	1	2	3	4	5	6	7	8	9	10	11	12
Number of sixes	1	3	5	2	4	6	3	4	6	0	4	4

(a) Use David's results to estimate the probability of getting a six using these dice.

....

1 mark

(b) David decides from his investigation that the paper is right.
Do you agree? Explain your answer.

1 mark

17. Look at this equation:

$$y^2 = \frac{4}{x^2 - 9}$$

(a) Find the two possible values of y when x = 5.

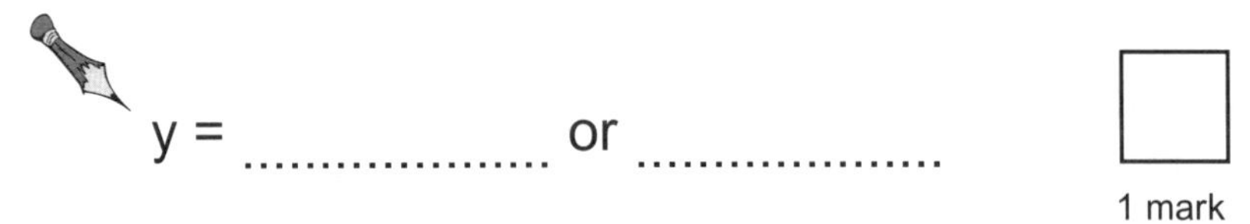

y = ... or ....

1 mark

(b) Is it possible to get the value y = 0 from this equation?
Explain your answer.

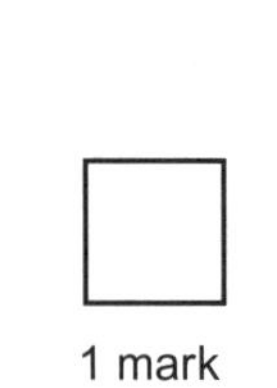

1 mark

(c) It is not possible to get a value for y if x takes any value from -3 to 3.
Give two reasons why.

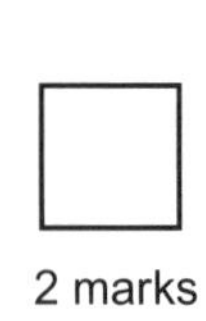

2 marks

18. A cylinder has radius r, height h, and a volume of 36π cm^3.
r and h are both whole numbers.

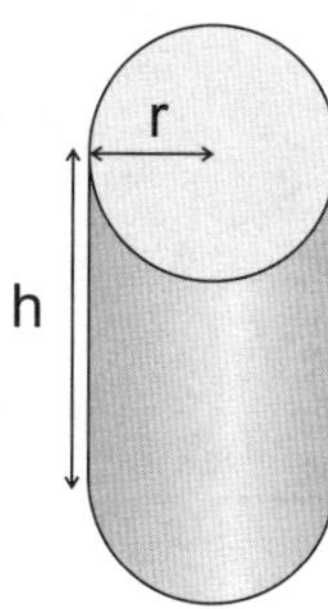

Write down two possible sets of values for r and h.

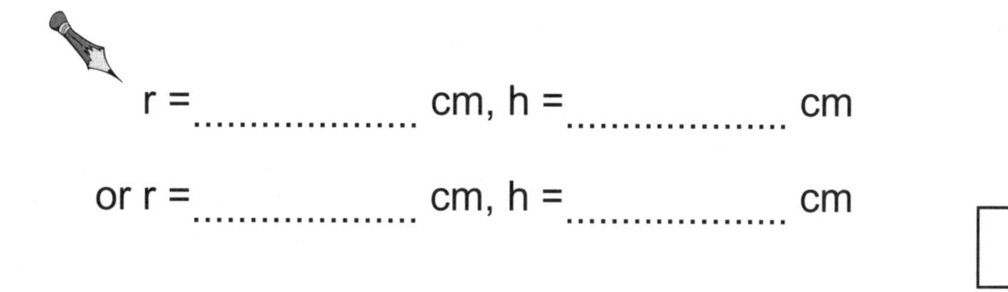

r = ... cm, h = ... cm

or r = ... cm, h = ... cm

2 marks

19. In the diagram below, triangles ABE and ACD are similar.

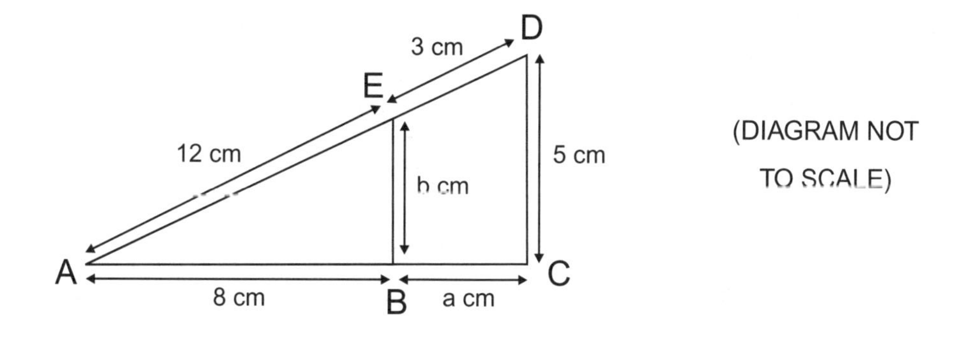

Find the lengths a and b.

a = ... cm

b = ... cm

2 marks

Key Stage 3 Mathematics Levels 5-8

Mental Arithmetic Practice Test 3

First Name ____________

Last Name ____________

School ____________

Score: [ ] 1st GO [ ] 2nd GO [ ] 3rd GO

Time: 5 seconds

1		130
2	Length Area Volume	
3		240
4	s	
5		
6		5.28
7	%	

Time: 10 seconds

8		420
9	52 54 55 51 55	
10	(,)	Graph: points P, Q, R; x from -2 to 2, y from 0 to 2
11		4 and 6
12	°C	-8°C -5°C 0°C 2°C
13	°	Triangle: angle a, 148°
14		-2
15		
16		25 m 800 m
17	$x =$	$x - \frac{3}{10} = \frac{7}{10}$
18		卌 卌 卌 ||
19		
20	°	P———Q
21		10n + 4
22		$7k^3$

Time: 15 seconds

23		5(n – 3)
24	p	75p £5
25		16 19
26		see table below
27		£2 in 10p coins £2 in 5p coins
28	g	4:3 360 g
29	$\sqrt{6}$ $\sqrt{12}$ $\sqrt{20}$ $\sqrt{24}$	Right-angled triangle with sides 2 and 4
30		

Table for question 26:

Number of cakes	Frequency
0	3
1	5
2	8
3	4

Coordination Group Publications

Key Stage 3

Mathematics

Answer Book

SATS Practice Papers

Levels 5-8

Contents

Using the Practice Papers P2
Answers P4
Mental Arithmetic Answers P16

These practice papers won't make you better at maths

... but they will show you what you **can** do, and what you **can't** do.

The papers are like the ones you'll get on the day — so they'll tell you what you need to **work at** if you want to do **better**.

Do a test, **mark it** and look at what you **got wrong**.
That's the stuff you need to learn.

Go away, **learn** those tricky bits, then **do the same test again**. If you're **still** getting questions wrong, you'll have to do even **more practice** and **keep testing** yourself until you get all the questions right.

It doesn't sound like a lot of **fun**, but how else do you expect to **learn** it?

There are two big ways to improve your score

1) **Keep practising the things you get wrong**
If you keep getting the fraction questions wrong, practise fractions. If you keep making a hash of the graph questions, practise graphs. And so on...

2) **Don't throw away easy marks**
Even if a question looks dead simple, you have to check your answer and make sure it's sensible.

Published by Coordination Group Publications Ltd

Contributors:
Cath Brown, Ali Palin
Jane Chow, Kieran Wardell
Sarah Hilton, Sarah Williams

Many thanks to Janet Dickinson *and* Dominic Hall *for proofreading.*

Groovy website: www.cgpbooks.co.uk
Jolly bits of clipart from CorelDRAW®
Printed by Elanders Hindson Ltd, Newcastle upon Tyne.

Doing the Tests

There are **three sets** of practice papers in this pack.
Each set has:

Paper A
1 hour test
no calculators allowed **60 marks**

Paper B
1 hour test
calculators are allowed **60 marks**

Mental Mathematics
should take about 20 minutes
no calculators allowed **30 marks**

Get someone to read the questions out for you — they're on the separate sheet that came with this pack.
You answer them on the page at the back of the calculator papers.

Follow all the instructions

1) This pencil means "**WRITE YOUR ANSWER HERE**". So make sure you do.

2) Write down your working. Even if you get the answer **wrong**, you could get a mark for trying to do the question in the **right way**. Questions which award marks for working have a **pencil** marking the space where you should **clearly show your working**.
3) The most important thing is to **understand** the questions.
Read everything really **carefully** to be sure you're doing what they want.

It you're going to do the practice papers more than once, then write your answers on a separate bit of paper.

Working out your Grade

- Do a complete exam (paper A, paper B and the mental mathematics test).
- Mark each exam paper, and add up all the marks (which gives you a mark out of 150).
- Look it up in this table to see what grade you got:

Mark	150 – 131	130 – 80	79 – 52	51 – 38	under 38
Level	8	7	6	5	N

Important

Getting Level 5, 6, 7 or 8 on one of these practice papers is **no guarantee** of getting that in the real SAT — **but** it is a pretty good guide.

1A KS3 Levels 5-8 Calculator NOT Allowed

Q	Marks	Correct answer	The bit in the middle tells you how to get to the answer	Useful tips

1. a — 1 — **53°** — Angles A and C are the same.

b — 2 — **127°** — Angles B and D are the same, so B = (360 – 53 – 53) ÷ 2 = 254 ÷ 2 = 127°.
(2 marks for correct answer, otherwise 1 mark for some correct working.)

2. a — 1 — **700, 0.7** — 1 cm^3 = 1 ml, so 700 cm^3 = 700 ml. 1000 ml = 1 litre, so 700 ml ÷ 1000 = 0.7 litres.

b — 1 — **63, 0.063** — 1000 g = 1 kg, so 63000 g ÷ 1000 = 63 kg. 1000 kg = 1 tonne, so 63 kg ÷ 1000 = 0.063 tonnes.

3. — 2

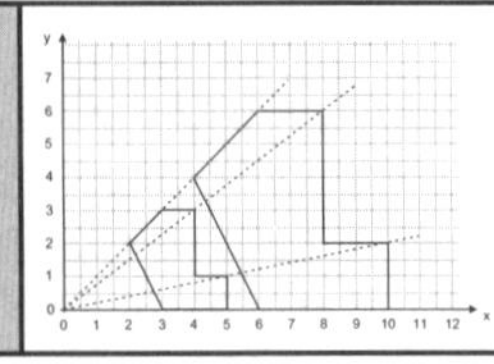

(2 marks for correct answer, otherwise 1 mark for correct enlargement but wrong position.)

TIP: A scale factor of ½ means the lines on your new shape should be half as long, and each point should be half the distance from the centre.

4. a — 2

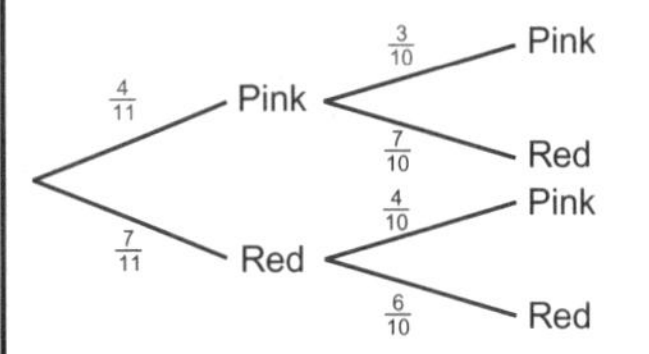

(2 marks for correct answer, otherwise 1 mark for getting at least two probabilities right.)

b — 1 — $\frac{6}{55}$ or $\frac{12}{110}$ — Multiplying along the pink branch gives $\frac{4}{11} \times \frac{3}{10} = \frac{12}{110} = \frac{6}{55}$

c — 2 — $\frac{28}{55}$ or $\frac{56}{110}$ — Multiplying along the pink and red branch gives $\frac{4}{11} \times \frac{7}{10} = \frac{28}{110}$

Multiplying along the red and pink branch gives $\frac{7}{11} \times \frac{4}{10} = \frac{28}{110}$, $\frac{28}{110} + \frac{28}{110} = \frac{56}{110} = \frac{28}{55}$

(2 marks for correct answer, otherwise 1 mark for some correct working.)

5. a — 1 — **035°**

b — 2

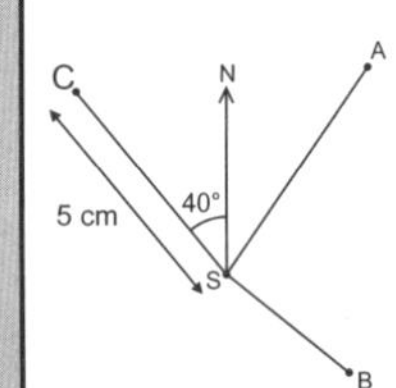

(1 mark for correct bearing, 1 mark for correct distance.)

TIP: Measuring 40° anticlockwise from the north line is just the same as measuring 320° clockwise, and it's a lot easier!

6. — 4

	6	
3	54	18
	9	

	21	
7	84	12
	4	

	25	
12.5	5^3	10
	5	

(4 marks for all six correct values, otherwise 3 marks for five correct, 2 marks for four correct or 1 mark for two or three correct.)

7. — 2 — **64 minutes** — £8.96 = 896p, 896 ÷ 14 = 64 minutes.
(2 marks for correct answer, otherwise 1 mark for some correct working.)

8. a — 1 — **x = -6** — $\frac{3x}{9} = -2$, 3x = -18, x = -6

b — 1 — **y = 15** — 2y – 6 = 24, 2y = 30, y = 15

c — 2 — **z = 18** — 3z – 7 = 29 + z, 3z – z = 29 + 7, 2z = 36, z = 18
(2 marks for correct answer, otherwise 1 mark for some correct working.)

TIP: Always check your answers by putting them back into the equations.

Q	Marks	Answer	Working
9. a	1	**25%**	$\frac{90}{360} \times 100 = 25\%$ *TIP: Remember — with pie charts, 360° always represents 100% of the data.*
b	2	**216°**	$\frac{60}{100} \times 360 = 216°$ **(2 marks for correct answer, otherwise 1 mark for some correct working.)**
c	2	**2000**	100 – 25 – 60 = 15% of people are not registered with a dentist. 15% = 300 people. So 1% = 300 ÷ 15 = 20. 100% = 20 × 100 = 2000 people. **(2 marks for correct answer, otherwise 1 mark for some correct working.)**
10. a	1	$\mathbf{\frac{1}{4}}$	$\frac{3}{4} - \frac{1}{2} = \frac{1}{4}$
b	2	$\mathbf{\frac{5}{8}}$	$\frac{3}{4} + \frac{5}{8} + \frac{1}{2} = \frac{6}{8} + \frac{5}{8} + \frac{4}{8} = \frac{15}{8}$. $\frac{15}{8} \div 3 = \frac{5}{8}$ *TIP: To add fractions you need to put them over a common denominator.* **(2 marks for correct answer, otherwise 1 mark for finding the sum of the fractions.)**
11.	3	**24 teachers and 84 pupils**	2 + 7 = 9, so 1 part = 108 ÷ 9 = 12. 12 × 2 = 24 teachers, 12 × 7 = 84 pupils. **(3 marks for correct answer, otherwise 1 mark for some correct working and 1 mark for either 24 or 84.)**
12. a	2	**x = 12**	4x + 30 = 78, 4x = 78 – 30, 4x = 48, x = 12 **(1 mark for correct algebraic expression and 1 mark for correct answer.)**
b	1	**1998**	2010 –12 = 1998
13. a	1	**-47**	y = (-2 × 25) + 3 = -47
b	1	**17**	-31 = -2x + 3, 2x = 34, x = 17 *TIP: You can also solve part (c) by using a simultaneous equations method.*
c	3	**(2.5, -2)**	-2x + 3 = 6x – 17, 3 + 17 = 6x + 2x, 20 = 8x, x = 2.5. So y = -2x + 3 = (-2 × 2.5) + 3 = -5 + 3 = -2. **(3 marks for a correct method and correct answer, otherwise 2 marks for a correct method and either x or y correct, or 1 mark for some correct working.)**
14. a	1	**24, 10**	
b	1	**33 minutes**	53 – 20 = 33
c	1	**8 minutes**	Median time for sudoku = 41 mins, median time for crossword = 33 mins. 41 – 33 = 8.
15.	3	**15%**	0.75 × 0.2 = 0.15, 0.15 × 100 = 15% **(3 marks for correct answer, otherwise 1-2 marks for some correct working.)**
16. a	1	$\mathbf{d = \frac{e-6}{2}}$	$2d + 6 = e,\ 2d = e - 6,\ d = \frac{e-6}{2}$
b	2	$\mathbf{f = \sqrt{\frac{3g-8}{5}}}$	$8 + 5f^2 = 3g,\ 5f^2 = 3g - 8,\ f^2 = \frac{3g-8}{5},\ f = \sqrt{\frac{3g-8}{5}}$ **(2 marks for correct answer, otherwise 1 mark for some correct working.)**
17. a	2	**36 cm**	Ratio of kites = 25 : 10 = 5 : 2. 1 part = 90 ÷ 5 = 18 cm. 2 × 18 = 36 cm. **(2 marks for correct answer, otherwise 1 mark for some correct working.)**
b	1	**120°**	Similar shapes have the same angles.
18. a	2	$\mathbf{2.5 \times 10^3}$	$5 \times 500 = 2500 = 2.5 \times 10^3$ **(2 marks for correct answer, otherwise 1 mark for 2500.)**
b	2	$\mathbf{2 \times 10^5}$	$(5 \times 10^8) \div (2.5 \times 10^3) = (5 \div 2.5) \times (10^8 \div 10^3) = 2 \times 10^{(8-3)} = 2 \times 10^5$ **(2 marks for correct answer, otherwise 1 mark for some correct working. Award marks for answer correctly calculated using incorrect answer to part a.)**

1B KS3 Levels 5-8 Calculator Allowed

Q	Marks	Correct answer	The bit in the middle tells you how to get to the answer	Useful tips
1. a	1	**1.175768662**		
b	1	**1.176**		*TIP: Remember — you need to use BODMAS to tell the calculator which order to do things in.*
c	1	**3.2**		
2. a	1	**Eight out of the twenty squares should be shaded.**	$\frac{4}{10} = \frac{8}{20}$	
b	1	**0.55**	22 out of 40 = 22 ÷ 40 = 0.55	
c	1	**62.5%**	40 out of 64, so (40 ÷ 64) × 100 = 62.5%	
3. a	2		**(2 marks for correct answer, otherwise 1 mark for at least 2 squares shaded correctly.)**	
b	2	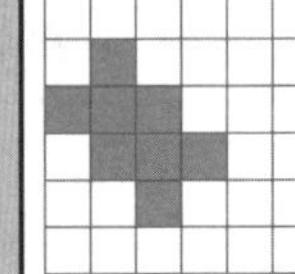 or 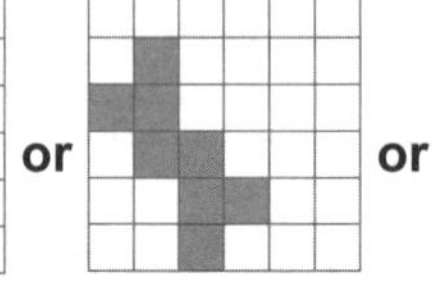 or or	**(2 marks for correct answer, otherwise 1 mark for at least 2 squares shaded correctly.)**	*TIP: When you've finished your pattern turn the page round through 360° and check that there are only two positions where it looks the same.*
4. a	1	$\frac{21}{40}$	There are 15 + 2 + 4 = 21 boys out of a total of 15 + 2 + 4 + 3 + 11 + 5 = 40 students.	
b	1	$\frac{9}{40}$	4 boys + 5 girls = 9 students play the keyboard out of a total of 40 students.	
c	1	$\frac{3}{18}$ or $\frac{1}{6}$	There are 3 girl guitarists out of a total of 15 boys + 3 girls = 18 students who play guitar.	
5. a	1	**£2.88**	36p × 8 = 288p = £2.88	
b	2	**Shop A by 9p**	At shop A it costs 36p × 18 = £6.48, at shop B it costs £2.19 × 3 = £6.57. £6.57 – £6.48 = 9p **(2 marks for correct working and answer, otherwise 1 mark for getting both £6.48 and £6.57.)**	
6.	2	**20 weeks**	105 – 77 = 28, 28 ÷ 1.4 = 20 weeks. **(2 marks for correct answer, otherwise 1 mark for some correct working.)**	
7. a	1	**2s + 4**		
b	1	**$11t^2 + 3t$**		
c	1	**$18u^2$**		
d	1	**$4v^2$**		
8. a	2	see table below	**(2 marks for all six correct values, otherwise 1 mark for at least three.)**	
b	1	**109.6 mph**	7125 ÷ 65 = 109.6 mph (to 1 d.p.)	

Table for 8. a:

Speed (s) in mph	frequency (f)	midpoint (x)	fx
$90 < s \leq 100$	12	95	1140
$100 < s \leq 110$	18	**105**	**1890**
$110 < s \leq 120$	28	**115**	**3220**
$120 < s \leq 130$	7	**125**	**875**
Total	65	-	7125

9.	4	**a = 50°, b = 40°, c = 200°, d = 70°**	a = 360° – 130° – 90° – 90° = 50°. b = 130° – 90° = 40°. c = 360° – 160° = 200°. d = 180° – 110° = 70°. **(1 mark for each correct angle.)** *TIP: These questions shouldn't cause any bother if you've learnt the angle rules.*
10. a	2	**£350**	£287 is 100% – 18% = 82% of the original price. 1% = 287 ÷ 82 = 3.5, so 100% = 3.5 × 100 = £350. **(2 marks for correct answer, otherwise 1 mark for some correct working.)**
b	2	**55%**	120 – 54 = 66 photos are discarded, $\frac{66}{120} \times 100 = 55\%$. **(2 marks for correct answer, otherwise 1 mark for some correct working.)**
11.	2	**339.3 cm³**	Volume = $\pi r^2 h = \pi \times 3^2 \times 12 = 339.3$ cm³ (to 1 d.p.) **(2 marks for correct answer, otherwise 1 mark for substituting correctly into the formula.)**
12.	2	**5.7 seconds**	Time = distance/speed, so the times are 40 ÷ 12.5 = 3.2 and 40 ÷ 16 = 2.5. 3.2 + 2.5 = 5.7 s. **(2 marks for correct answer, otherwise 1 mark for either 3.2 or 2.5.)**
13.	3	**24 newspapers**	Let x = number of newspapers delivered on Tuesday. So 3.5x + 30 = 114, 3.5x = 114 – 30 = 84, x = 24. **(3 marks for correct answer, otherwise 1 mark for correct equation and 1 mark for attempting to solve it.)**
14.	2	**$x^2 + 3x - 28$**	$(x + 7)(x - 4) = x^2 - 4x + 7x - 28 = x^2 + 3x - 28$. **(2 marks for correct answer, otherwise 1 mark for getting 2 out of 3 terms correct.)**

15. 4

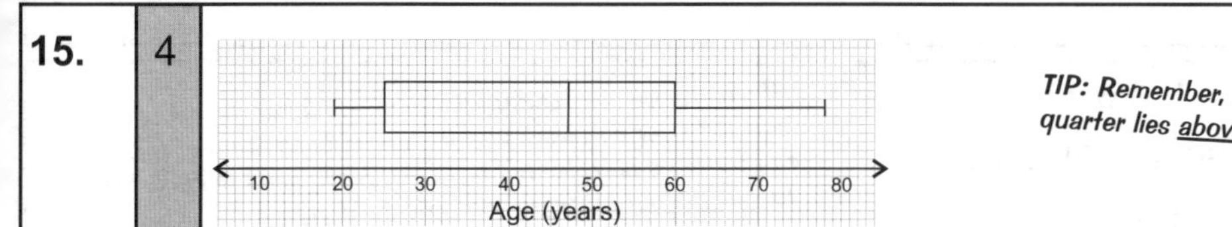

TIP: Remember, a quarter of data lies below the lower quartile, and a quarter lies above the upper quartile. So here the upper quartile is 60.

(4 marks for correct answer, otherwise 1 mark for drawing the box with correct median, 1 mark for either the upper or lower quartile correct and 1 mark for showing upper and lower ranges correctly.)

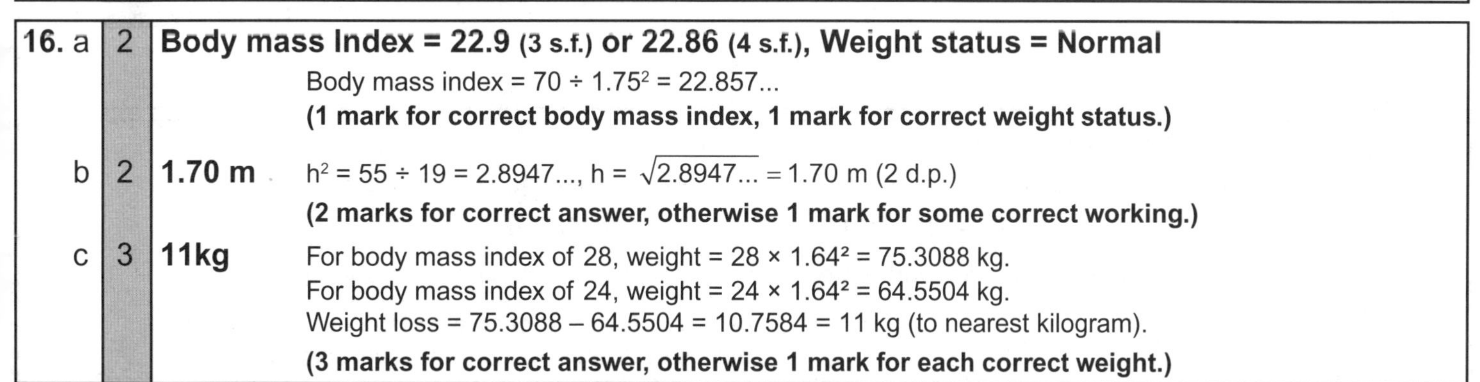

16. a	2	**Body mass Index = 22.9 (3 s.f.) or 22.86 (4 s.f.), Weight status = Normal**	Body mass index = 70 ÷ 1.75² = 22.857... **(1 mark for correct body mass index, 1 mark for correct weight status.)**
b	2	**1.70 m**	$h^2 = 55 \div 19 = 2.8947...$, $h = \sqrt{2.8947...} = 1.70$ m (2 d.p.) **(2 marks for correct answer, otherwise 1 mark for some correct working.)**
c	3	**11kg**	For body mass index of 28, weight = 28 × 1.64² = 75.3088 kg. For body mass index of 24, weight = 24 × 1.64² = 64.5504 kg. Weight loss = 75.3088 – 64.5504 = 10.7584 = 11 kg (to nearest kilogram). **(3 marks for correct answer, otherwise 1 mark for each correct weight.)**
17. a	2	**78 m**	$(AB)^2 = 30^2 + 72^2 = 900 + 5184 = 6084$, $AB = \sqrt{6084} = 78$ m **(2 marks for correct answer, otherwise 1 mark for some correct working.)**
b	2	**22.6°**	$a = \tan^{-1}\left(\frac{30}{72}\right) = 22.6°$ **(2 marks for correct answer, otherwise 1 mark for some correct working.)**
18. a	1	**0.4**	1 – 0.6 = 0.4
b	1	**12 days**	0.4 × 30 = 12
c	1	**0.216**	0.6 × 0.6 × 0.6 = 0.216

TIP: To work out the expected number of days you just multiply the probability for one day by the total number of days. Easy.

2A KS3 Levels 5-8 Calculator NOT Allowed

Q	Marks	Correct answer	The bit in the middle tells you how to get to the answer	Useful tips
1. a	1	**4/15**	There are four raspberry flavour out of a total of fifteen.	
b	1	**9/15 or 3/5**	There are nine sweets that are not blackberry out of fifteen.	
c	1	**Cannot tell**	**You don't know how many sweets are in his bag so you don't know if half of them is more or less than the five Debbie has.** **(Only award mark for "Cannot tell" and a correct explanation.)**	
2. a	3		To construct the triangle draw the base the correct length first. Use compasses set to 5 cm and 4 cm from each end of the base to draw arcs. Where the arcs cross gives the position for B. **(3 marks for correct answer, otherwise 2 marks for two sides the correct length, or 1 mark for one side the correct length.)**	
b	1	**40 – 43°**		
3.	2	**£115**	Use 50 as an estimate of the number of calculators and £2.30 as an estimate of the cost. So $2.30 \times 50 = 2.30 \times 10 \times 5 = 23 \times 5 =$ £115. **(2 marks for correct answer (also accept 2 × 50 = £100), otherwise 1 mark for evidence of sensible rounding.)**	
4. a	1	**£99**	$(7 \times 12) + 15 = 84 + 15 =$ £99	
b	2	**11 days**	Work backwards through the number machine: $147 - 15 = 132$, $132 \div 12 = 11$. **(2 marks for correct answer, otherwise 1 mark for some correct working.)**	
c	1	**The delivery charge**		
5. a	1	**x = 6**	$3x + 7 = 25$, $3x = 18$, $x = 18 \div 3 = 6$	*TIP: There are several different methods for solving equations. Trial and error can work well for simple ones like part (a). But for more complicated ones you really need to know how to multiply out brackets and collect like terms.*
b	1	**x = 9.5**	$4(x - 2) = 30$, $4x - 8 = 30$, $4x = 38$, $x = 9.5$	
c	1	**x = -4**	$2x - 9 = 5x + 3$, $-3x = 12$, $x = -4$	
6. a	1	**-5**		*TIP: Remember the rules for adding and subtracting negative numbers — "+ +" and "– –" mean add, but "+ –" means subtract.*
b	1	**-3**		
c	1	**4**		
d	1	**12**		
7. a	1	**144 cm³**	$6 \times 6 \times 4 = 144$ cm³	
b	2	**168 cm²**	Area of side faces = $6 \times 4 = 24$. Area of top and bottom faces = $6 \times 6 = 36$. Total surface area = $(4 \times 24) + (2 \times 36) = 96 + 72 = 168$ cm². **(2 marks for correct answer, otherwise 1 mark for some correct working.)**	
c	2	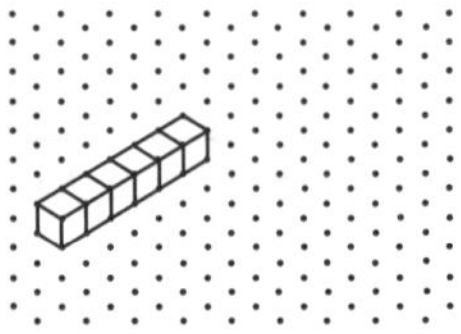 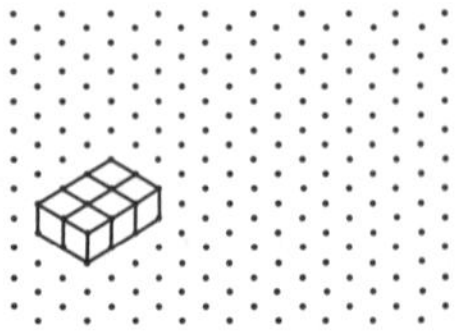 [cuboid drawing] OR [cuboid drawing]	**(2 marks for correct answer (the cuboids can be drawn in different positions), otherwise 1 mark for a cuboid with two dimensions correct.)**	*TIP: The easiest way to think about this is that the volume of a 2 cm cube is $2^3 = 8$ cm³. So to make a cuboid of volume 48 cm³, you need $48 \div 8 = 6$ cubes.*
8. a	1	**20%**	$3 + 5 + 2 = 10$, $(2 \div 10) \times 100 = 20\%$	
b	2	**30 geese, 12 swans**	18 ducks are 3 parts of the bird population, so 1 part is $18 \div 3 = 6$. Geese = $5 \times 6 = 30$, swans = $2 \times 6 = 12$ **(1 mark for each correct answer.)**	
9.	2	(see table below)	**(2 marks for correctly completed table, otherwise 1 mark for at least three correct values.)**	

	Theme Park	Seaside	Total
Boys	41	23	64
Girls	42	14	56
Total	83	37	120

10. a — 1 — **y = 2x** — Gradient = 2, y-intercept = 0

b — 1 — **(1 mark for an equation containing "-½x".)** — Gradient = -1 ÷ gradient of line through A and D = -½

c — 1 — **y = 6 – x** — Gradient = -1, y-intercept = 6

d — 1 — **(1 mark for an equation containing "-x".)** — Gradient = gradient of line through C and D = -1.

---

11. a — 1 — **50°F** — $F = \frac{9C}{5} + 32 = \frac{9 \times 10}{5} + 32 = 18 + 32 = 50°F$

b — 2 — **-4°F** — $F = \frac{9C}{5} + 32 = \frac{9 \times -20}{5} + 32 = -36 + 32 = -4°F$

TIP: When you're working things out without a calculator remember to simplify as much as possible. (9 × -20) ÷ 5 becomes a lot easier if you cancel the 5 first. Then it's just 9 × -4 which is -36.

(2 marks for correct answer, otherwise 1 mark for substituting -20 into formula but then making one error.)

c — 2 — $\mathbf{C = \frac{5(F - 32)}{9}}$ — $F = \frac{9C}{5} + 32,\ F - 32 = \frac{9C}{5},\ 5(F - 32) = 9C,\ C = \frac{5(F - 32)}{9}$

(2 marks for correct answer, otherwise 1 mark for completing the first step to get $F - 32 = \frac{9C}{5}$ **.)**

---

12. — 2 — **No. The numbers do not fit Pythagoras' Theorem. $6^2 = 36$ but $5^2 + 4^2 = 25 + 16 = 41$.**

(2 marks for No and correct explanation, otherwise 1 mark for showing use of Pythagoras' Theorem.)

---

13. — 2 — $\mathbf{x^2 + 9x + 20}$ — $(x + 5)(x + 4) = x^2 + 4x + 5x + 20 = x^2 + 9x + 20$

(2 marks for correct answer, otherwise 1 mark for an unsimplified expression with at least three terms correct.)

TIP: You'll have no trouble with these if you've learnt the foolproof FOIL method.

---

14. a — 2

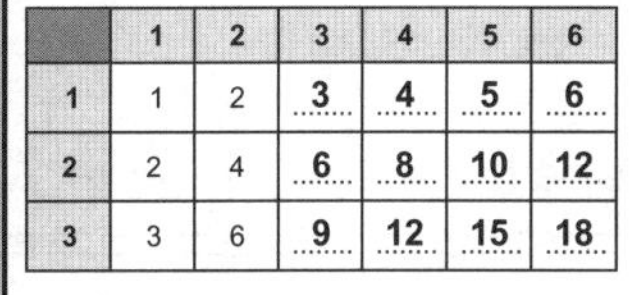

	1	2	3	4	5	6
1	1	2	3	4	5	6
2	2	4	6	8	10	12
3	3	6	9	12	15	18

(2 marks for all twelve correct values, otherwise 1 mark for at least six correct values.)

b — 1 — **6/18 or 1/3** — Six out of the eighteen scores are odd.

---

15. — 2 — **A = (-2, 0), B = (0, 8)** — At A y = 0, so $0 = x^3 + 8$, $x^3 = -8$, x = -2. At B x = 0, so y = 0 + 8 = 8.

(1 mark for each correct pair of coordinates.)

---

16. a — 1 — **14 cm**

b — 1 — **19 cm**

c — 1 — **5 cm** — 21 – 16 = 5

TIP: There's no excuse for dropping marks here — as long as you know what the different bits of a box plot mean, you can just read off the values.

d — 3

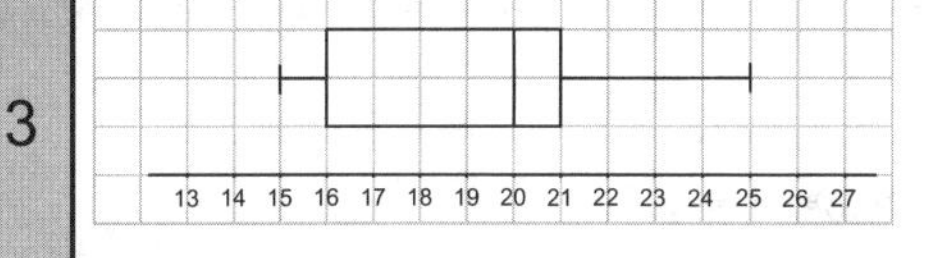

(3 marks for correct answer, otherwise 1 mark for correct median and 1 mark for both quartiles correct or for the correct range.)

---

17. a — 1 — **29030**

b — 2 — $\mathbf{2.462 \times 10^4}$ — $29030 - 4410 = 24620 = 2.462 \times 10^4$

(2 marks for correct answer, otherwise 1 mark for correct calculation but answer not in standard form.)

---

18. a — 1 — **y = 0** — Anything to the power 0 is 1.

b — 1 — **y = 4**

c — 1 — **y = 2** — $72 = y^3 \times 3^2,\ y^3 = 72 \div 9 = 8,\ \sqrt[3]{8} = 2$

TIP: Parts (b) and (c) look tricky, but don't panic — you can work them out by trial and error. Sub in values of y (1, 2, etc.) and you soon get the right answer.

2B KS3 Levels 5-8 Calculator Allowed

Q	Marks	Correct answer	The bit in the middle tells you how to get to the answer	Useful tips

1. a — 1
b — 1

TIP: With rotations, use tracing paper to help find the centre of rotation. With reflections, each point of the new shape should be exactly the same distance away from the mirror line as the corresponding point of the old shape.

2. — 3

Number of 5p coins	Number of 10p coins	Number of 20p coins
1	0	2
1	2	1
3	1	1
5	0	1
1	4	0
3	3	0
5	2	0
7	1	0
9	0	0

(3 marks for all eight different ways, otherwise 2 marks for five to seven ways or 1 mark for at least three ways.)

3. a — 1 — E.g. — 4/7 × 21 = 12 (shade any 12 squares)

b — 1 — E.g. — 0.3 × 20 = 6 (shade any 6 squares)

c — 1 — E.g. — 45/100 × 20 = 9 (shade any 9 squares)

TIP: Just count the number of squares and times by the proportion. Easy!

4. a — 1 — **35 minutes** — 52 – 17 = 35

b — 1 — **31 minutes** — order list: 17 26 31 43 52, middle number = 31.

c — 2 — E.g. **20 23 25 30 40** **(1 mark for a list with 25 as the median, 1 mark for a list with a range of 20.)**

5. a — 2 — **30** — 108 ÷ 9 = 12° per student. 360° ÷ 12 = 30
(2 marks for correct answer, otherwise 1 mark for some correct working.)

b — 1 — **Cannot tell**
A bigger proportion of 9A have dogs, but you don't know how many students are in 9B.
(Only award the mark for "Cannot tell" and a correct explanation.)

6. a — 2 — E.g. **(0, 7), (1, 6), (2, 5)**
(2 marks for three pairs that fit the rule, otherwise 1 mark for two pairs that fit the rule.)

b — 2

TIP: In part (a) you handily found three points on the line x + y = 7. So just plot them and join with a straight line.

(1 mark for plotting at least three correct points and 1 mark for joining them with a straight line.)

7. — 2

Keeping your compass setting the same, draw two arcs from each cross.
Draw a straight line between the two points where the arcs cross. This is the perpendicular bisector.
(2 marks for correct answer, otherwise 1 mark for drawing arcs (or circles) to give at least two points on the locus.)

8. a — 2 — **11.2%** — Increase in salary = £3600, (3600 ÷ 32 200) × 100 = 11.180... = 11.2% (1 d.p.).
(2 marks for correct answer, otherwise 1 mark for 3600.)

b — 2 — **£ 26 542** — 28 400 = 107%, so 1% = 28 400 ÷ 107 = 265.4205..., so 100% = 100 × 265.4205... = 26 542.05... = £26 542 (nearest £) **(2 marks for correct answer, otherwise 1 mark for some correct working.)**

Q	Marks	Answer	Working
9. a	1	**28**	$4 + 9 + 8 + 5 + 2 = 28$
b	3	**6 hours and 40 minutes**	Multiply all frequencies by the mid values of the groups: $(4 \times 1.5) + (9 \times 4.5) + (8 \times 7.5) + (5 \times 10.5) + (2 \times 13.5) = 186$, $186 \div 28 = 6.642...$ hours. $0.642...$ hours $\times 60 = 38.57...$ mins, so 6 hours 40 mins to the nearest 10 mins. **(3 marks for correct answer. Otherwise 2 marks for correct calculations but answer not rounded, or 1 mark for getting 186.)**
10. a	2	**10**	Circumference $= 2\pi r = 2\pi = 6.28...$ cm. $65 \div 6.28... = 10.34...$, so 10 complete revolutions. **(2 marks for correct answer, otherwise 1 mark for correctly finding circumference.)**
b	2	**3.14 cm²**	Area $= \pi r^2 = \pi \times 1^2 = 3.14$ cm² (3 s.f.) **(2 marks for correct answer, or 1 mark for using correct formula but with a calculation error.)**
c	3	**43**	Radius of real wheel $= \sqrt{(0.58 \div \pi)} = 0.429...$ m $= 0.43$ m (2 d.p.). Radius of toy wheel = 1 cm = 0.01 m. So scale factor $= 0.43 \div 0.01 = 43$. **(3 marks for correct answer, otherwise 1 mark for finding radius of real wheel and 1 mark for finding radius of toy wheel in same units as real wheel.)**
11. a	1	**18°**	$180° - 162° = 18°$
b	1	**20**	$360° \div 18° = 20$ sides. *TIP: Remember the rule: exterior angle = 360° ÷ no. of sides. So just rearrange to find the number of sides.*
12. a	1	**30.9 mph**	$\frac{18}{35} \times 60 = 30.9$ mph (3 s.f.)
b	1	**28.4 minutes**	$\frac{18}{38} \times 60 = 28.4$ minutes (3 s.f.) *TIP: Watch out with these. You need to multiply or divide by 60 to change the time from minutes into hours or vice versa.*
c	1	**16.7 miles**	$\frac{25}{60} \times 40 = 16.7$ miles (3 s.f.)
13. a	2	**x = 8.05 cm**	$x^2 = 3.4^2 + 7.3^2 = 64.85$, $\sqrt{64.85} = 8.05$ cm (3 s.f.) **(2 marks for correct answer, otherwise 1 mark for correct use of Pythagoras' theorem.)**
b	2	**x = 2.68 cm**	$x^2 = 6.3^2 - 5.7^2 = 7.2$, $\sqrt{7.2} = 2.68$ cm (3 s.f.) **(2 marks for correct answer, otherwise 1 mark for correct use of Pythagoras' theorem.)**
14. a	2	**195.4 cm³**	$V = \frac{4}{3} \times \pi \times 3.6^3 = 195.432... = 195$ cm³ (3 s.f.) **(2 marks for correct answer, otherwise 1 mark for correct substitution into formula.)**
b	2	**1.89 cm**	$r = \sqrt[3]{\frac{3V}{4\pi}} = \sqrt[3]{\frac{3 \times 28.3}{4\pi}} = \sqrt[3]{6.756} = 1.89$ cm (3 s.f.) **(2 marks for correct answer, otherwise 1 mark for correctly rearranging formula for r.)**
15. a	2	**a = 21.3°**	$\tan a = \frac{4.8}{12.3}$, $a = \tan^{-1}\left(\frac{4.8}{12.3}\right) = 21.317... = 21.3°$ (3 s.f.) **(2 marks for correct answer, otherwise 1 mark for use of tan.)**
b	2	**b = 2.60 cm**	$\sin 32° = b/4.9$, so $b = \sin 32° \times 4.9 = 2.596... = 2.60$ cm (3 s.f.) **(2 marks for correct answer, otherwise 1 mark for use of sin.)**
16. a	2	**3a + 2c = 31, 2a + 5c = 39**	**(1 mark for each equation.)**
b	2	**a = £7, c = £5**	To get 6a in both equations, multiply the first by 2 and the second by 3 to get $6a + 4c = 62$ and $6a + 15c = 117$. Now subtract the first from the second to get $11c = 55$ and so $c = 5$. $3a + 2c = 31$, so $3a = 21$ and $a = 7$. **(2 marks for correct working and answer, otherwise 1 mark for some correct working and either a or c.)**
17. a	2	**x = 4.8 cm, y = 8.75 cm**	From rectangle B, ratio of length and width is $8 \div 5 = 1.6$. $x = 3 \times 1.6 = 4.8$ cm and $y = 14 \div 1.6 = 8.75$ cm. **(1 mark for each correct length.)**
b	1	**12/35 or 0.34**	A is smaller than C so the scale factor is less than 1. $4.8 \div 14 = 48/140 = 12/35$ (or 0.34 (2 s.f.)). **(2 marks for correct answer, otherwise 1 mark for some correct working.)**

3A KS3 Levels 5-8 Calculator NOT Allowed

Q	Marks	Correct answer	The bit in the middle tells you how to get to the answer	Useful tips
1. a	1	**8 × 30 = 240, 8 × 7 = 56, 240 + 56 = 296**	**(or do a multiplication showing that a 5 must be carried).**	
b	2	**1184**	32 × 37 is 4 lots of 8 × 37, 4 × 296 is 4 × (300 – 4) = 1200 – 16 = 1184. **(2 marks for correct answer, otherwise 1 mark for saying that you need to find 4 lots of 296, or trying to do that multiplication sum.)**	
2. a	1	**d + 10**		
b	1	**k – 7**		
c	1	**3d**		
d	1	**3d – d = 2d**		
e	2	**2d – k**	The difference between their ages is d – k, so in d – k years time Katya will be David's age now. His age then is d + d – k, which is 2d – k. **(2 marks for correct answer, otherwise 1 mark for getting d – k.)**	
3. a	1	**$x \le 5$**	$3x + 2 \le 17$, so $3x \le 15$, so $x \le 15 \div 3 = 5$	*TIP: Put your answers back into the inequalities to check they work.*
b	1	**$y \le 2$**	$4 - 6y \ge -8$, so $-6y \ge -12$, so $6y \le 12$, so $y \le 2$	
4. a	2	**No — Because some multiples of 3 are even, e.g. 6.**	**(1 mark for saying no, and 1 mark for the correct explanation.)**	
b	2	**"It is a multiple of 3" and "It is divisible by 6" should be ticked.**	**(2 marks for correct answer, otherwise 1 mark for 1 correct and 1 wrong statement ticked.)**	
5. a	1	**11**	The number of grey crosses is one more than the pattern number.	
b	1	**20**	The number of white crosses is double the pattern number.	
c	1	**301**	101 grey + 200 white = 301 crosses altogether.	
6. a	1	**$\frac{12}{35}$**	$\frac{1}{7}+\frac{1}{5}=\frac{5}{35}+\frac{7}{35}=\frac{12}{35}$	*TIP: Don't always just times the two denominators — you're looking for the smallest number both denominators go into.*
b	1	**$\frac{4}{39}$**	$\frac{2}{13}-\frac{2}{39}=\frac{6}{39}-\frac{2}{39}=\frac{4}{39}$	
7.	3	**x = 2, y = 3**	Multiplying the 2nd equation by 6 gives 18x – 6y = 18. By adding this to the 1st equation you get 23x = 46, x = 46 ÷ 23 = 2. Substituting back gives (3 × 2) – y = 3, y = 6 – 3 = 3. **(1 mark for EITHER multiplying 2nd equation by 6 and attempting to add, OR multiplying the first equation by 3 and the second by 5, and attempting to subtract. 1 mark each for correct values of x and y found using an algebraic method. If no method shown, no marks.)**	
8. a	1	**Width = y cm, Length = 2x cm**		
b	2	The scale factor of the enlargement is new length ÷ old length = 2x ÷ y, or new width ÷ old width = y ÷ x, so $\frac{2x}{y}=\frac{y}{x}$.	**(2 marks for correct explanation, otherwise 1 mark for referring to scale factor of enlargement or use of ratios.)**	
c	1	**$y = \sqrt{2}x$**	Sophie is incorrect because she hasn't square rooted both sides of the equation correctly. $\frac{2x}{y}=\frac{y}{x}$, so $y^2 = 2x^2$, so $y=\sqrt{2x^2}=\sqrt{2}x$	

Q	Part	Marks	Answer
9.	a	1	**2 cm** $4\pi = \pi r^2$, $r^2 = 4$ so r = 2 cm
	b	2	Hypotenuse is the diameter = 4 cm. Using Pythagoras, $(\sqrt{8})^2 + AC^2 = 4^2$, so $AC^2 = 16 - 8 = 8$, so $AC = \sqrt{8}$. AC = BC, so the triangle is isosceles. **(1 mark for using Pythagoras and 1 mark for showing AC = $\sqrt{8}$.)**
	c	1	**4 cm²** ½ × base × height = ½ × $\sqrt{8}$ × $\sqrt{8}$ = 4 cm²
10.	a	1	**1. modal age, 2. median age, 3. mean age**
	b	1	**The mean is largest because it takes into account the ages of the adults, the others don't.** *TIP: You can see straight away that the modal age is 3. And the median must be either 3 or 4. A quick count up of the people gives 51 in total, so the median is 4.*
11.	a	1	$\mathbf{\frac{1}{8}}$ $\frac{3}{24} = \frac{1}{8}$
	b	3	**Small** Probability of small tin being peaches is 3/10, probability of large tin being peaches is 4/14 = 2/7. 2/7 = 20/70, 3/10 = 21/70. So probability is higher with small tin. **(1 mark for saying "small", 1 mark for 3/10 and 2/7, and 1 mark for showing 3/10 is larger.)**
12.	a	2	Angle PTQ is y because triangle PTQ is isosceles, so angle PQT is 180° – 2y. Angle PQT + x = 180°, so PQT = 180° – x. So 180° – 2y = 180° – x, -2y = -x, x = 2y. **(2 marks for correct explanation, otherwise 1 mark for getting angle PQT = 180° – 2y or 180° – x.)** *TIP: It's often a good idea to try and work out as many angles as you can. Then see what information you can use to answer the question.*
	b	2	**y = 30°** Angle TSQ = x as triangle TSQ is isosceles. Angle PTS = 90°. So using triangle PTS, 180° = 90° + y + x, 180° = 90° + y + 2y, 3y = 90°, y = 30°. **(2 marks for correct answer, otherwise 1 mark for some correct working.)** *TIP: Remember to use x = 2y from part (a).*
13.	a	1	**£20** 200 ÷ 10 = 20
	b	1	**£5** 2½% is 10% ÷ 4, 20 ÷ 4 = 5
	c	2	**£269.50** 10% = 22, 2½% = 5.50, so 22½% = 22 + 22 + 5.5 = 49.50. Total price = 220 + 49.50 = £269.50 **(2 marks for correct answer. otherwise 1 mark for finding 10% and 2½% correctly.)**
14.	a	2	**(x + 10)(x – 2)** **(2 marks for correct answer, otherwise 1 mark if the signs are the wrong way round.)**
	b	1	**(x + 10)(x – 10)** *TIP: Remember the handy rule — $a^2 - b^2 = (a + b)(a - b)$.*
15.		2	**2, 2, 3, 4, 9 or 2, 2, 3, 5, 8 or 2, 2, 3, 6, 7** **(2 marks for correct answer, otherwise 1 mark for 2, 2, 3 and two other numbers.)** *TIP: You need to narrow down the options. The list has to begin 2, 2, 3,... and a mean of 4 means the five numbers have to sum to 20.*
16.	a	2	**57 cm²** ½ × (12 + 7) × 6 = ½ × 6 × 19 = 3 × 19 = 57 cm² **(2 marks for correct answer, otherwise 1 mark for some correct working.)**
	b	2	**684 cm³** Cross-sectional area × depth = 57 × 12 = 684 cm³. **(2 marks for correct answer, otherwise 1 mark for attempting to multiply area by depth. Award marks for correctly calculated answer using incorrect value from part (a).)**
17.	a	1	**Negative correlation**
	b	2	**Intercept must be more than 20. Gradient must be negative.** **(1 mark for each correct reason.)**
18.	a	1	$\mathbf{5.02 \times 10^3}$
	b	2	$\mathbf{1.4 \times 10^{-2}}$ $a \times b = (3.5 \times 10^3) \times (4 \times 10^{-6}) = 14 \times 10^{-3} = 1.4 \times 10^{-2}$ **(2 marks for correct answer, otherwise 1 mark for getting 14×10^{-3}.)**

3B KS3 Levels 5-8 Calculator Allowed

Q	Marks	Correct answer	The bit in the middle tells you how to get to the answer	Useful tips
1. a	1	2		TIP: Careful with powers — in part (c) you only square the x, not the whole thing.
b	1	-10		
c	1	8		
2. a	2	**BestXchange**	BetaTravel gives 82 ÷ 60 = 1.366... euros for £1, or 60 ÷ 82 = £0.731... for 1 euro. BestXchange gives 100 ÷ 72 = 1.388... euros for £1, or 72 ÷ 100 = £0.72 for 1 euro. So BestXchange is better value. **(1 mark for correct calculation of either rate and 1 mark for correct answer.)**	
b	1	**138.89 euros**	$\frac{100}{72} \times 100 = 138.89$ euros	
3. a	1	**a = 65°**	PQR is an isosceles triangle, so a must be = 65°.	
b	1	**b = 65°**	b is the alternate angle to a and so must be the same.	
c	1	**c = 115°**	b + c = 180°, so c = 180° – 65° = 115°.	
d	1	**d = 45°**	Angles in triangle RQS add to 180°, 180° – a = 115°, so d = 180° – 115° – 20° = 45°.	
4. a	1	n^2	TIP: You need to recognise common sequences like square and cube numbers.	
b	1	$n^2 + 1$	Each term is 1 more than the square numbers.	
c	1	$3n^2$	Each term is three times the square numbers.	
d	1	$2n^2 + 1$	You get each number by doubling the square numbers and adding 1.	
5.	2	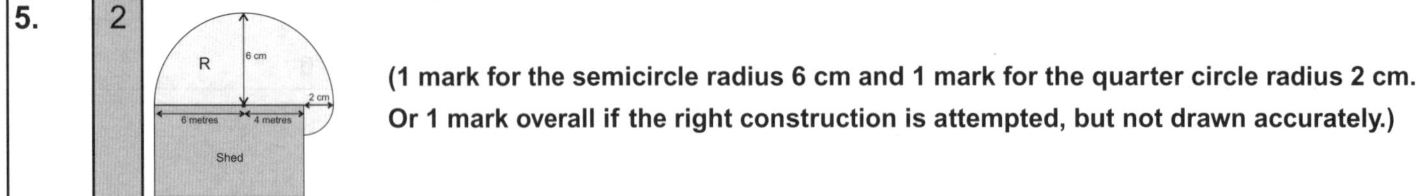	**(1 mark for the semicircle radius 6 cm and 1 mark for the quarter circle radius 2 cm. Or 1 mark overall if the right construction is attempted, but not drawn accurately.)**	
6. a	1	E.g. **y = 2x**, you can have y = 2x + or – anything.		
b	1	E.g. **y = 3x + 4**, you can have y = anything x + 4.		
c	2	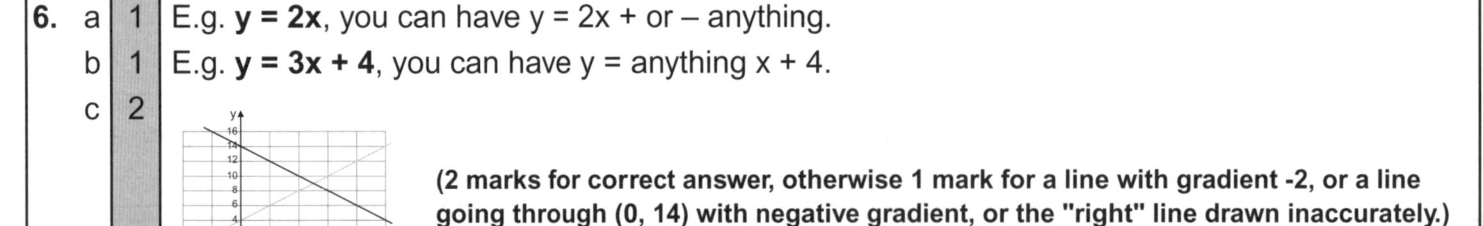	**(2 marks for correct answer, otherwise 1 mark for a line with gradient -2, or a line going through (0, 14) with negative gradient, or the "right" line drawn inaccurately.)**	
7.	3	$\frac{1}{4}$	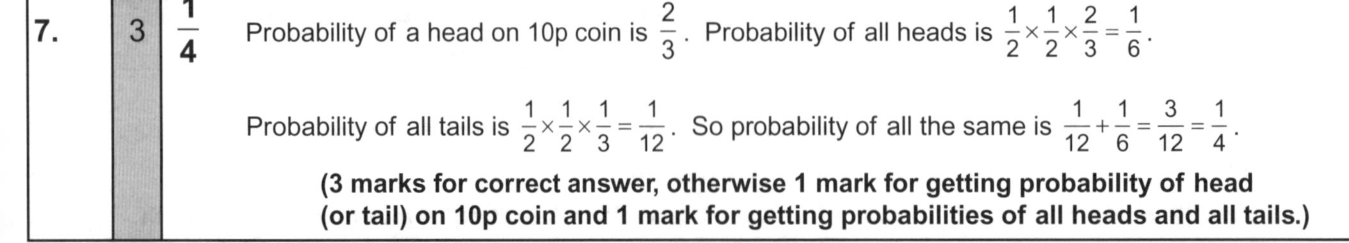 Probability of a head on 10p coin is $\frac{2}{3}$. Probability of all heads is $\frac{1}{2} \times \frac{1}{2} \times \frac{2}{3} = \frac{1}{6}$. Probability of all tails is $\frac{1}{2} \times \frac{1}{2} \times \frac{1}{3} = \frac{1}{12}$. So probability of all the same is $\frac{1}{12} + \frac{1}{6} = \frac{3}{12} = \frac{1}{4}$. **(3 marks for correct answer, otherwise 1 mark for getting probability of head (or tail) on 10p coin and 1 mark for getting probabilities of all heads and all tails.)**	
8.	2	**72 kg**	New weight is $\frac{17}{16}$ of old weight. $\frac{1}{16}$ of old weight is 76.5 ÷ 17 = 4.5 kg. Old weight is 4.5 × 16 = 72 kg. **(2 marks for correct answer, otherwise 1 mark for attempting to divide by 17 and multiply by 16.)**	
9.	2		Suppose ABC was a right-angle. EITHER: we would have BC = 9.3 × sin 30° = 4.65 cm, OR AC = 4.9 ÷ sin 30° = 9.8 cm. OR: angle BAC = $\sin^{-1}(4.9/9.3)$ = 31.79...°. But angle BAC = 30°, so angle ABC cannot be a right angle. **(2 marks for a correct explanation and calculation, or 1 mark for any attempt at relevant calculation without explanation.)**	

Q	Marks	Answer	Working
10. a	2	**$7x - 15$**	$3x - 9 - 6 + 4x = 7x - 15$ **(1 mark for correctly multiplying out without simplifying and 1 mark for simplification.)**
b	2	**$2x^2 - 7x + 3$**	$2x^2 - x - 6x + 3 = 2x^2 - 7x + 3$ **(1 mark for correctly multiplying out without simplifying and 1 mark for simplification.)**
11.	2	**134**	Billie eats (4 ÷ 7) × 70 = 40, Anjum eats (3 ÷ 5) × 40 = 24, Catie eats 70. 40 + 24 + 70 = 134. **(2 marks for correct answer, otherwise 1 mark for calculating either Anjum or Billie's total.)**
12. a	1	**0.15 m**	*TIP: Remember: 1 m = 1000 mm, so 1^2 m^2 = 1000^2 mm^2.*
b	1	**0.00015 m^2**	
c	1	**145 mm and 155 mm**	Lower bound = 150 – 5 = 145 mm. Upper bound = 150 + 5 = 155 mm.
13. a	1	**48**	57 – 9 = 48
b	1	**38**	16th value = 38
c	2	**19%**	40% of 60 is 24, 6 pupils got less than 24, (6 ÷ 31) × 100 = 19%. **(2 marks for correct answer, otherwise 1 mark if the retest mark is wrongly calculated, but the % of pupils is correct using the incorrect retest mark.)**
14. a	1	**Anna earns £6 per hour, David earns £8 per hour.**	Anna marks 3 papers per hour, 3 × 2 = £6. David marks 4 papers per hour, 4 × 2 = £8.
b	3		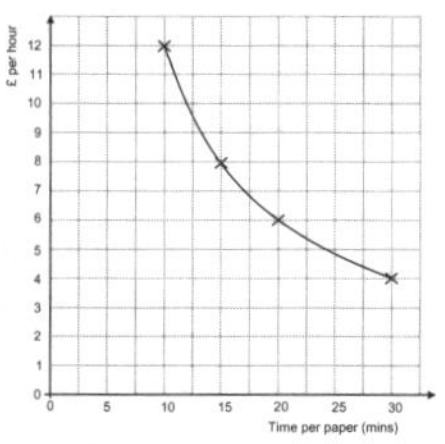 Some possible points include: (10, 12), (30, 4), (12.5, 9.6) and (22.5, 5.33). The first two are shown on the graph. **(1 mark for points plotted for David & Anna, 1 mark for at least 2 further points, 1 mark for smooth curve.)**
15. a	2	**Right** —	both of them get 20% of the questions right. **(1 mark for right and 1 mark for a suitable explanation.)**
b	2	**Wrong** —	sale price is 90% of original price. New price is 110% of sale price = 110% of 90% = 99%. So new price is not the same as original price. **(1 mark for wrong and 1 mark for a suitable explanation.)**
c	2	**Wrong** —	price in April is 120% of previous price. Price in May is 120% of price in April = 120% of 120% = 144%. That's a 44% rise in two months. **(1 mark for wrong and 1 mark for a suitable explanation.)**
16. a	1	**0.175**	Total no. of sixes = 42, total no. of throws = 240. Estimated probability = 42 ÷ 240 = 0.175.
b	1	**No, as this is only a little above $\frac{1}{6}$ (0.167) and this is close enough to $\frac{1}{6}$ to suggest that the paper is wrong.**	**(For 1 mark, must have comparison with 1/6.)**
17. a	1	**y = -½ or +½**	$y^2 = \frac{4}{16} = \frac{1}{4}$, $y = \pm\sqrt{\frac{1}{4}} = \pm\frac{1}{2}$
b	1	**No, because we'd need a number that when 4 was divided by it, gave zero.**	
c	2	**3 or -3 make the denominator zero, it is not possible to divide by zero. Cannot have numbers between -3 and 3 because they would give negative values for y^2.**	**(1 mark for each statement.)**
18.	2	E.g. Any two of: **r = 1, h = 36; r = 2, h = 9; r = 3, h = 4; r = 6, h = 1.**	**(1 mark for each correct set.)**
19.	2	**a = 2 cm, b = 4 cm**	Scale factor of enlargement = AD ÷ AE = 15 ÷ 12 = 1.25. AC = AB × 1.25 = 8 × 1.25 = 10, so a = 2 cm. BE = CD ÷ 1.25 = 5 ÷ 1.25 = 4, so b = 4 cm. **(1 mark for each correct value, otherwise 1 mark overall for some correct working.)**

1206 - 4784

1 KS3 Levels 5-8 Mental Mathematics Test 1 — Answers

1. 23 cm
2. 3 500 000
3. 360°
4. -7
5. $\frac{3}{5}$
6. E.g. $\frac{4}{6}$ or $\frac{6}{9}$ etc.
7. $6y^2$
8. 165.5 cm
9. 999
10. 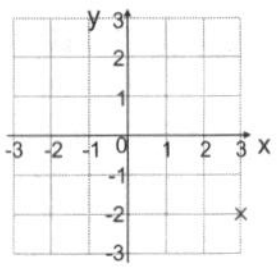
11. 0.35
12. 23
13. a + 10b
14. 114
15. 14
16. 1.21
17. 15%, $\frac{1}{4}$, 0.3
18. 1, -5
19. -1
20. 63 cm^2
21. 2×10^4
22. 21 miles
23. 35
24. 90
25. 97°
26. $y = 2x - 1$
27. 400 ml
28. £7
29. 48 cm
30. 6 & 14

Each answer = 1 mark

2 KS3 Levels 5-8 Mental Mathematics Test 2 — Answers

1. 7
2. 85°
3. 4
4. 140
5. 400
6. 3.03
7. 0.7
8. -3
9. 23.50
10. 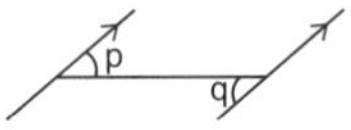
11. 70%
12. 14
13. 14
14. £17.50
15. median
16. 95 m
17. £59.97
18. 20 500
19. $x^2 - 3$
20. 2.2, 2.5
21. B
22. 50
23. 2.5×10^{-1}
24. £61.60
25. 300°
26. $\frac{4}{25}$
27. 100
28. 243 cm^2
29. £2.31
30. $\frac{4}{5}$

Each answer = 1 mark

3 KS3 Levels 5-8 Mental Mathematics Test 3 — Answers

1. 80
2. Volume
3. 120
4. 600
5. 5
6. 5.3
7. 35%
8. 105
9. 54
10. (-2, 2)
11. 36
12. 10°C
13. 16°
14. -8
15. Kite
16. 32
17. $x = 1$
18. 17
19. $\frac{1}{3}$
20. 270°
21. $5n + 2$
22. $7k^2$
23. 25
24. 50p
25. 25
26. 33
27. 60
28. 270 g
29. $\sqrt{20}$
30. $\frac{9}{16}$

Each answer = 1 mark

Science
EY STAGE
3
EVELS
5-7
RACTICE PAPER
1A

CGP

Key Stage 3

Science Test

Practice Paper 1A

Read this page, but don't open the booklet until your teacher says you can start. Write your name and school in the spaces below.

First Name ______________________

Last Name ______________________

School ______________________

Remember

- The test is one hour long.
- Make sure you have these things with you before you start: pen, pencil, rubber, ruler, angle measurer or protractor, calculator.
- The easier questions are at the start of the test.
- Try to answer all of the questions.
- Don't use any rough paper — write all your answers and working in this test paper.
- Check your work carefully before the end of the test.
- If you're not sure what to do, ask your teacher.

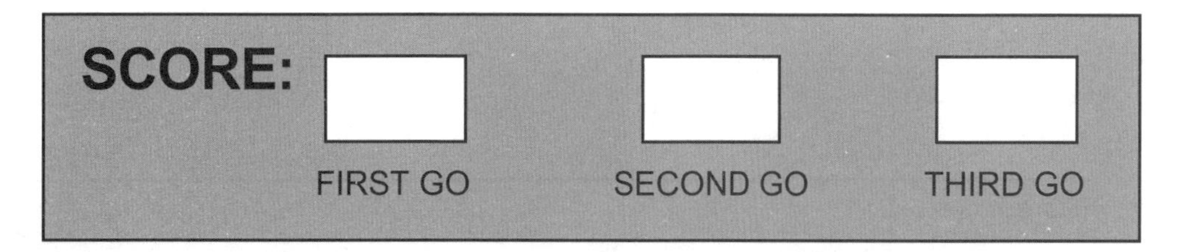

Exam Set SHGP31

1. Each of the organ systems listed below has one function.
Draw a line from each system to the correct function.
One function will be unused.

ORGAN SYSTEM	FUNCTION
	Transports substances such as food and oxygen around the body.
Immune	
	Replaces oxygen and removes carbon dioxide from the blood.
Reproductive	
	Produces sperm or egg cells.
Digestive	
	Helps protect the body against infections.
Circulatory	
	Breaks down complex food molecules and absorbs them.
Respiratory	
	Causes movement by contracting and relaxing.

1 mark

1 mark

1 mark

1 mark

1 mark

Maximum 5 marks

2. Peter is running in the 200 metre race on his school sports day.

(a) As he is running, Peter's muscles are transforming energy.
Which **two** of the statements below are true? Tick the correct boxes.

☐ Peter's muscles convert heat energy into movement energy.

☐ Peter's muscles convert chemical energy into movement energy.

☐ Peter's muscles convert movement energy into sound energy.

☐ Peter's muscles convert chemical energy into heat energy.

☐ Peter's muscles convert movement energy into chemical energy.

2 marks

(b) Peter's mum is standing next to the winning post.
She sees the smoke from the starting pistol before she hears the bang.
Explain why.

....

....

1 mark

(c) Peter's time for the race is 25 seconds.
Calculate his average speed. Remember to show your working.

....

....

2 marks

Maximum 5 marks

3. Tim is investigating how quickly a cup of tea cools down with different amounts of tea in the cup.

(a) What factor would Tim need to change as he carried out his investigation (the independent variable)?

.... 1 mark

(b) What factor would Tim need to measure as he carried out his investigation (the dependent variable)?

.... 1 mark

(c) Write down one factor Tim would need to keep the same to make his investigation a fair test.

....

.... 1 mark

Maximum 3 marks

4. The diagram shows the arrangement of particles in water as it changes state.

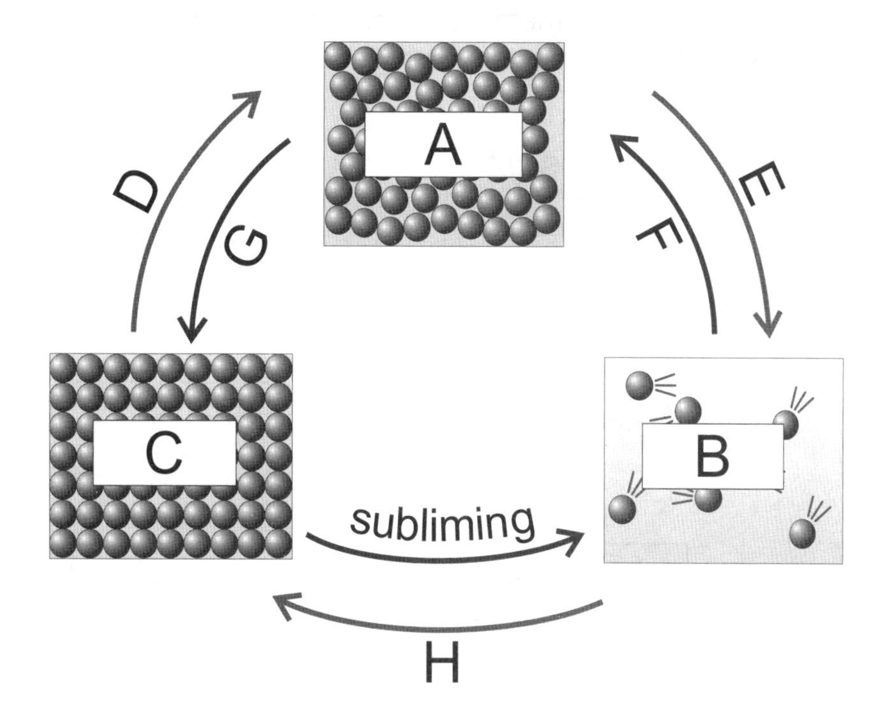

(a) Write the correct letter from the diagram next to each term below.

(i) Solid ....

(ii) Melting ....

(iii) Condensing ....

(iv) Liquid ....

(v) Freezing ....

(vi) Gas ....

(vii) Boiling ....

7 marks

(b) Give one change of state during which heat is given out.

....

1 mark

Maximum 8 marks

5. Some metals react with acids to produce metal salts and hydrogen gas.

(a) Draw lines to join each of the metal salts below with the metal and the acid that could have reacted to produce it.

METAL	**METAL SALT**	**ACID**
zinc	lead chloride	sulfuric acid
iron	zinc nitrate	hydrochloric acid
lead	iron sulfate	nitric acid

1 mark

1 mark

1 mark

(b) (i) What could you do to determine the pH of an acid?

....

1 mark

(ii) What would be observed in this pH test?

....

1 mark

(c) In a reaction between a metal and an acid, which reactant does the hydrogen gas that is produced come from?

....

1 mark

Maximum 6 marks

6. The diagram below shows a plant cell.

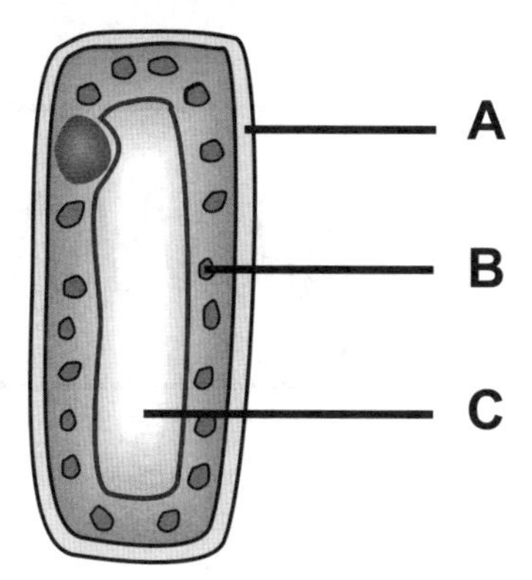

(a) Give the correct names for the structures labelled on the diagram.

A ....

B ....

C ....

3 marks

(b) What is the function of structure A?

....

1 mark

(c) Sarah was looking at the root cells of a plant under the microscope.
Why did the cells have no structures like structure B?

....

....

2 marks

Maximum 6 marks

7. Some pupils connected a microphone to an oscilloscope. They monitored the shape of the signals produced when someone sang into the microphone.

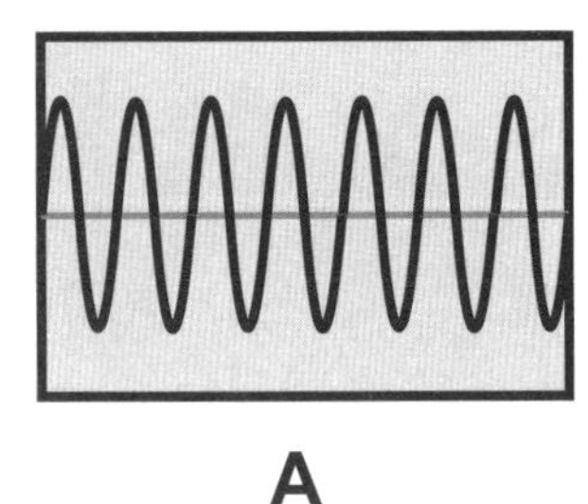

A

B

C

D

(a) Which of the wave patterns above, **A**, **B**, **C** or **D**, would be produced when the singer sang:

A quiet high note? ....

A quiet low note? ....

A loud high note? ....

A loud low note? ....

4 marks

(b) One of the pupils blows a dog whistle into the microphone.
A wave pattern appears on the screen, but no one can hear the whistle.
Explain why no one can hear the sound from the dog whistle.

....

....

1 mark

Maximum 5 marks

8. Use some of the words and chemical formulas in the box to complete the following passage about industrial pollution.

HCl	$CaCO_3$	HNO_3	increased	reduced	H_2SO_4

Acid rain from industrial pollution contains dilute sulfuric acid (which has

the formula ....) and dilute nitric acid (which has the formula

..........................).

Lakes can become contaminated with acid rain, which causes their pH to

be .... The pH can be ....

by neutralising the acid in the water with crushed calcium carbonate

(which has the formula ....).

5 marks

Maximum 5 marks

---

9. All cigarette packets sold in Britain are now printed with a government health warning.

(a) The following chemicals are all inhaled by smokers.
For each one, describe the health problems it causes.

(i) Nicotine

....

1 mark

(ii) Tar

....

1 mark

(iii) Carbon monoxide

....

1 mark

Continued over the page

The table below shows the percentages of low birth weight babies who had mothers who smoked during pregnancy.

Baby's mass at birth (kg)	2.25 or less	2.26 – 2.70	2.71 – 3.15	3.16 – 3.60	3.61 – 4.05	over 4.05
% of mothers who smoked	50	42	36	29	21	20

(b) Plot this information as a bar chart below.

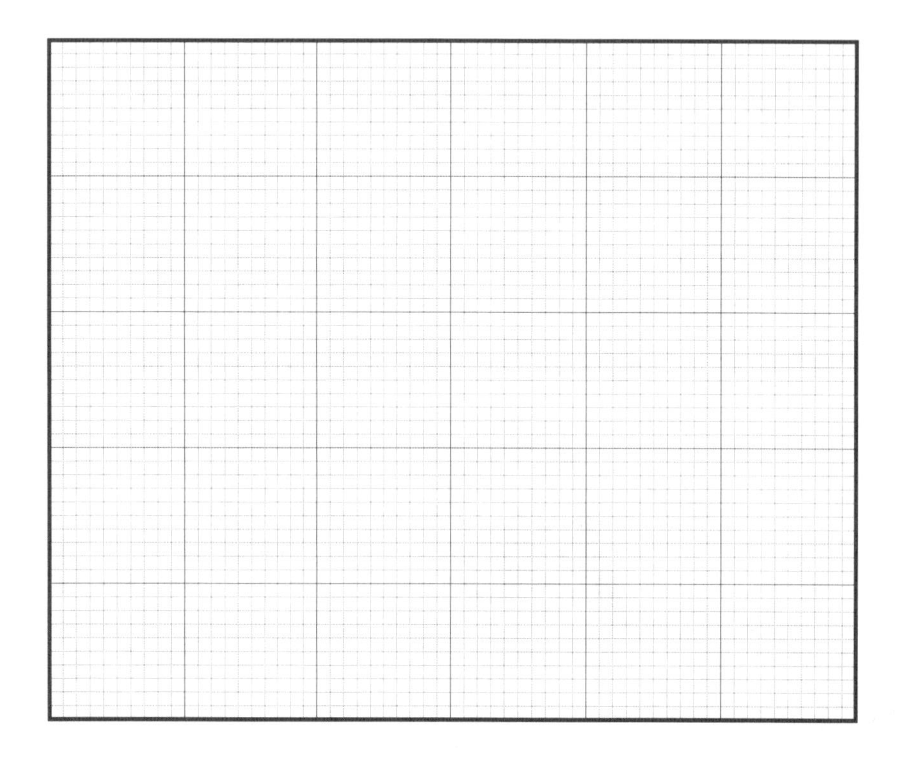

3 marks

(c) Low birth weight has been linked with health problems in babies. Use your bar chart to suggest why women are advised not to smoke while they are pregnant.

....

....

1 mark

Maximum 7 marks

10. A starship reaches a distant star and discovers five planets orbiting it.

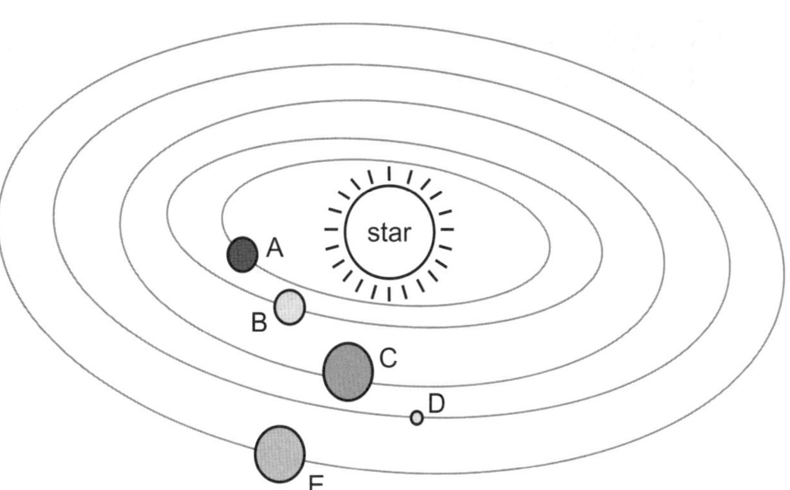

Here is some information about the planets.

Planet	Diameter (km)	Mass (compared with Earth)	Distance from star (km)	Time taken to orbit star (Earth years)
A	8000	1.2	60 million	0.6
B	10 000	0.9	150 million	1.1
C	20 000	15	225 million	1.5
D	2000	2.0	350 million	1.9
E	18 000	20	780 million	3.5

(a) Which planet will have the hottest surface temperature? ....

Explain your answer.

....

2 marks

(b) Which planet will have the strongest gravitational field ? ....

Explain your answer.

....

2 marks

Maximum 4 marks

11. Camels are adapted in various ways for life in their desert habitats.

Explain how the following adaptations are useful for the camel.

(a) Flat, splayed feet.

....

....

1 mark

(b) One or two humps for storing fat.

....

....

1 mark

(c) Long eyelashes.

....

....

1 mark

(d) Tough, leathery mouth.

....

....

1 mark

Maximum 4 marks

12. Stefan held a piece of magnesium ribbon with tongs and placed it in a hot Bunsen flame. He saw it burn with a bright flame and produce a white ash.

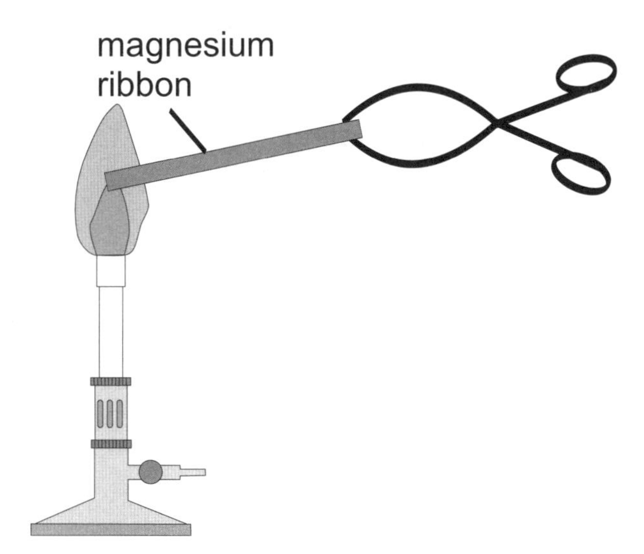

(a) Write down one observation that showed that a chemical reaction had taken place.

....

1 mark

(b) What is the chemical name for the white ash produced?

....

1 mark

(c) Write a word equation for the chemical reaction that took place.

....

1 mark

Maximum 3 marks

13. The diagram shows a fractional distillation column used in a laboratory to separate crude oil into its different parts (called fractions).

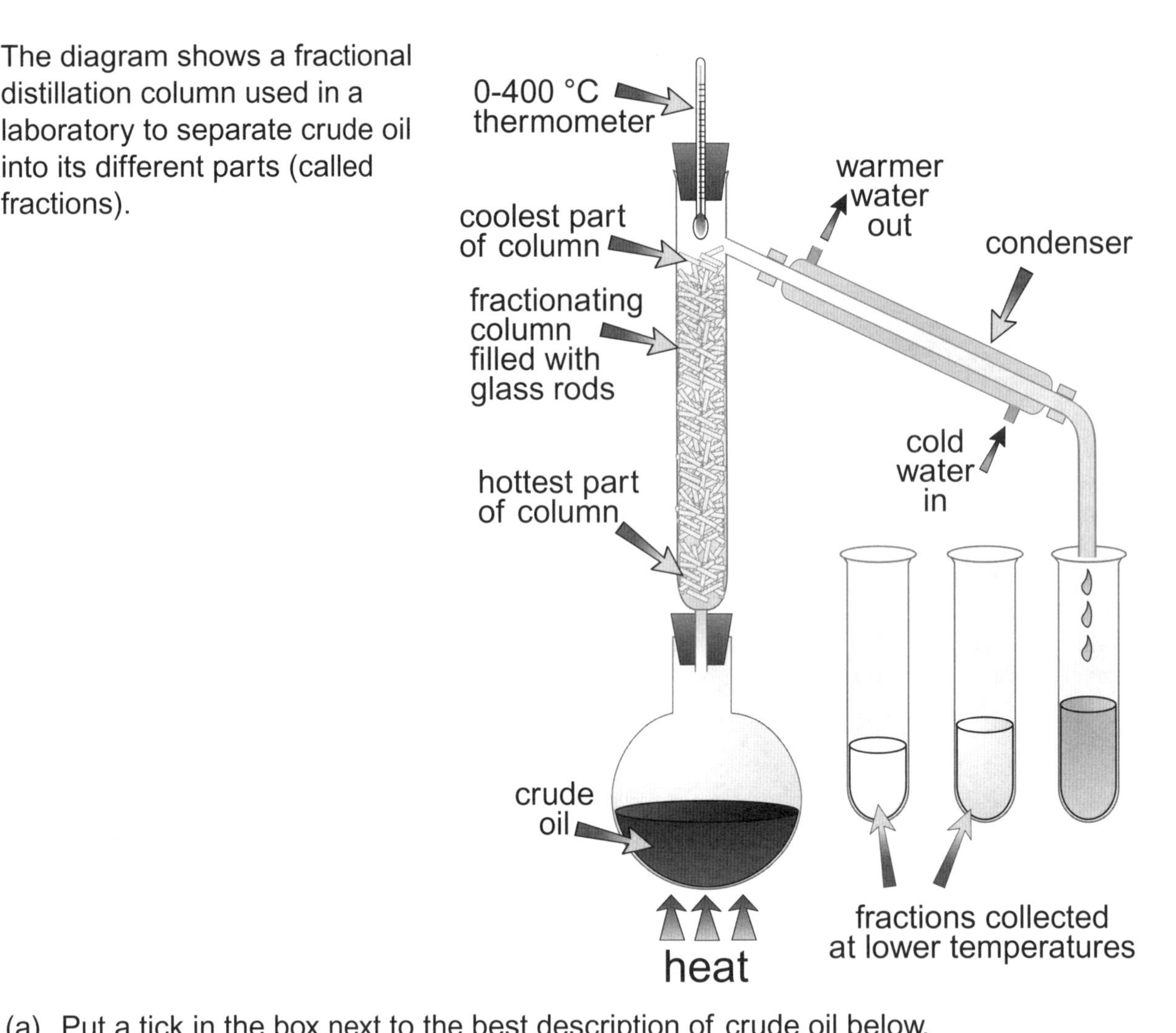

(a) Put a tick in the box next to the best description of crude oil below.

☐ A pure element ☐ A pure compound

☐ A mixture of elements ☐ A mixture of compounds

1 mark

(b) The fraction being collected in the diagram is a substance called naphtha.

(i) What physical state is naphtha in while it's in the fractionating column?

....

1 mark

(ii) Explain how the condenser works to cause the naphtha to change state.

....

1 mark

Maximum 3 marks

14. Shahana set up the following experiment to investigate the effect of light intensity on photosynthesis. Her results are shown in the table.

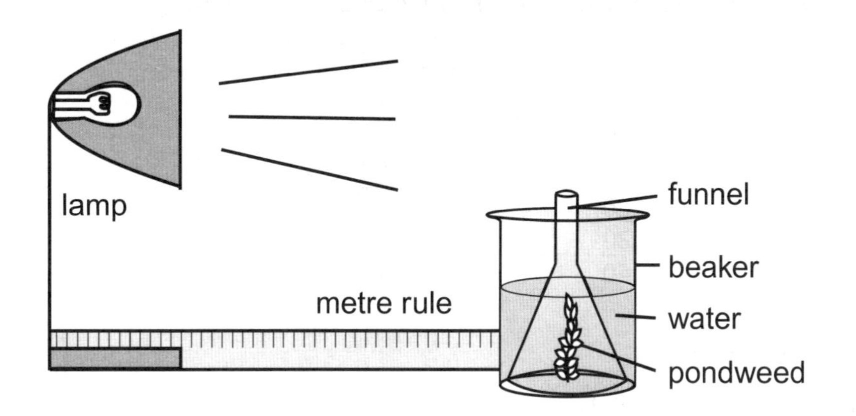

Distance of lamp from beaker (cm)	Number of bubbles produced by pondweed in 1 minute
100	2
80	5
60	9
40	20
20	39

(a) Plot the results of this experiment on the axes below.
Draw a smooth curve through the points and label the axes.

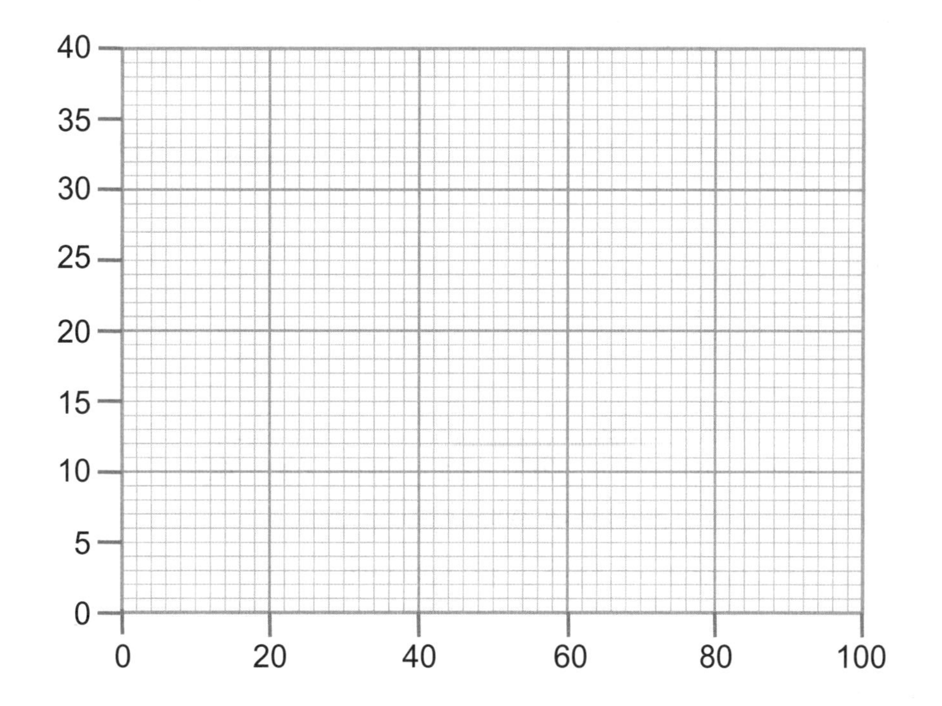

3 marks

(b) What conclusions could Shahana draw from her results?

....

....

2 marks

Maximum 5 marks

15. Jeremy used the following circuit to investigate the resistance of different lengths of wire. For each different length of wire, he measured the voltage and the current and used these to calculate the resistance. His results are shown in the table.

Different lengths of wire
Ammeter
Voltmeter

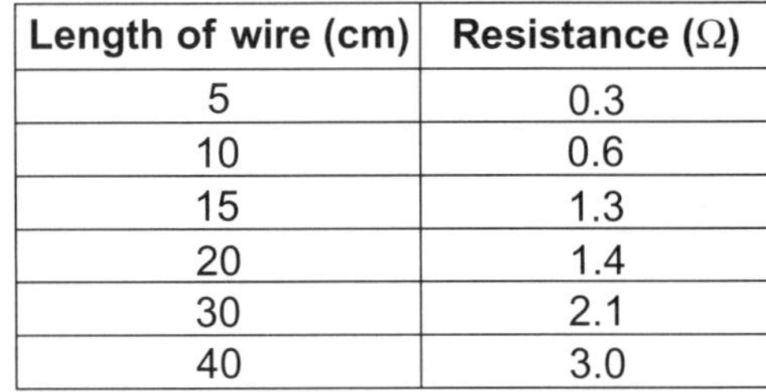

Length of wire (cm)	Resistance (Ω)
5	0.3
10	0.6
15	1.3
20	1.4
30	2.1
40	3.0

(a) (i) Plot the results on the grid below.
The first three have been done for you. — 1 mark

(ii) Draw a line of best fit. — 1 mark

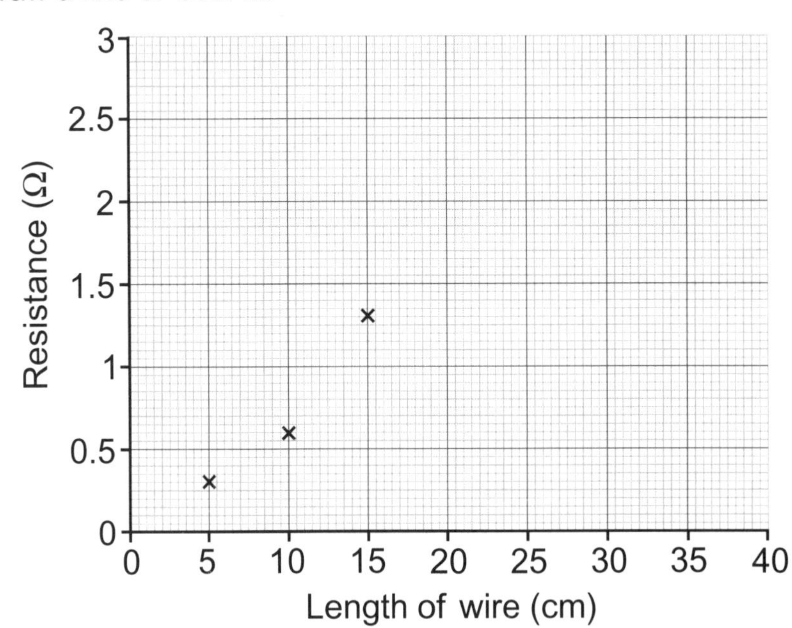

(b) One of Jeremy's results does not fit the overall pattern.
Circle this point on the graph. — 1 mark

(c) Use your graph to predict:

(i) the resistance of a wire that is 25 cm long. .... Ω — 1 mark

(ii) the length of a wire with the resistance 2.5 Ω. .... cm — 1 mark

(d) Describe the relationship between resistance and wire length.

.... — 1 mark

Maximum 6 marks

Science
KEY STAGE
3
LEVELS
5-7
PRACTICE PAPER
1B

CGP

Key Stage 3

Science Test

Practice Paper 1B

Read this page, but don't open the booklet until your teacher says you can start. Write your name and school in the spaces below.

First Name ______________________________

Last Name ______________________________

School ______________________________

Remember

- The test is one hour long.
- Make sure you have these things with you before you start: pen, pencil, rubber, ruler, angle measurer or protractor, calculator.
- The easier questions are at the start of the test.
- Try to answer all of the questions.
- Don't use any rough paper — write all your answers and working in this test paper.
- Check your work carefully before the end of the test.
- If you're not sure what to do, ask your teacher.

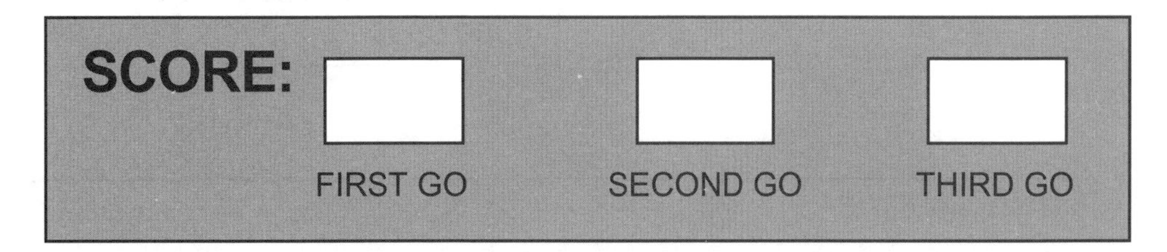

Exam Set SHGP31

1. Neil is making syrup by dissolving sugar in water in a beaker.

(a) Identify the solvent, solution and solute.

(i) Solvent ....

(ii) Solution ....

(iii) Solute ....

3 marks

(b) Suggest one thing Neil could do to the mixture to get more sugar to dissolve.

....

1 mark

Maximum 4 marks

2. Draw lines to match the parts of the body with the function they carry out in human digestion.

Parts of the body	Functions
Small intestine	absorbs the water from the food waste.
Stomach	absorbs nutrients into the bloodstream.
Teeth	churns up food and mixes it with acid and enzymes.
Large intestine	moves food to the next part of the digestive system by peristalsis.
Gullet	stores waste water.
	grind up food and mix it with saliva.

5 marks

Maximum 5 marks

3. The particles that make up various substances are shown below.

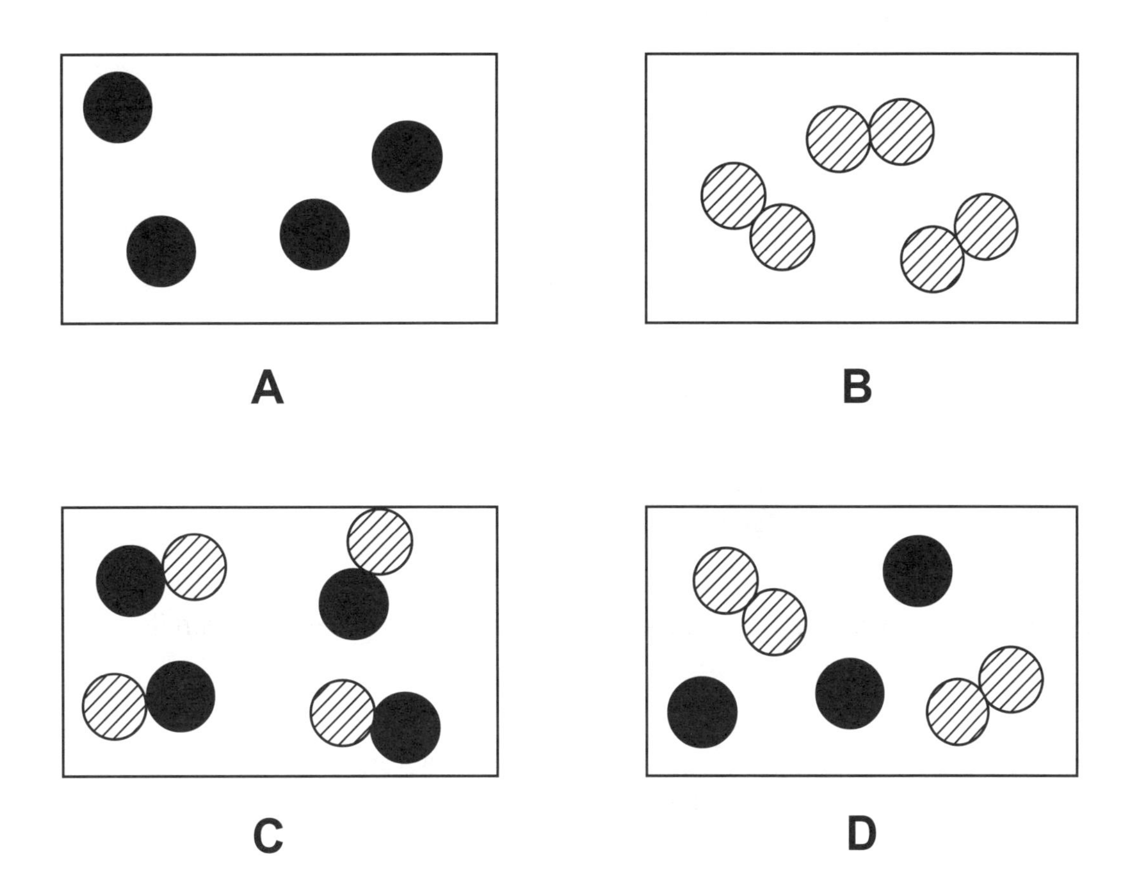

Complete the table by writing the letter of each diagram opposite its correct description.

Description	Letter
An element made up of molecules	
Molecules in a compound	
A mixture of different elements	
An element made up of atoms	

3 marks

Maximum 3 marks

4. Sophie and Colin make a seesaw from a plank and a log they found in the woods.

The seesaw won't work properly because Colin is unable to lift Sophie with it.

(a) Colin has a mass of 60 kg. What is his weight in newtons?
(On Earth, a mass of 1 kg weighs 10 N.)

....

1 mark

(b) What can you say about Sophie's weight compared with Colin's?

....

1 mark

(c) Write down two things they could do to get the seesaw to work properly.

1. ....

2. ....

2 marks

(d) Describe a simple laboratory experiment that they could carry out to investigate the two things suggested in part (c). You may use diagrams to illustrate your answer.

2 marks

Maximum 6 marks

5. The levels of various gases in the atmosphere vary over time, partly due to the action of green plants. During the day plants photosynthesise. Photosynthesis can be represented by the following equation:

$$\textbf{gas B} + \textbf{water} \xrightarrow[\text{CHLOROPHYLL}]{\text{LIGHT}} \textbf{glucose} + \textbf{gas A}$$

(a) Name gas A and gas B.

Gas A ....

Gas B ....

2 marks

At night photosynthesis stops but plants still carry out another chemical reaction which affects the levels of the two gases.

(b) What is the name of this reaction?

....

1 mark

(c) Write down the word equation for this reaction.

....

1 mark

Maximum 4 marks

6. The symbol equation for the reaction between calcium carbonate and sulfuric acid is:

$$CaCO_3 + H_2SO_4 \rightarrow CaSO_4 + H_2O + CO_2$$

(a) Write down the word equation for the reaction.

....

.... ☐ 2 marks

(b) Calcium carbonate neutralises acids but is not soluble in water.
Tick the box next to the statement that best describes calcium carbonate.

☐ An acid ☐ An alkali

☐ A base ☐ An oxide

☐ 1 mark

Maximum 3 marks

---

7. The body can defend itself against disease in a variety of ways.
Match up each defence to the correct description from those listed below.

DEFENCE

Defence	Description
Skin	Chemical that kills most microbes.
Mucus	Made up of white blood cells that engulf microbes or release antibodies.
Clotting of blood	Seals wounds quickly to prevent entry of microbes.
Stomach acid	Sticky substance that traps microbes in places like the nose and lungs.
Immune system	Forms a physical barrier to most microbes.
	Enzyme that kills bacteria.

☐ 1 mark
☐ 1 mark
☐ 1 mark
☐ 1 mark
☐ 1 mark

Maximum 5 marks

8. The diagram shows the rock cycle. Write the correct letter from the diagram next to each of the labels given below.

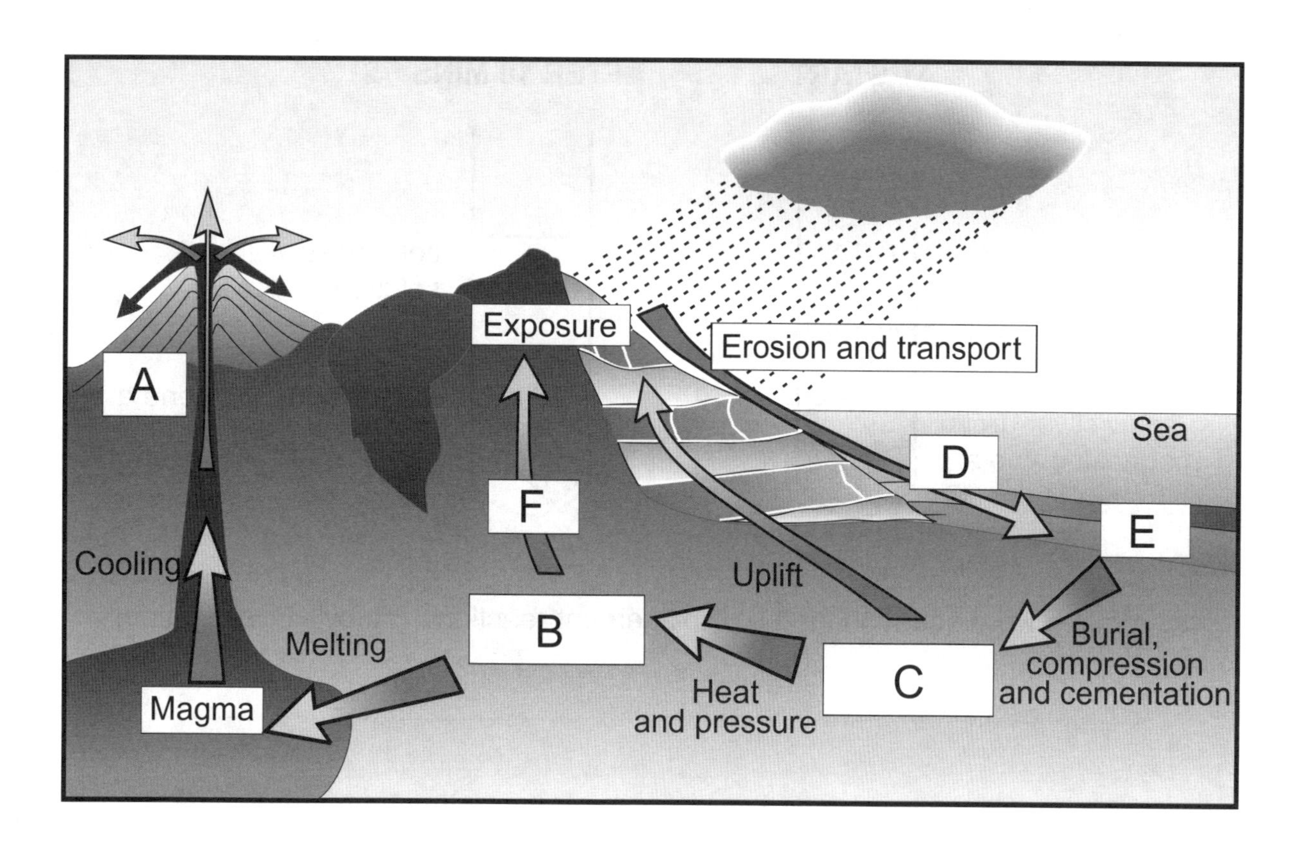

	Label	**Letter**
(a)	Metamorphic rocks	....
(b)	Igneous rocks	....
(c)	Deposition	....
(d)	Sediments	....
(e)	Sedimentary rocks	....

5 marks

Maximum 5 marks

9. Ruby is investigating displacement reactions.
The diagram shows her experiment and its results.

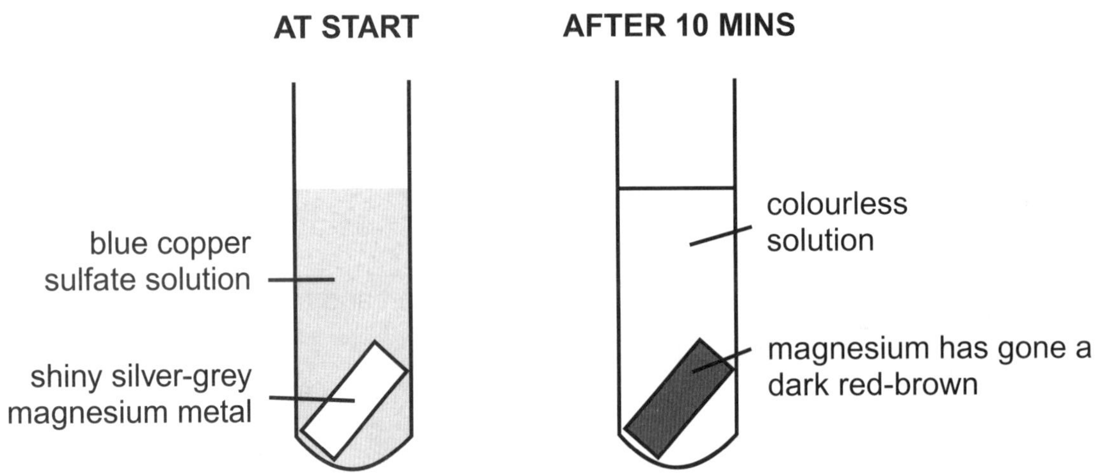

AT START	AFTER 10 MINS
blue copper sulfate solution	colourless solution
shiny silver-grey magnesium metal	magnesium has gone a dark red-brown

(a) Write a word equation for the displacement reaction in Ruby's investigation.

....

.... 2 marks

(b) Explain why this type of reaction is called a displacement reaction.

....

.... 1 mark

(c) Which of the two metals involved in the reaction was the more reactive?

.... 1 mark

Maximum 4 marks

10. Peter lives in England. He is talking on the telephone to his friend Manuel, who lives in Ecuador. Ecuador is a country which lies on the Earth's equator.

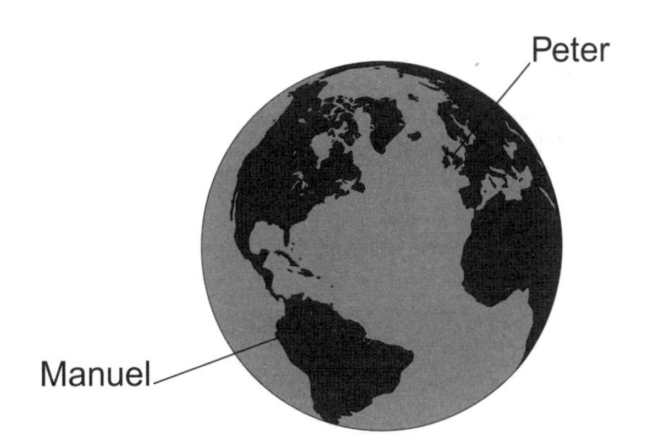

Peter says, "It's summer here. The days are eighteen hours long and it gets really hot — 25 °C sometimes."

Manuel says, "The days are always about twelve hours long here and the temperature often reaches 35 °C."

(a) When it's summer in England, why does England have longer days than Ecuador?

....

....

2 marks

(b) Explain why the shadow an object casts at midday in winter is longer than the shadow cast by the same object at midday in summer.

....

....

2 marks

Maximum 4 marks

11. Jill did an experiment to investigate how quickly marble chips dissolve in different concentrations of hydrochloric acid. As the reaction proceeded she recorded the mass of the beaker containing the reaction mixture at five minute intervals. The apparatus she used is shown below.

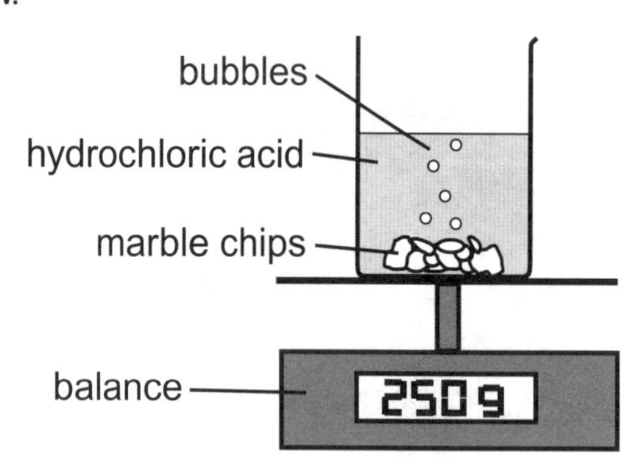

(a) What factor did Jill change as she carried out her investigation (the independent variable)?

....

1 mark

(b) Give two factors she should have kept the same to make it a fair test.

1. ....

2. ....

2 marks

(c) What could Jill do to make her results more reliable?

....

....

1 mark

(d) The table shows the results obtained from Jill's first experiment. She used 220 g of marble chips.

Time (mins)	Mass of beaker and contents (g)
0	250.0
5	245.0
10	242.0
15	240.5
20	239.5
25	239.5

(i) Draw a fully labelled graph to show these results on the grid below, joining the points with a smooth curve.

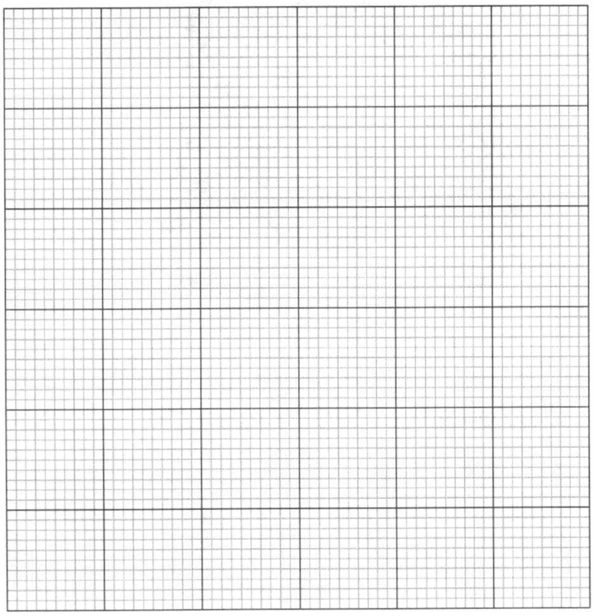

3 marks

(ii) Describe the trend shown by the results.

....

1 mark

(iii) The reaction stopped at one of the times listed below.
Tick the correct box.

☐ 14 minutes ☐ 18½ minutes

☐ 22½ minutes ☐ 25 minutes

1 mark

(iv) By how much did the mass of the beaker and its contents decrease in 25 minutes?

....

2 marks

Maximum 11 marks

12. At a theatre red, green and blue spotlights are used.
By mixing these, any other colour of lighting can be made.

(a) What name is given to colours that can be mixed to make any other colour?

....

1 mark

(b) An actress is wearing a yellow dress. However, when the red and blue spotlights shine on her, the dress appears red.

(i) Explain why the dress appears red when only the red and blue spotlights are shining on it.

....

....

2 marks

(ii) When only a red and a green spotlight are shining on it, the dress appears yellow. Explain why.

....

....

2 marks

(iii) Predict what colour the dress would look when all three lights are used.

....

1 mark

Maximum 6 marks

13. When Liam fell off his bike, he dislocated his shoulder. A doctor examined Liam's shoulder joint and the muscle surrounding it.

(a) What type of joint is the shoulder joint?

....

1 mark

(b) Muscles work in antagonistic pairs. What does this mean?

....

....

2 marks

The diagram shows the bones and muscles in the arm.

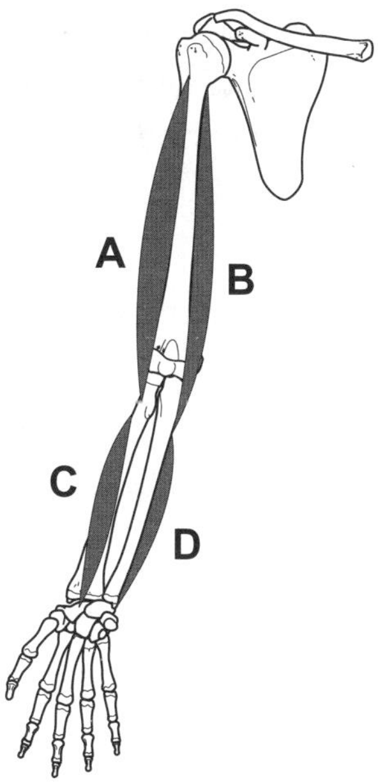

A
B
C
D

(c) Which of the muscles in the diagram, **A**, **B**, **C** or **D**, contracts to bend the arm at the elbow?

....

1 mark

Maximum 4 marks

14. The diagram shows an electromagnet used to control a device for locking a door.

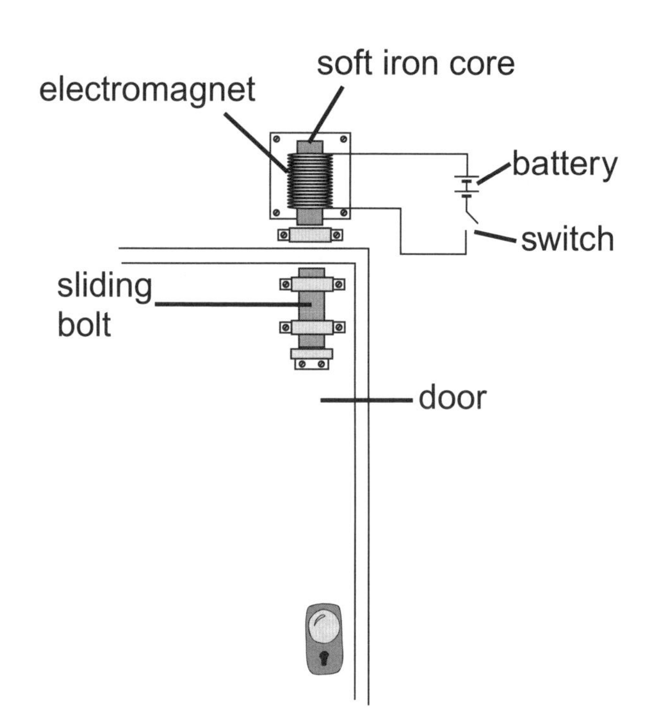

When the electromagnet is switched on, the door is locked.

When the electromagnet is switched off, the door is unlocked.

(a) The sliding bolt is made from a magnetic material.
Draw an arrow on the diagram to show which way the sliding bolt moves when the electromagnet is switched on.

1 mark

(b) What is the name of the force that moves the bolt when the electromagnet is switched **off**?

....

1 mark

(c) Suggest a material the bolt could be made from.

....

1 mark

(d) Write down one way of making the electromagnet stronger.

....

1 mark

Maximum 4 marks

15. Read the following description of a garden ecosystem and answer the questions that follow.

> The 'cabbage white' butterfly feeds on brassica plants. It shares this food source with slugs and snails, but the slugs and snails will also eat lettuce. Small birds like blue tits and thrushes eat the butterflies, slugs and snails. Cats eat the blue tits and the thrushes.

(a) Draw out the food web in the space provided.

3 marks

(b) Why is it harder to collect reliable data when working in the field than when working in the laboratory? Tick the correct box.

- ☐ It's hard to get a large enough sample.
- ☐ There are many variables that cannot be controlled when working in the field.
- ☐ Scientists cannot record their data properly when they work outdoors.

1 mark

Continued over the page

(c) Suggest a way that slugs and snails could be counted in a garden.

....

1 mark

(d) A gardener uses slug pellets to kill slugs and snails, to stop them eating his plants.

Describe and explain the effect you would expect this to have on the number of blue tits in the garden.

....

....

....

2 marks

Maximum 7 marks

cience

EY STAGE

3

EVELS

5-7

RACTICE PAPER

2A

Key Stage 3

Science Test

Practice Paper 2A

Read this page, but don't open the booklet until your teacher says you can start. Write your name and school in the spaces below.

First Name ______________________________

Last Name ______________________________

School ______________________________

Remember

- The test is one hour long.
- Make sure you have these things with you before you start: pen, pencil, rubber, ruler, angle measurer or protractor, calculator.
- The easier questions are at the start of the test.
- Try to answer all of the questions.
- Don't use any rough paper — write all your answers and working in this test paper.
- Check your work carefully before the end of the test.
- If you're not sure what to do, ask your teacher.

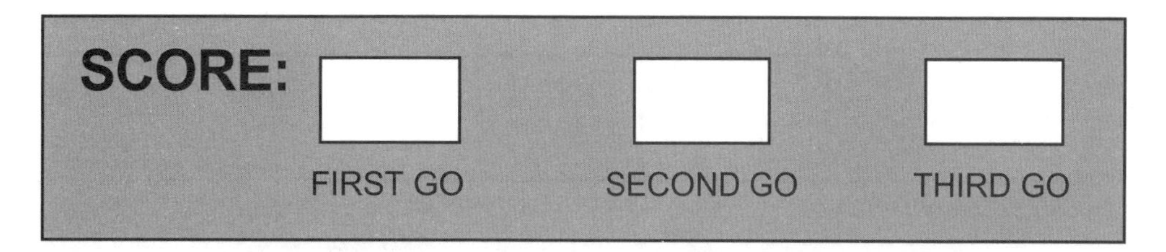

Exam Set SHGP31

1. Burning fossil fuels in vehicle engines produces exhaust gases and particles that are linked with environmental and health problems.

Draw lines to connect each exhaust gas or particle listed below to the environmental or health problem it is linked with.

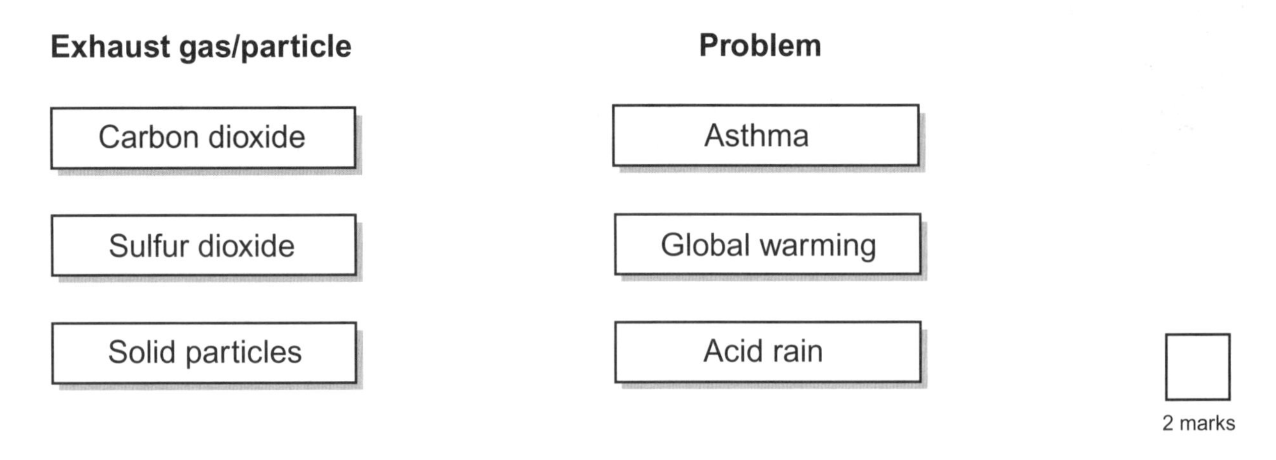

2 marks

Maximum 2 marks

2. The diagrams show laboratory tests used to identify three common gases.

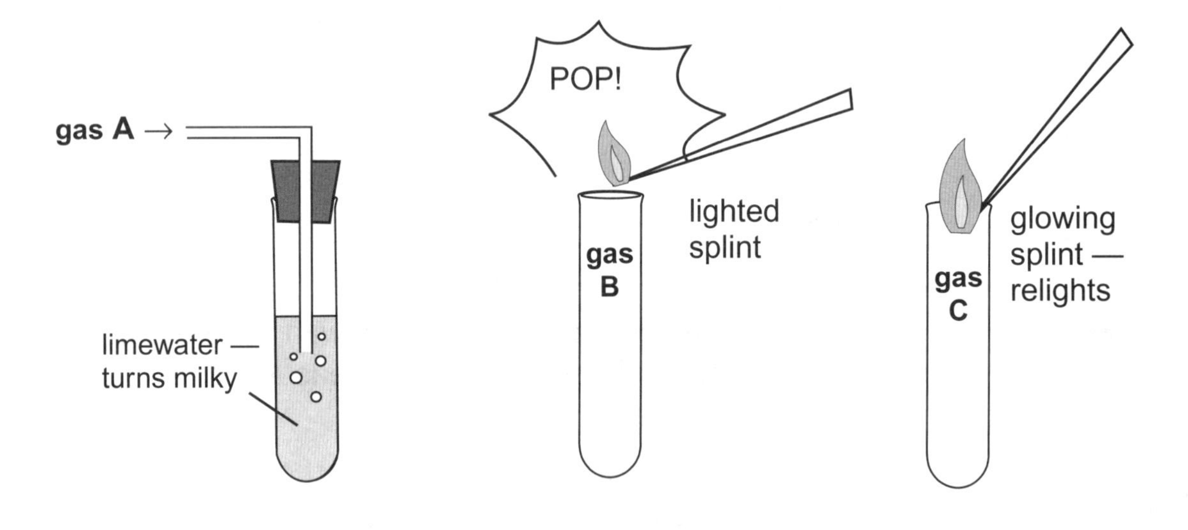

GAS	NAME
A	
B	
C	

3 marks

Maximum 3 marks

3. Marie is playing a note on her guitar.

(a) What difference would it make if she plucked the string harder?

....

1 mark

(b) Which two of the following describe a high note?
Tick the two correct boxes.

☐	High frequency	☐	Low frequency
☐	High amplitude	☐	Low amplitude
☐	High pitch	☐	Low pitch

2 marks

Maximum 3 marks

4. Tick the boxes to show whether each part of the body listed below is a cell, a tissue or an organ. The first one has been done for you.

	cell	**tissue**	**organ**
Stomach	☐	☐	✓
Muscle	☐	☐	☐
Heart	☐	☐	☐
Sperm	☐	☐	☐
Brain	☐	☐	☐
Neurone	☐	☐	☐

3 marks

Maximum 3 marks

5. Tina used the apparatus shown below to investigate how an electric heater heats up an aluminium block.

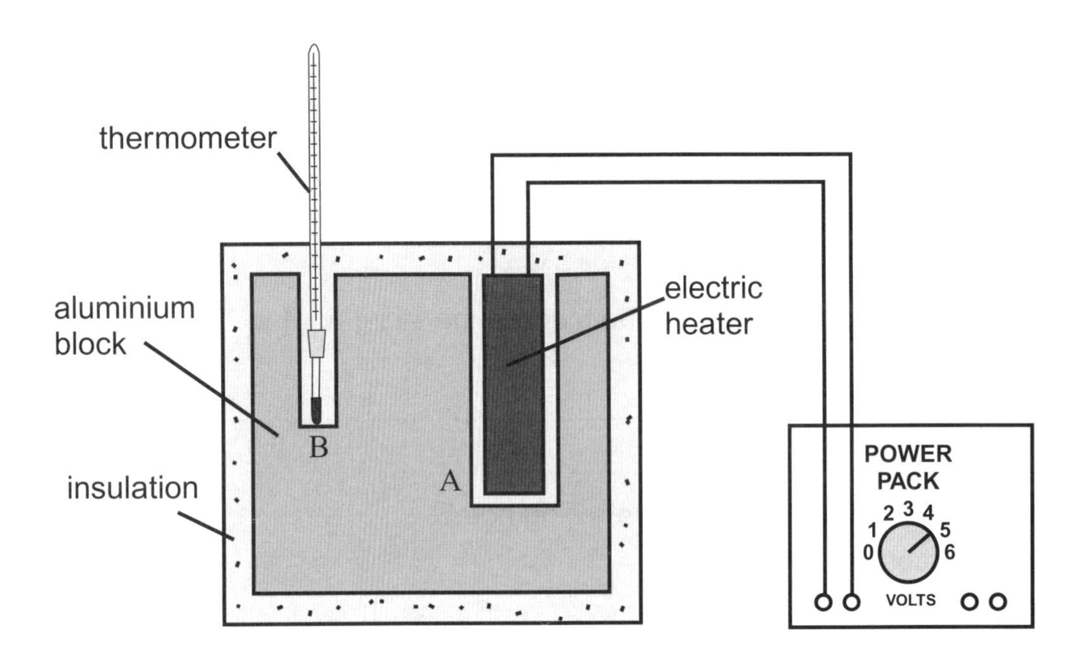

Here are her results:

Time (min)	Temperature (°C)
0	20
5	28
10	35
15	45
20	52
25	61
30	68

(a) What process causes heat from point A to reach point B?

....

1 mark

(b) Use these results to draw a graph on the grid over the page.

- Decide the scale for each axis and label them clearly.
- Plot the points.
- Draw a line of best fit.

Continued over the page

3 marks

(c) Tina predicts that all metals will heat up at the same rate.
Describe how she could test this prediction using the apparatus.

....

....

2 marks

(d) What was the temperature of the aluminium block at 22 minutes?

....

1 mark

(e) Give **one** reason why it is more useful to present the results as a line graph rather than a table?

1 mark

....

Maximum 8 marks

6. An ice cube was placed in a beaker of water and the temperature of the water was measured every minute for 30 minutes. The water was originally at room temperature.

The results are shown on the graph below.

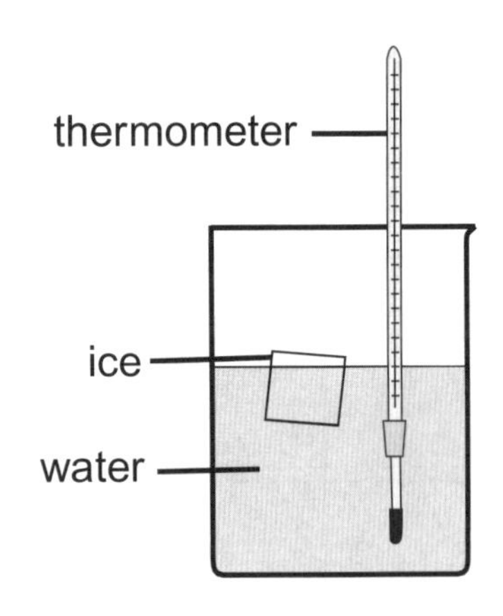

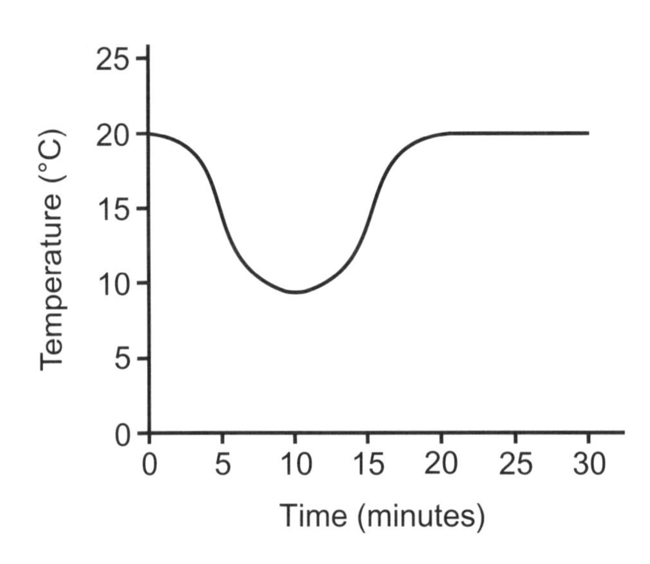

(a) What physical change do you think happened to the ice between 0 and 10 minutes?

....

1 mark

(b) How did the kinetic energy of the ice particles change during this time?

....

1 mark

(c) How did the kinetic energy of the water particles change during this time?

....

1 mark

(d) What was the minimum temperature reached by the water?

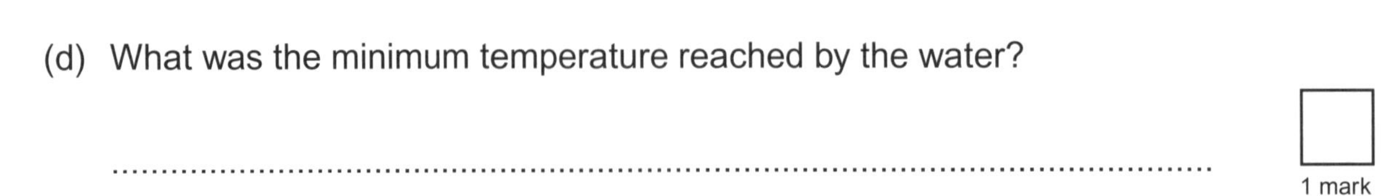

....

1 mark

(e) What was the room temperature during this experiment?

....

1 mark

Maximum 5 marks

7. Kath predicts that the boys in her Year 8 class will grow at a faster rate than the girls. She measured the height of the boys in her class, using a tape measure, on the 1st of every month for ten months. She then calculated an average height for each month. Kath also measured herself on the 1st of each month using a tape measure and compared her height to the average height of the boys. She recorded the heights to the nearest centimetre, and her results are shown in the graph below.

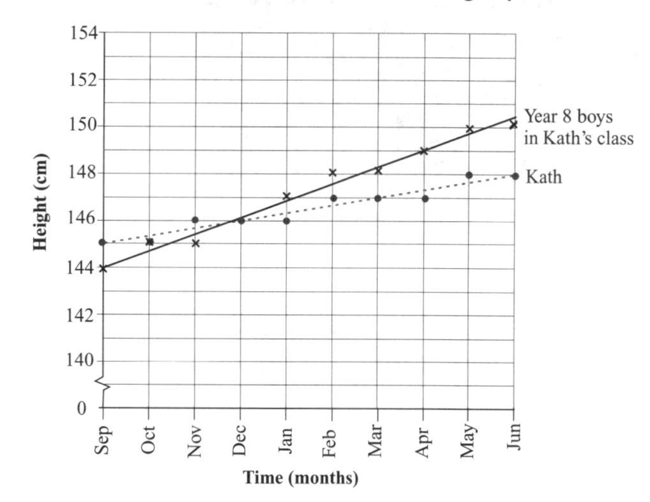

(a) What is the difference in height between Kath and the boys in March?

....

1 mark

(b) Suggest an improvement to Kath's method.

....

1 mark

(c) Does the graph show that all girls grow at a slower rate than boys during year 8? Explain your answer.

....

....

2 marks

(d) List two changes (other than an increase in height) that happen to boys and two changes that happen to girls during adolescence.

(i) Boys ....

....

2 marks

(ii) Girls ....

....

2 marks

Maximum 8 marks

8. Newlands School has a wind turbine for generating electricity.

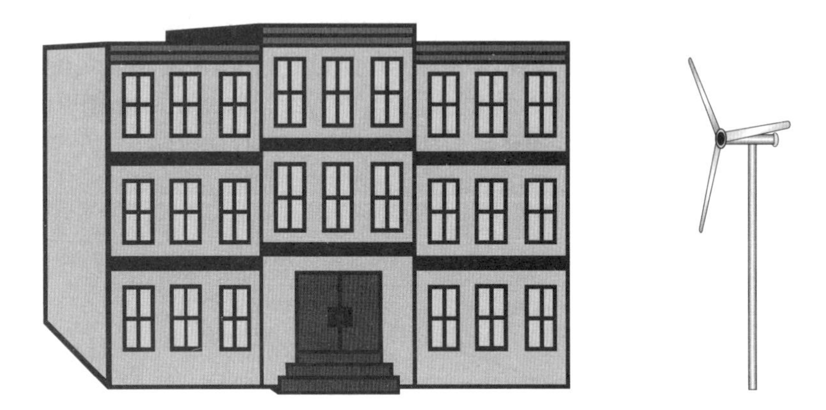

(a) Complete the sentence below to describe the useful energy change that happens when the wind turbine is generating electricity.

The wind turbine changes .... energy

into electrical energy for the school.

1 mark

(b) Write down one advantage of using a wind turbine to make electricity instead of using mains electricity.

....

1 mark

(c) Write down one disadvantage of using a wind turbine to make electricity instead of using mains electricity.

....

1 mark

(d) Electricity can also be created using coal, oil and gas.
What is the ultimate source of the energy that these resources contain?

....

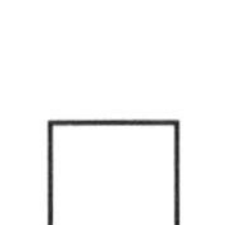

1 mark

Maximum 4 marks

9. Jill carried out chromatography on samples of three known substances, A, B and C, and two unknown substances, X and Y.

Her results are shown in the diagram.

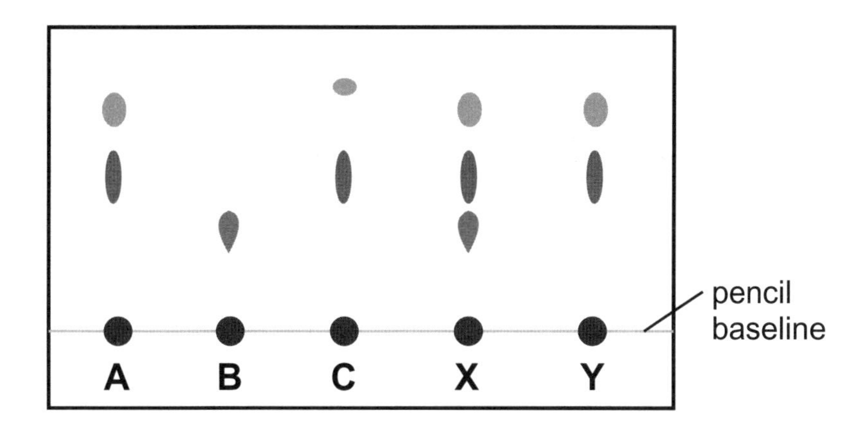

(a) Which two substances are the same?

....

1 mark

(b) Which two known substances make up substance X?

....

1 mark

(c) Explain why the baseline is drawn in pencil and not in ink.

....

....

1 mark

(d) Jill put the baseline above the solvent surface, not below it. Explain why.

....

....

1 mark

Maximum 4 marks

10. Read the following passage and answer the questions that follow.

> Carol and David have two daughters. Paige has her father's blonde hair and hazel eyes. Rhiannon is Paige's twin, and she has her mother's brown hair and blue eyes. Rhiannon is 2 cm taller than Paige.

(a) List two of Rhiannon's features mentioned above that are due to her genes only.

1. ....

2. ....

2 marks

(b) Explain why Paige and Rhiannon can't be identical twins.

....

....

1 mark

(c) Carol and David have another daughter, called Anna, who looks a little bit like both of them. Explain why Anna has a mixture of her parents' characteristics.

....

1 mark

Maximum 4 marks

11. Mr Jones has a light inside his caravan. It uses a battery.

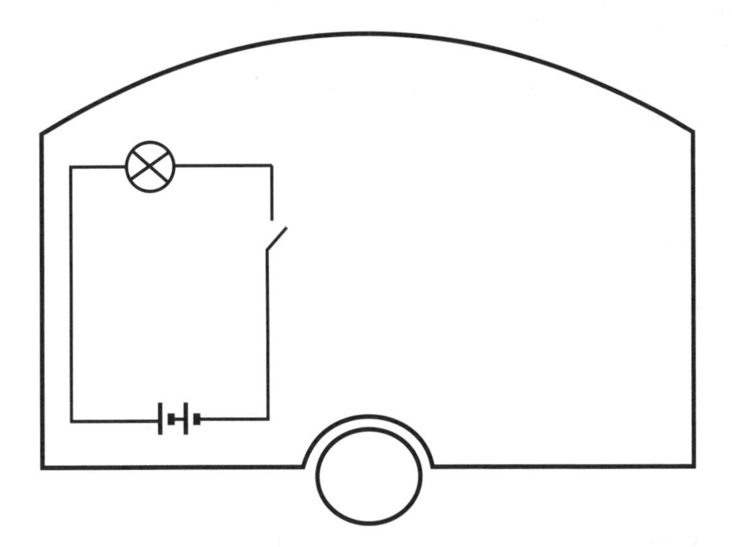

Mr Jones decides he wants another light that he can switch on when he needs it.

(a) Complete the diagram below to show how he should connect up the lights in his caravan. Include the light switches.

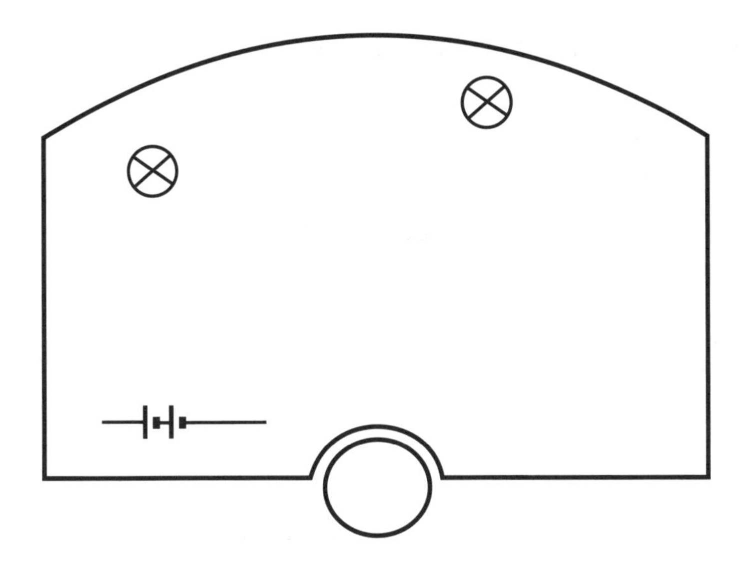

3 marks

(b) What problem might Mr Jones expect if he uses both lights in his caravan? Give a reason.

....

....

2 marks

Maximum 5 marks

12. Draw lines to match up the kingdoms of classification given below with the correct types of organism.

Protista	Include algae and amoeba
Fungi	Insects, fish, birds
Plants	Moulds, yeasts, mushrooms and toadstools
Animals	Ferns, mosses, conifers and flowers

4 marks

Maximum 4 marks

13. Hot magnesium ribbon reacts with steam to produce magnesium oxide and hydrogen.

(a) Write a word equation for the reaction described above.

....

1 mark

(b) Potassium reacts with cold water to produce a gas and a solution that turns universal indicator solution dark blue.

(i) Write a word equation for this chemical reaction.

....

....

2 marks

(ii) Is the resulting solution an acid, an alkali or neutral?

....

1 mark

(iii) Tick the pH value you would expect for the dark blue solution.

☐ 0 ☐ 1 ☐ 4 ☐ 7 ☐ 12

1 mark

Maximum 5 marks

14. Rabbits have long ears. They use them not only for hearing, but also to help them lose excess heat in hot weather. Look at the pictures of the following rabbits.

Group A —
live in the hot desert.

Group B —
live in cool, open grassland.

(a) Why is it an advantage for rabbits in Group A to have the longest ears?

....

1 mark

(b) Why is it important for rabbits to be able to hear well?

....

1 mark

(c) Another group of rabbits live in a very cold, snowy area.
Describe what you would expect their ears to look like and explain your answer.

....

....

2 marks

(d) Elephants also have large ears for their body size.
Which of the following do you think is the best explanation for this adaptation?

- ☐ They use their large ears to detect predators.
- ☐ They use their large ears to keep cool in their warm climate.
- ☐ They use their large ears to help them stalk their prey.
- ☐ They use their large ears to signal to their herd.

1 mark

Maximum 5 marks

15. Julie is a skydiver. As she falls to Earth the forces on her change and affect her speed. Here are some possible reasons for her different speeds.

A Her weight is greater than the air resistance.

B Her weight is less than the air resistance.

C Her weight is equal to the air resistance.

D She has no weight.

E There is no air resistance.

Choose from these reasons to explain each of the following things that happen to Julie. Write the correct letter next to each description.

What happens to Julie	Reason	
(a) When she first jumps out of the aeroplane she falls faster and faster.	....	1 mark
(b) Eventually she reaches a steady speed, moving very fast.	....	1 mark
(c) She slows down suddenly when her parachute opens.	....	1 mark
(d) She falls at a steady speed, more slowly than before.	....	1 mark

(e) Julie falls 100 metres in 15 seconds. Calculate her speed.

....

....

2 marks

Maximum 6 marks

16. Dylan compared two indigestion tablets, A and B, to see which was better at neutralising stomach acid (hydrochloric acid). The active ingredient in both tablets was calcium carbonate.

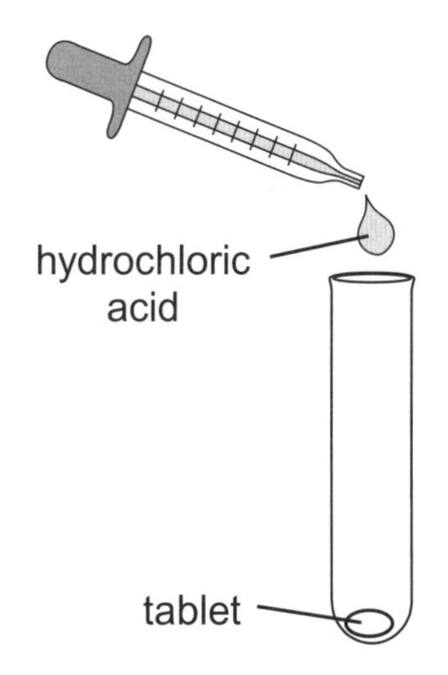

He put each tablet in a separate test tube and added hydrochloric acid, one drop at a time, until no further reaction occurred. He recorded the number of drops needed to neutralise each tablet.
His results are shown below.

Tablet	No. of drops needed
A	22
B	30

(a) Which tablet was better at neutralising stomach acid? Explain your answer.

....

2 marks

(b) Give two factors that Dylan should have kept the same to make the comparison a fair test.

1. ....

2. ....

2 marks

(c) What factor did Dylan change as he carried out his investigation (the independent variable)?

....

1 marks

(d) Give one way in which Dylan could improve the experiment to make the results more reliable?

....

....

1 mark

Maximum 6 marks

END OF TEST

Science
EY STAGE
3
EVELS
5-7
RACTICE PAPER
2B

CGP

Key Stage 3

Science Test

Practice Paper 2B

Read this page, but don't open the booklet until your teacher says you can start. Write your name and school in the spaces below.

First Name ________________________________

Last Name ________________________________

School ________________________________

Remember

- The test is one hour long.
- Make sure you have these things with you before you start: pen, pencil, rubber, ruler, angle measurer or protractor, calculator.
- The easier questions are at the start of the test.
- Try to answer all of the questions.
- Don't use any rough paper — write all your answers and working in this test paper.
- Check your work carefully before the end of the test.
- If you're not sure what to do, ask your teacher.

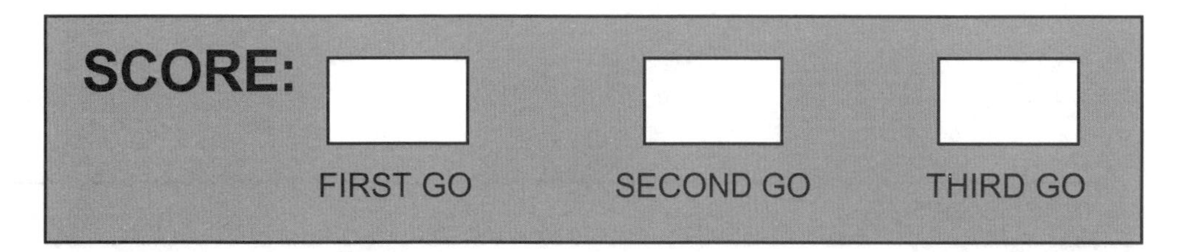

Exam Set SHGP31

1. The chemical formula for a common salt is: $\mathbf{CuSO_4}$

(a) Write down the names of all the elements in this compound and state how many atoms of each are present.

....

....

.... 3 marks

(b) Name the salt. .... 1 mark

Maximum 4 marks

2. A double-decker bus has some mirrors to let the driver see the passengers on the top deck.

(a) On the diagram, draw the path of a ray of light to show how the driver sees the naughty child upstairs. Use a ruler.

2 marks

(b) Cyclists often use special reflectors that shine in the dark so that drivers behind them can see them. The reflector always sends light back to where it came from.

Complete the diagram to show how the reflector sends light back to where it came from.

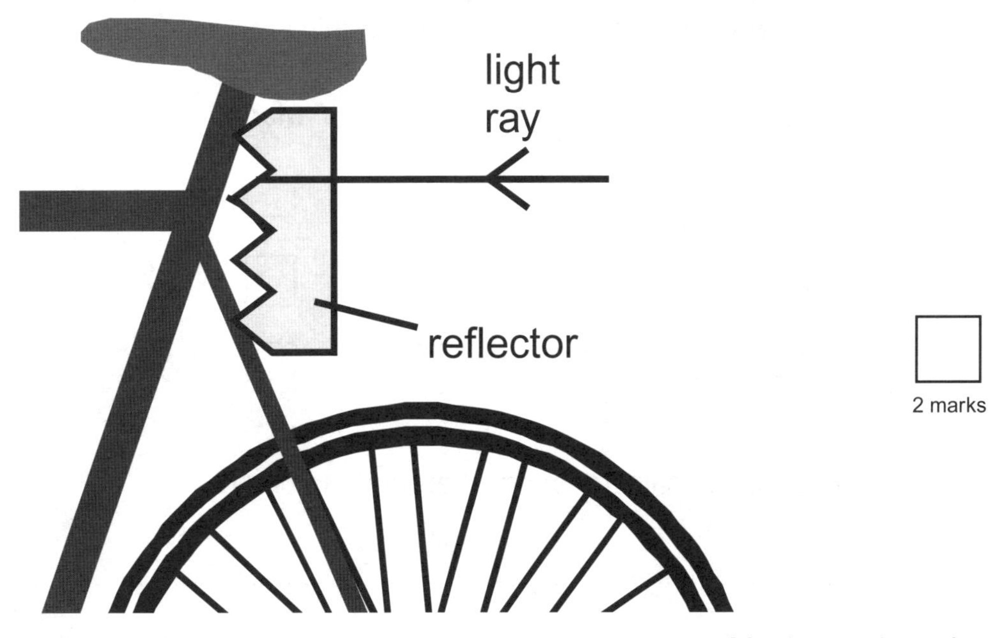

2 marks

Maximum 4 marks

3. The diagram shows a generalised human body cell.

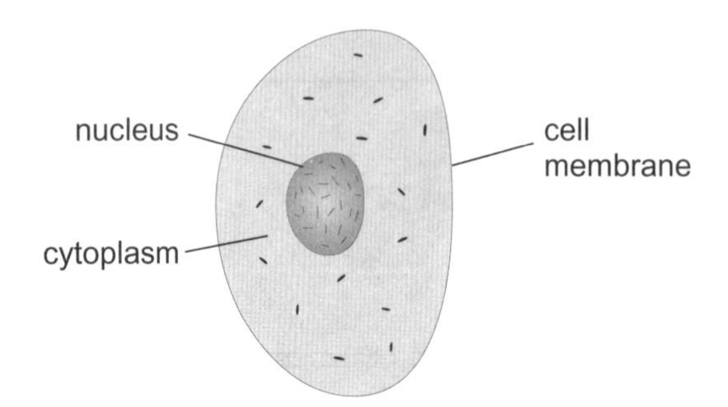

(a) Draw lines to match up the parts of the cell with their function.

Nucleus	controls what passes into and out of the cell.
Cytoplasm	controls the cell.
Cell membrane	where all the chemical reactions take place.

2 marks

(b) (i) Name the chemical process that happens in all body cells to release energy.

....

1 mark

(ii) For each of these substances, tick the correct box to show whether it is used or made during this process.

	Used	**Made**
Oxygen	☐	☐
Glucose	☐	☐
Carbon dioxide	☐	☐

3 marks

(c) How are chemicals transported around the body?

....

1 mark

Maximum 7 marks

4. The following table contains some data about different species of bird within a community.

Species of bird	Average no. of eggs laid per year by a female bird	% death rate per year
A	8	35
B	1	10
C	3	8
D	5	40
E	11	48
F	6	18

(a) Plot this information as a scatter graph on the axes below. Draw a line of best fit.

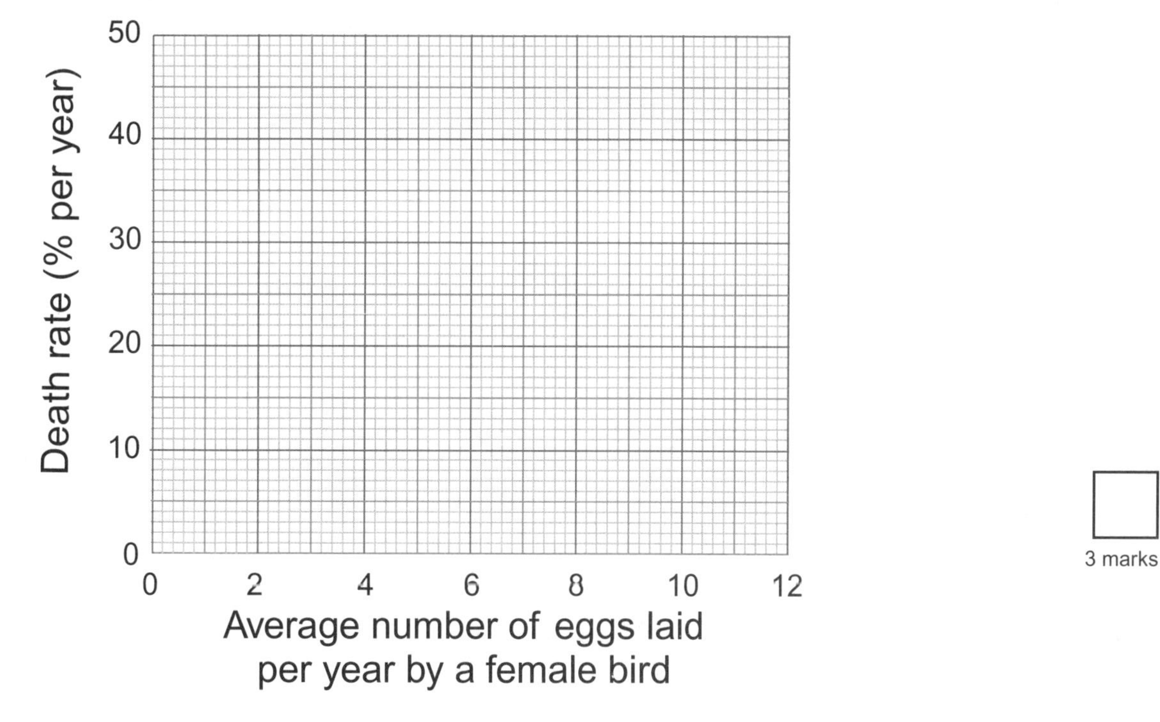

3 marks

(b) Look at the graph you have plotted. Which species do you think has an unusually high death rate considering its annual egg production?

....

1 mark

(c) If 30% of bluetits die each year, use your graph to estimate the number of eggs laid per year by the average female bluetit.

....

1 mark

Maximum 5 marks

5. A pupil is using the apparatus shown below to investigate how strong different magnets are.

He tests two magnets, A and B.

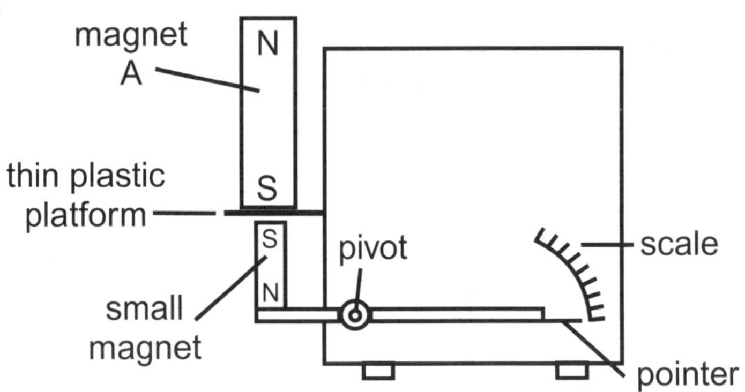

(a) Explain what happens to the small magnet when magnet A is placed on the platform as shown.

....

....

2 marks

(b) Why is it important to put the two south poles next to each other?

....

....

2 marks

(c) Suggest a reason why the pivot has been placed nearer to the small magnet than to the pointer.

....

....

1 mark

(d) How can the pupil tell which is the stronger magnet, A or B?

....

....

1 mark

Maximum 6 marks

6. Becky says that if she blows through a straw into water, the carbon dioxide in her breath will turn the water acidic. She does an experiment to test this. Her apparatus and results are shown below.

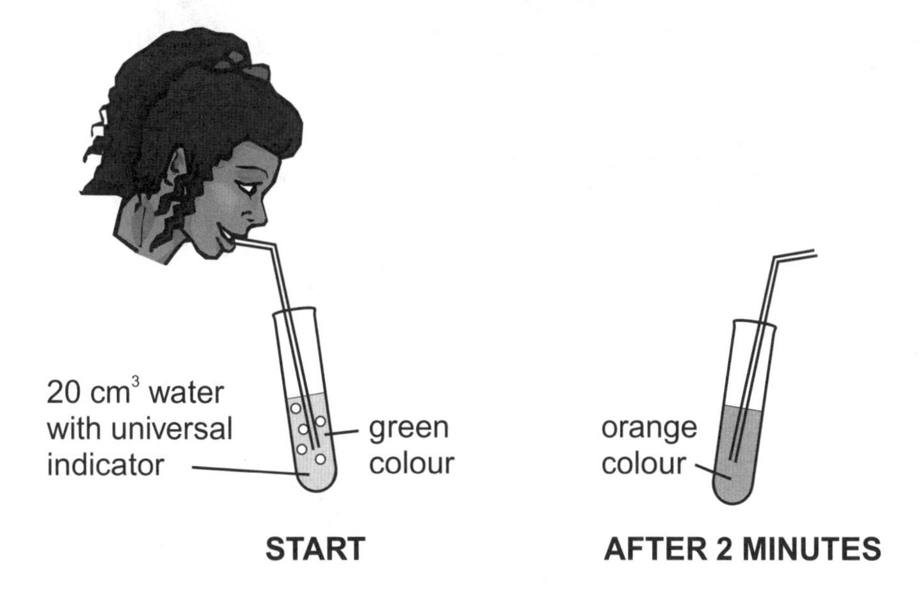

(a) What conclusion can you draw from Becky's results?

....

.... 2 marks

(b) Huang says that Becky should have repeated the experiment using ordinary air as a control. He does this, using an air pump instead of blowing out, and finds that after one minute the solution is still green.

What conclusion can you draw from Huang's results?

....

.... 2 marks

(c) How do the two experiments support Becky's statement?

....

....

.... 2 marks

Maximum 6 marks

7. The digestion of food relies on the action of chemicals.
Each type of chemical digests a different kind of food.

(a) What is the general name for these chemicals?

....

1 mark

(b) What is the name for the chemical found in saliva that breaks down starch into sugar?

1 mark

(c) Name the substances X and Y shown on the diagram below.

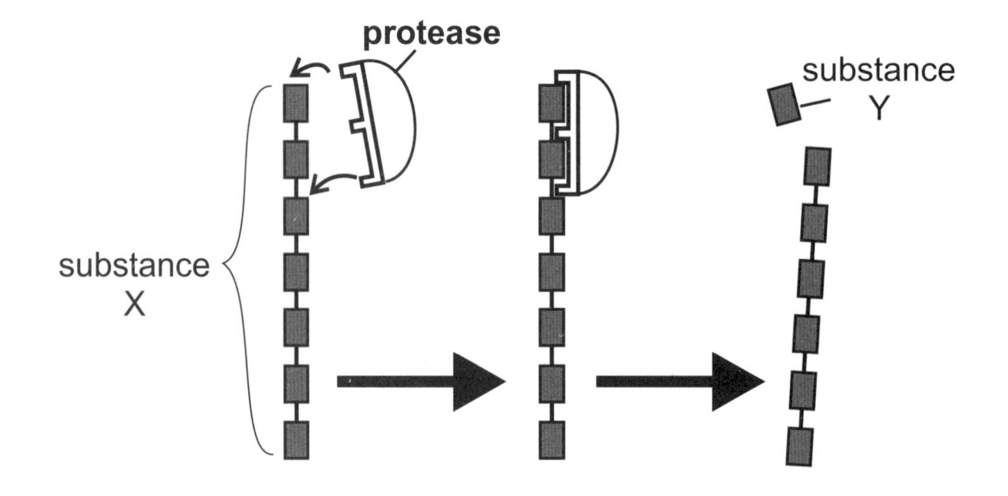

Substance X ....

Substance Y ....

2 marks

(d) Give one food in which you would expect to find a high proportion of substance X.

....

1 mark

Maximum 5 marks

8. The diagram shows how extrusive and intrusive igneous rocks are formed.

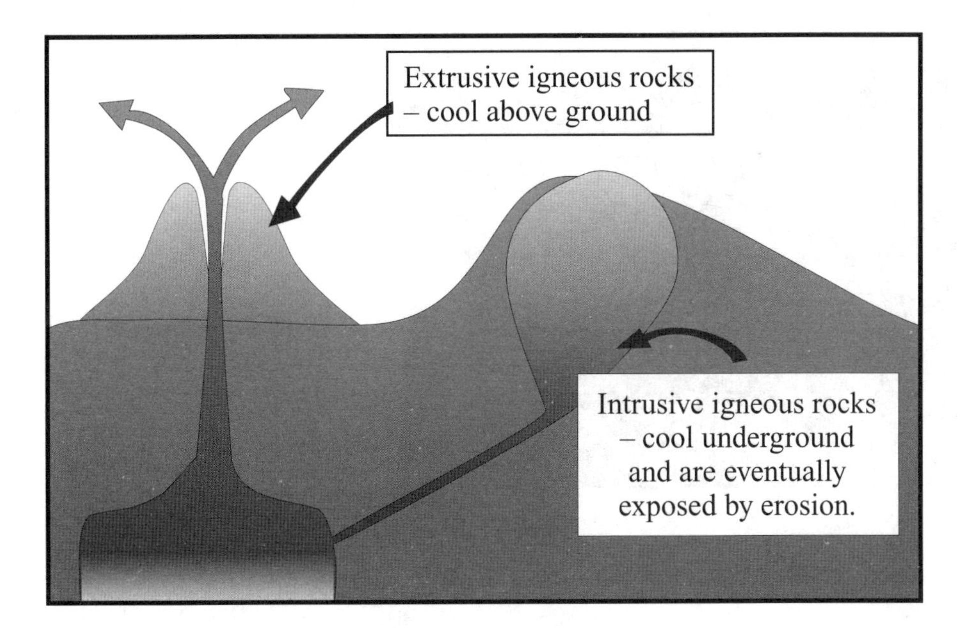

Below are diagrams showing the crystals in two igneous rock samples, A and B.

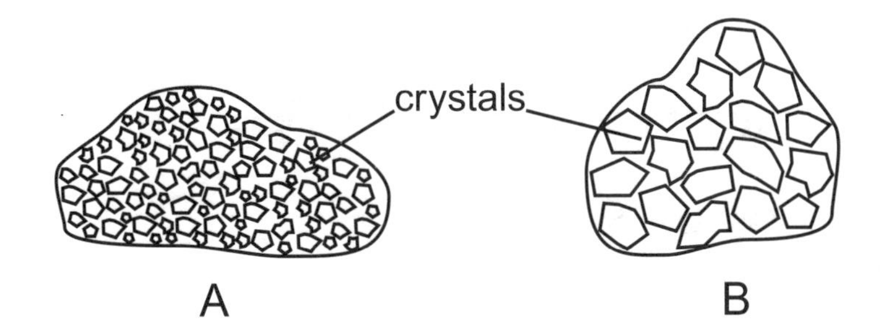

(a) Which rock sample is an intrusive igneous rock? Explain your answer.

....

.... ☐ 2 marks

(b) Draw lines to connect each of the rocks below to the correct rock type.

Rock	Rock type
Marble	Sedimentary
Limestone	Igneous
Granite	Metamorphic

☐ 2 marks

Maximum 4 marks

9. Satellites are used to beam television pictures to Europe.

(a) Tick two boxes next to the correct statements about satellites.

☐ Satellites do not fall to Earth because there is no gravity in space.

☐ It needs an engine to stay in orbit.

☐ Its speed stays constant because there's no friction to slow it down.

☐ It needs to be moving to stay in orbit.

2 marks

(b) Suggest one other use for satellites.

....

1 mark

(c) Name a natural satellite which orbits Earth.

....

1 mark

Maximum 4 marks

10. Mark and Bill were letting toy cars roll down a ramp onto a wooden floor to see how far they went.

The cars all stopped at different points after travelling across the floor.

(a) Name a force that acts to slow down and stop the cars.

....

1 mark

(b) They measured the distances travelled by four cars.
Their results are shown in the table.

CAR	DISTANCE TRAVELLED (cm)
1	50
2	22
3	30
4	37

Complete the following bar chart showing the distance travelled by each car.

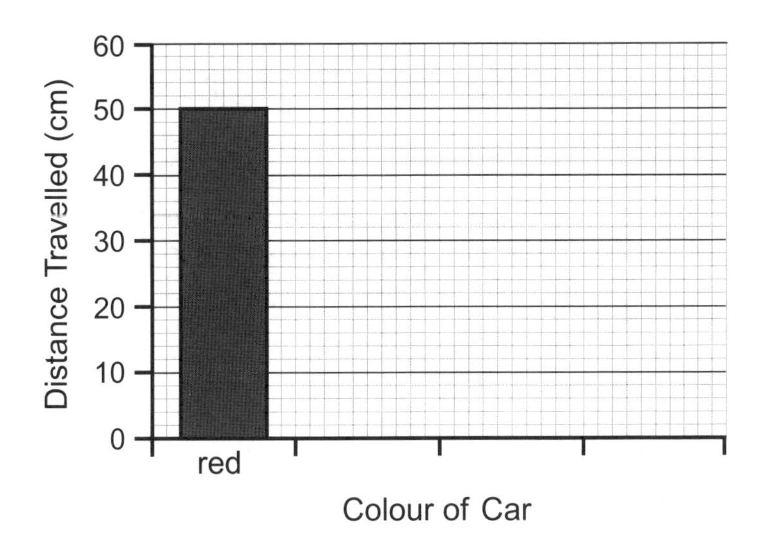

2 marks

(c) Suggest three reasons why the cars travelled different distances.

....

....

3 marks

Maximum 6 marks

11. Mrs Goldsmith needs to buy a light bulb. She has to choose between an ordinary 100 watt filament bulb and a 20 watt low-energy bulb. Both bulbs give out the same amount of light energy, but the low-energy bulb uses less electrical energy.

An advertising panel beside the low energy bulbs says:

> A low energy bulb only uses 20% of the energy used by an equivalent filament bulb. A low energy bulb lasts eight times as long as a filament bulb. A low energy bulb saves you money in the long term.

(a) What happens to the energy that is not converted to light in the filament bulb?

....

1 mark

(b) Write down two other pieces of information Mrs Goldsmith needs before she can decide whether the low-energy bulb really is cheaper in the long term.

1. ....

2. ....

2 marks

(c) Write down two reasons why Mrs Goldsmith might decide to buy the low-energy bulb even if it works out to be more expensive in the long run.

1. ....

2. ....

2 marks

(d) Mrs Goldsmith also needs to replace an ordinary 60 watt filament bulb. Which low energy bulb should she choose? Tick the correct box.

☐ 20 watt ☐ 16 watt ☐ 12 watt ☐ 8 watt

1 mark

Maximum 6 marks

12. Rahel heated 28.5 g of zinc powder in air. The mass of the white powder left behind after heating was 30.5 g.

(a) Explain the mass of the products is never less than the mass of the reactants.

....

1 mark

(b) (i) What substance reacted with the zinc metal?

....

1 mark

(ii) Calculate the mass of this substance that reacted.

....

1 mark

(c) Write down the chemical name of the powder formed after burning.

....

1 mark

Maximum 4 marks

13. The diagram shows a pair of lungs in a human.

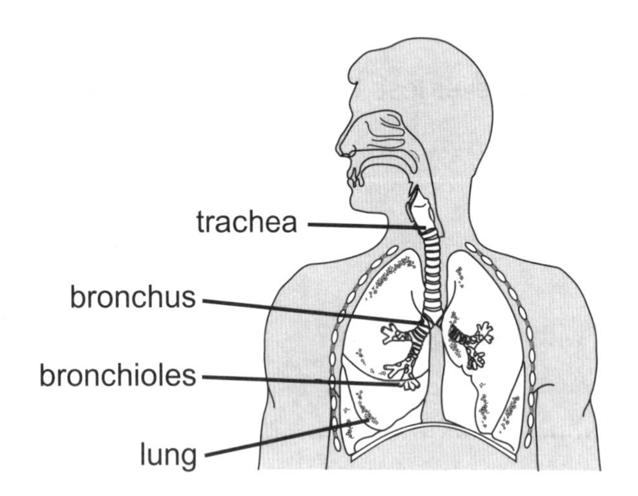

(a) Describe two ways in which the lungs are designed to keep out particles and microorganisms that you breathe in.

1. ....

2. ....

2 marks

(b) Smoking affects the functioning of the lungs. What chemical in cigarettes is addictive?

....

1 mark

(c) Suggest one reason why smokers tend to suffer from more chest infections than non-smokers do.

....

....

1 mark

(d) Cigarette smoke contains a gas called carbon monoxide.
Describe one health problem caused by carbon monoxide.

....

1 mark

Maximum 5 marks

14. Dave is investigating the solubility of potassium nitrate at different temperatures. His results are shown below.

Solubility of potassium nitrate (g / 100 g)	Temp (°C)
20	7
30	24
40	27
50	34
60	39

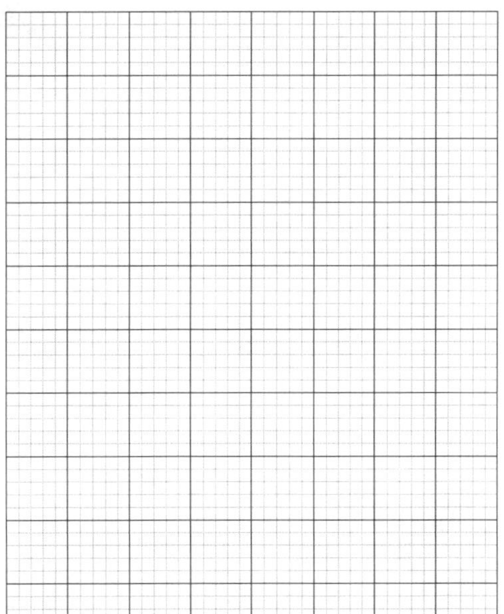

(a) What is a saturated solution?

.... 1 mark

(b) (i) Plot the results on the graph above. 2 marks

(ii) Put a ring around the result that does not fit the general pattern. 1 mark

(iii) Suggest how this anomalous result could have occurred.

.... 1 mark

(iv) Plot a smooth curve through the points (ignoring the anomaly). 1 mark

(c) Describe how the solubility of potassium nitrate changes with temperature.

.... 1 mark

(d) What is the solubility of potassium nitrate at:

(i) 20 °C? .... 1 mark

(ii) 30 °C? .... 1 mark

Maximum 9 marks

END OF TEST

cience
EY STAGE
3
EVELS
-7
RACTICE PAPER
A

Key Stage 3

Science Test

Practice Paper 3A

Read this page, but don't open the booklet until your teacher says you can start. Write your name and school in the spaces below.

First Name ______________________________

Last Name ______________________________

School ______________________________

Remember

- The test is one hour long.
- Make sure you have these things with you before you start: pen, pencil, rubber, ruler, angle measurer or protractor, calculator.
- The easier questions are at the start of the test.
- Try to answer all of the questions.
- Don't use any rough paper — write all your answers and working in this test paper.
- Check your work carefully before the end of the test.
- If you're not sure what to do, ask your teacher.

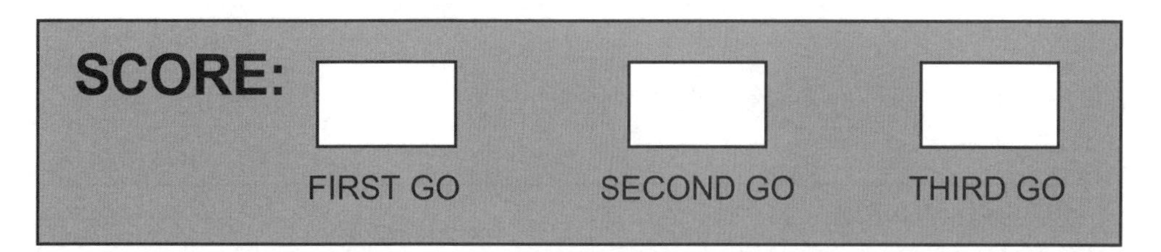
SCORE:
FIRST GO
SECOND GO
THIRD GO

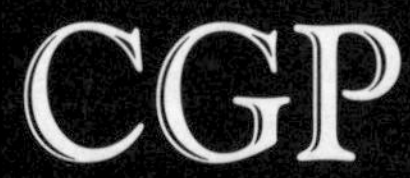

Exam Set SHGP31

1. The diagram shows a circuit containing various different components.

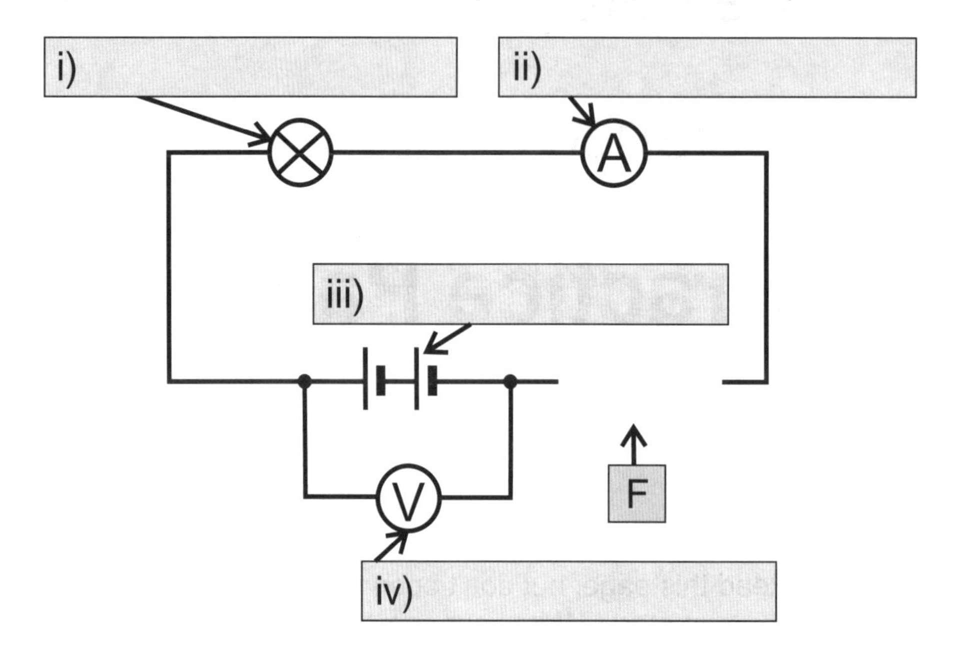

(a) Write the names of the components in the boxes next to their symbols.

4 marks

(b) Draw the symbol for a fuse in the space labelled F on the diagram.

1 mark

Maximum 5 marks

2. Draw lines to connect each of the everyday chemicals listed below to the colour it would turn universal indicator, and to its most likely pH value.

Indicator colour	Chemical	pH
blue	Stomach acid	10
orange	Soap powder	1
green	Lemon juice	3
red	Salt water	7

4 marks

Maximum 4 marks

3. In 1969 the astronaut Neil Armstrong was the first human to walk on the Moon.

(a) Choose the correct reason for each of the following statements by ticking one box to complete the sentence.

(i) Neil Armstrong needed a space suit because ...

- [ ] ... there is no air on the Moon.
- [ ] ... it stopped him from flying off into space.
- [ ] ... he needed it to carry his equipment.
- [ ] ... it protected him from the dangerous moon rocks.

1 mark

(ii) Objects weigh less on the Moon than on Earth because ...

- [ ] ... the objects have less mass.
- [ ] ... there is no gravity in space.
- [ ] ... they are in orbit around the Earth.
- [ ] ... the Moon has a much smaller mass than the Earth.

1 mark

(b) A radio message sent from the Moon takes about 1.25 seconds to reach Earth. The speed of a radio wave is 300 000 km/s.

Calculate the distance from the Earth to the Moon.

....

2 marks

Maximum 4 marks

4. Will carried out the following experiment:

Three geranium plants of about the same size were chosen.

- Plant A was placed in a dark cupboard.
- Plant B was placed in a room near the window.
- Plant C was placed in a room away from the window.

Each plant was left in position for two weeks and watered daily.

(a) Give one factor that Will kept the same to make his experiment a fair test.

....

1 mark

(b) At the beginning of the experiment all the plants were green and healthy.
Complete the table below to show why each plant looked as it did after two weeks.

Plant	Appearance after 2 weeks	Explanation
A	Spindly with yellow leaves	
B	Growing straight with large green leaves	
C	Bending with large green leaves	

3 marks

(c) Which of these conclusions is the best one that Will could draw from his experiment? Tick the correct box.

☐ My results show that all plants need to be near a window.

☐ My results show that all plants need water and light to grow.

☐ My results show that plants are sensitive to the amount of light available.

☐ My results show that plants can grow with or without light.

1 mark

Maximum 5 marks

5. One way to generate electricity is to build a dam across a deep river valley and use the energy in the stored water to drive a generator.

(a) Write down one reason why this method of generating electricity is:

(i) good for the environment.

....

....

1 mark

(ii) bad for the environment.

....

....

1 mark

(b) Name two other sources of energy that can be used for making electricity.

1. ....

2. ....

2 marks

Maximum 4 marks

6. Yew Fai and Helen investigated the energy values of five different brands of cornflakes using the method shown below. They measured the increase in temperature of the water for each brand of cornflakes.

Their results are shown in the table on the right.

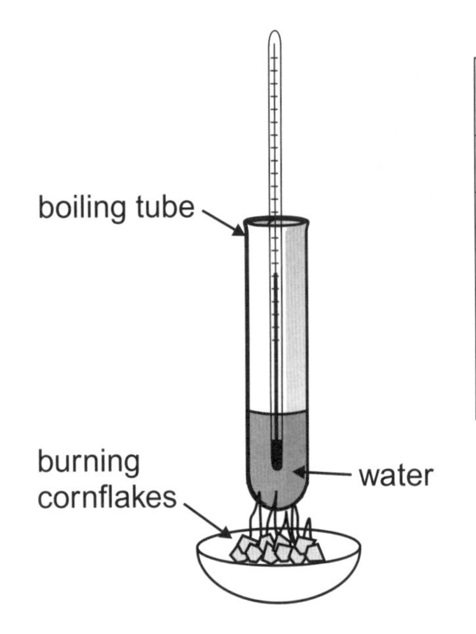

brand	starting temperature (°C)	final temperature (°C)	temperature change (°C)
A	21	41	
B	19	43	
C	20	49	
D	21	42	
E	22	50	

(a) Fill in the temperature change (°C) column of the table.

2 marks

(b) Give **two** things that Yew Fai and Helen needed to do to make this a fair test.

1. ....

2. ....

2 marks

(c) What could they do to improve the reliability of their results?

....

1 mark

(d) Suggest one change they could make to their apparatus to improve the accuracy of the results.

....

1 mark

Maximum 6 marks

7. Wine is about 10% alcohol and 90% water. The table shows some information about water and alcohol, and the diagram shows the equipment used to turn wine into brandy.

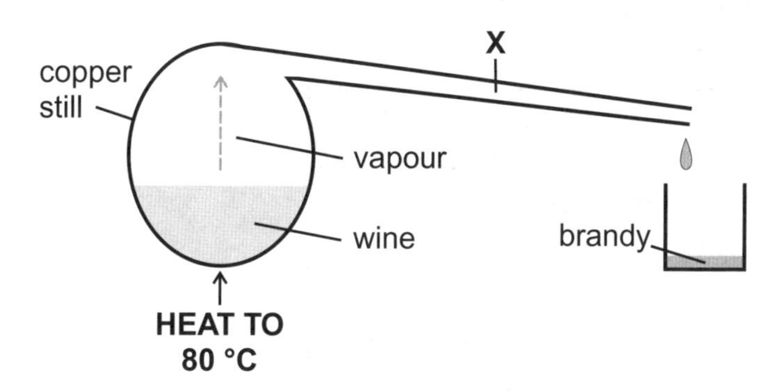

Substance	Boiling Temp.
Water	100 °C
Alcohol	78 °C

(a) What is the name of this separation process?

....

1 mark

(b) Why can you separate water and alcohol using this process?

....

1 mark

(c) What process is taking place at point X on the diagram?

....

1 mark

(d) Which do you think contains a greater percentage of alcohol, wine or brandy? Explain how you can tell from the method shown above.

....

....

....

2 marks

Maximum 5 marks

8. Farmers sometimes breed different varieties of pig together in order to develop useful characteristics.

Look at the data below on five varieties of pig.

Breed	Characteristics
Hampshire	Short, stocky body. Lean meat (little fat).
Landrace	Long body, lean meat.
Large White	Long back. Has large litters of piglets.
Saddleback	Very hardy and easy to keep. High body fat.
Welsh	Lean meat, light weight. Has large litters.

A farmer wants to produce a pig that will live outdoors in a hilly area.
He wants it to produce large litters of piglets with lean meat that he can sell.

(a) What name is given to this type of breeding?

....

1 mark

(b) Which two varieties from the table would you suggest the farmer should breed together? Explain your answer.

....

....

2 marks

(c) Explain how this type of breeding could eventually produce a new variety of pig.

....

....

....

2 marks

Maximum 5 marks

9. Look at the diagram below showing part of the human skeleton.

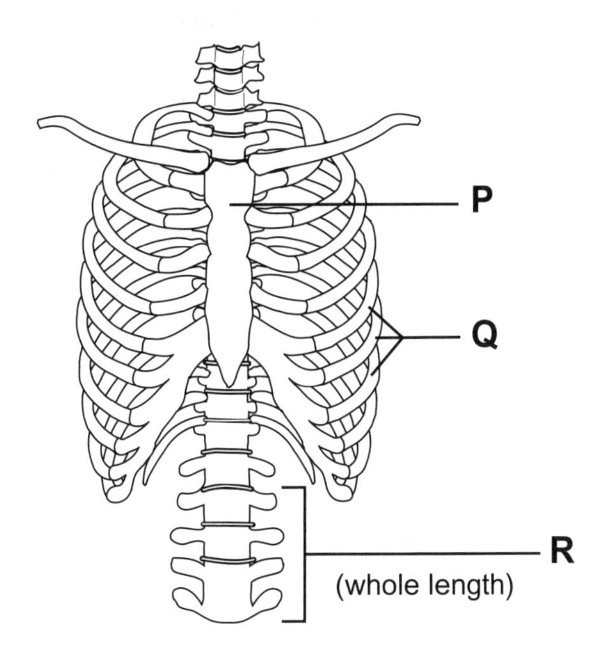

(a) Write down the names of the structures P, Q and R in the spaces below.

P ....

Q ....

R ....

3 marks

(b) The skeleton is designed for **movement**, **support** and **protection**.
Which of these is the primary function of:

(i) Structure Q? ....

1 mark

(ii) Structure R? ....

1 mark

Maximum 5 marks

10. Mr Grey likes making toast in front of his open fire.

(a) He made his toasting fork himself. He had a choice of these materials:

copper **steel** **plastic** **wood**

Suggest a good choice of material for:

(i) The handle. ....

Give a reason for your choice.

....

2 marks

(ii) The prongs. ....

Give a reason for your choice.

....

2 marks

(b) Smoke from his fire always goes up the chimney. Explain why this happens.

....

....

1 mark

(c) Explain how heat gets from the fire to the slice of toast.

....

....

1 mark

Maximum 6 marks

11. Libby investigated the chemical reaction between sulfur powder and iron filings. She mixed them together in a crucible and heated them strongly in a Bunsen flame for five minutes.

She recorded her observations in the table below.

Substance	Description	Appearance	Magnetic?
1	Iron filings	Grey filings	Yes
2	Sulfur powder	Yellow powder	No
3	Mixture	Yellow and grey powder	Grey bits only
4	Final product	Shiny black solid	No

(a) Write down one safety precaution Libby will need to take in this investigation.

....

1 mark

(b) Write down the substance number of one element and one compound from the table above.

Element: .... Compound: ....

2 marks

(c) (i) Write down the **name** of the substance produced in the chemical reaction.

....

1 mark

(ii) When iron (Fe) and sulfur (S) atoms join together, one atom of iron combines with one atom of sulfur.

Write down the **chemical formula** of the substance produced.

....

1 mark

(d) Libby began the experiment with 5.6 g iron and reacted it all with sulfur.

Tick the box you think is the most likely mass of the product.

☐ 5.6 g ☐ 2.8 g ☐ 8.8 g ☐ 1.0 g

1 mark

Maximum 6 marks

12. Imran has the flu. His mum takes him to the doctor.

(a) The doctor says that antibiotics won't work against the microorganism causing Imran's illness. Circle the correct word to complete the sentence below.

Imran's flu is caused by a **virus / fungus / bacterium.**

1 mark

(b) Imran's baby sister doesn't catch the flu because she's been vaccinated against it.

(i) Explain what this means.

....

....

2 marks

(ii) Imran says that his sister's immune system doesn't need to fight the flu microorganism because the vaccine does it instead.
Is he right? Explain your answer.

....

....

2 marks

Maximum 5 marks

13. Part of the reactivity series of elements is shown on the right.

Potassium
Sodium
Calcium
Magnesium
Aluminium
Carbon
Zinc
Iron
Lead
Hydrogen
Copper
Silver
Gold

Use this information to complete the table below, which shows what happened when samples of different metals were added to solutions of various metal salts.

Use a tick (✓) to show a reaction, and a cross (✗) to show no reaction.

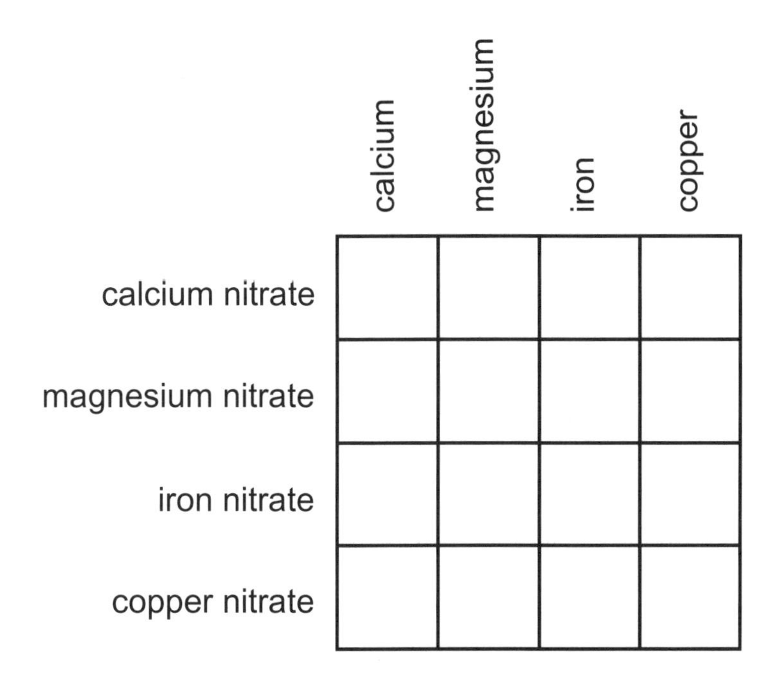

	calcium	magnesium	iron	copper
calcium nitrate				
magnesium nitrate				
iron nitrate				
copper nitrate				

4 marks

Maximum 4 marks

14. The graph below shows how the numbers of sparrows and sparrowhawks vary over time. Sparrows are the main prey of sparrowhawks.

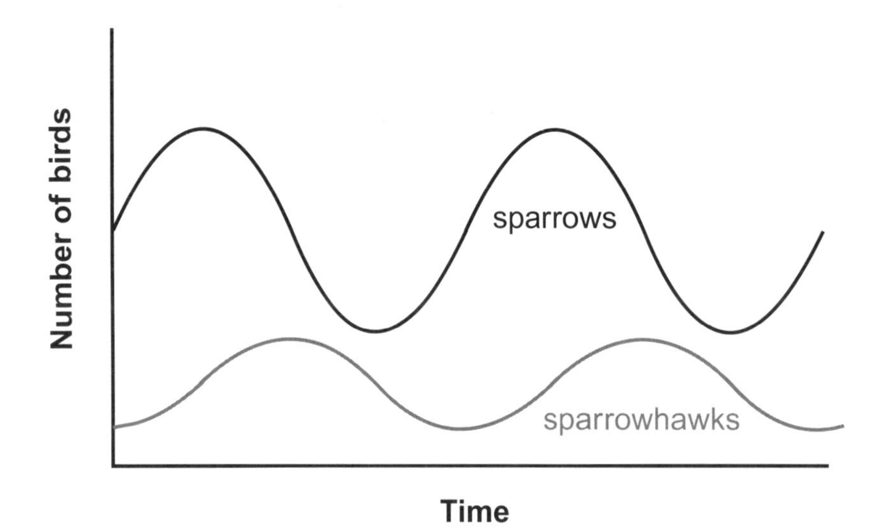

(a) Identify two factors that might cause changes in the number of sparrows each year.

1. ....

2. ....

2 marks

(b) Describe the pattern seen on the graph above.

....

....

....

2 marks

(c) Explain the pattern.

....

....

....

2 marks

Maximum 6 marks

15. Mrs Lightfoot and her elephant walk across a wooden floor.
Mrs Lightfoot's high heels leave marks on the floor. The elephant's feet do not.

The elephant has a mass of 3000 kg. Mrs Lightfoot has a mass of 50 kg.

Explain why Mrs Lightfoot's heels mark the floor
but the elephant does no damage.

....

....

2 marks

Maximum 2 marks

16. Sid makes a stack of 800 kg of bricks on top of a board.
The board has an area of 0.25 square metres.

(a) Work out the weight of the bricks in newtons (g = 10 N/kg).

....

1 mark

(b) Calculate the pressure under the board.

....

....

....

2 marks

Maximum 3 marks

END OF TEST